FORENSIC PSYCHIATRY

By

HENRY A. DAVIDSON, M.D.

AMERICAN ACADEMY OF FORENSIC SCIENCES
FELLOW, AMERICAN PSYCHIATRIC ASSOCIATION

THE RONALD PRESS COMPANY ⟋ NEW YORK

Library of Congress Catalog Card Number: 52-10289
PRINTED IN THE UNITED STATES OF AMERICA

TO

MY WIFE

PREFACE

This manual has been written as a psychiatric-legal guide for physicians. Anyone who seeks to treat the human mind or to diagnose its vagaries must expect to be asked, now and then, to give oral or written testimony to some judicial tribunal. In such a situation, he has no choice but to accept, grudgingly or gracefully, the role of expert witness thus thrust upon him.

But when he enters the legal arena, the expert witness may well feel the need of practical medico-legal help. The psychiatrist, for example, may find it necessary to prepare a court report on the responsibility of an accused person, or on some question concerning the welfare of a child. The doctor may be harassed by questions concerning the propriety of a commitment, the competency of a patient, the reliability of an alcoholic. What the practitioner needs is a book which will tell him, among other things, how to examine a patient or claimant, how to evaluate disability, how to measure responsibility, and how to prepare an acceptable legal report. To provide such help is one of the aims of this volume.

Lawyers frequently complain of trouble in establishing a common meeting ground with psychiatrists. Unfortunately, the lawyer too often gets from the psychiatrist or from the professional textbook interesting, but from his standpoint unusable, accounts of such things as unconscious factors in motivation. This manual will, I hope, serve as a bridge across which understandable communication may be established between the two professions. To be sure, Part II is elementary for a lawyer. It will, nonetheless, be helpful to him if for no other reason than that it gives his expert witnesses something of the ABC's of courtroom mechanics.

The social worker will find the chapters on placement of children, competency, criminal responsibility, marriage and divorce, and juvenile delinquency particularly relevant to his day-to-day contact with the law. The probation officer, whether in child welfare, adult criminal, or domestic relations work, is often asked to investigate or to supervise emotionally disturbed people. If his functions are to maintain their truly professional status, the probation officer will want to have some understanding of the impact of emotional disturbance on behavior. Because the relationship between personal injury and subsequent emotional symptoms is not as simple as it often seems, the insurance adjuster should find Chapter 4 particularly useful.

The reader of these pages will quickly find that theoretical material has been largely eliminated. To write a useful volume in which the essential points will stand out in bold relief, it was necessary to strip away most of the interesting theoretical material on the psychology of injury, the dynamics of juvenile delinquency, the childhood background of alcoholics, the subtleties of marital adjustment, and the unconscious motivations of criminal behavior.

What I have written is chiefly the fruit of my own experience, enriched by citations to the medical and the legal literature. It is all that, plus the enthusiastic contributions of many people in many professions. For some years I have been lecturing at law schools and to bar associations on the forensic aspects of psychiatry. Nearly always, the talk was thrown open to discussion and thus dozens of lawyers and psychiatrists in all corners of the country contributed to the fashioning of these chapters. Mr. Leslie S. Kohn, of the New Jersey bar, was my principal legal mentor. My brother, Gordon I. Davidson, also a lawyer, screened some of the chapters and did his best to weed out legal errors.

I am grateful to my wife for enduring many evenings in solitude while the manuscript was in preparation, to my children for not begrudging me the time, and to my secretary, Mrs. Miriam Armstrong, not only for typing it so neatly but also for her eagle eye in detecting minor errors.

HENRY A. DAVIDSON, M.D.

Arlington, Virginia
July, 1952

CONTENTS

PART I

THE CONTENT OF FORENSIC PSYCHIATRY

PART II

THE TACTICS OF TESTIMONY

CONTENTS

APPENDIX

PART I

THE CONTENT OF
FORENSIC PSYCHIATRY

Chapter 1

CRIMINAL RESPONSIBILITY

When a crime is committed, the offender sometimes says that he did not know what he was doing. When this issue is raised, a psychiatrist is called on to examine the defendant and give an expert opinion. There is a popular but erroneous idea that the test of responsibility is whether the offender "knew right from wrong." This would require the appraisal of an abstract ethical concept (good and evil) and it has no place in modern criminal jurisprudence. The criterion of responsibility is known as the McNaghten formula. The basic question is whether the accused knew that *his particular act* was wrong. This is quite different from knowing right from wrong in the abstract.

The McNaghten Formula

To escape responsibility, the defendant must show that "he was laboring under such a defect of reason from disease of the mind as not to know the nature and quality of the act; or, if he did know it, that he did not know he was doing what was wrong." This is the "McNaghten formula," [1] and it is the basis for determination of criminal responsibility in every state of the Union and in the federal courts. The criterion is sometimes considered obsolete, since it was laid down in 1843 and psychiatry has made much progress since then. However, there seems little chance that the rule will be abandoned or rewritten in the foreseeable future. As one court has remarked, ". . . the formula is now so completely imbedded in the administration of criminal law as to be considered no longer subject to challenge." [2]

The psychiatrist's job is to match the defendant's mental state to the formula and to report his opinion to the jury, who in turn determines responsibility. It is frequently alleged that the law is inconsistent for supposing that a person could be legally sane and medically insane, or vice versa. However, this is not the state of affairs.

[1] Rex v. McNaghten, 10 Clark and Finelly, House of Lords Cases, 200.
[2] State v. Mackin, 36 Atlantic 1040.

When a psychotic patient is convicted of crime, he is not thereby declared to be "legally sane." He is merely held to be legally "responsible"—that is, "answerable" for his acts. The distinction between insanity and irresponsibility is perfectly valid. As every psychiatrist knows, some psychotic patients do respond to fear of punishment or promise of reward (that is, they are "responsible"— they respond) and others do not. There is a vast sociologic difference between these two groups of psychotic persons.

In analyzing the patient's mental state, the psychiatrist must first consider what each clause of the McNaghten formula means.

Defect of Reason from Disease of the Mind.—The examiner first determines whether in fact there was a mental disorder which impaired feeling or thinking. If no mental disorder is found, it is scarcely necessary to proceed with the rest of the formulation.

Knowledge of the Nature of the Act.—This means that the offender can perceive the physical characteristics of his act. The nature of the act of pulling a trigger is that something will be hurled out of the gun barrel. Almost every defendant knows the nature of his act, since only an idiot would be unaware of such simple physical characteristics as the fact that a sharp knife cuts skin. Few subjects will fail this test.

Knowledge of the Quality of the Act.—While the word "quality" is variously defined, I have elsewhere,[3] in an analysis of decisions, pointed out that the nearest definition of "quality" would be the word "harmfulness." A child who turns on the gas knowing that a vapor will escape and spread through the building certainly knows the "nature" of the act of turning the jet. But if he does not know that this would be harmful to the people in the house, he does not know the "quality" of the act. Or consider this example: "Sir Fitzjames Stephen instances the case of an idiot who cut off the head of a sleeping man, remarking that it would be great fun to see him looking for it when he woke." [4] Here the idiot knew the nature of the act, since the nature of decapitation is that it removes the head from the body—this he obviously understood. But, as is indicated by his remark, he did not know the harmfulness of such an act. In fact, this is the only stipulation in the McNaghten formula which would permit

[3] Henry A. Davidson, "Criminal Responsibility," *New Jersey Law Review,* I (May, 1935), 123. Also "Orientation to Forensic Psychiatry," *Archives of Neurology and Psychiatry,* LVII (June, 1947), 730.

[4] Charles Mercier, *Criminal Responsibility* (New York: Physicians and Surgeons Book Co., 1926), p. 215.

the idiot to escape conviction. Mercier [5] believes that the third clause ("not knowing that it was wrong") might exculpate him, but this is unlikely, since it is probable (as Fitzjames Stephen himself put it) that "the idiot would know that people in authority would not approve of this"; thus he would know that the act is wrong. The psychiatrist frequently finds that the patient knew *what* he was doing but that he had no implication of the *harmfulness* of his act. If this lack of realization was due to ignorance, poor education or unsophistication, it is of no help in exculpating him under the formula. But if this lack of realization is due to mental deficiency, an involuntary toxic state, or a psychosis, it comes squarely under this "quality" clause.

In some states the word "consequences" is used instead of "quality" at this point in the formula. If it means "consequences to the victim," it has practically the same meaning as "quality." If it means "consequences to the perpetrator" it has no meaning except, possibly, ignorance of the law.

Knowledge that the Act Is Wrong.—This is usually the clause on which the entire defense turns. The psychiatrist should know two things about the word "wrong." First, it is a concrete, not an abstract, concept. It means, "Did he know the particular act was wrong?" and not "Did he have a philosophic concept of good and evil?" Second, it implies that he knew society considered the act wrong and not that he himself considered it wrong. For example, a burglar says that he sees nothing wrong in stealing from rich people who already have more money than they can use. It cannot be argued that he should be excused because he did not know that burglary was wrong. While in his own private ethical code it may not have been wrong, he did know that the law (the community) considers burglary wrong. On the other hand, suppose a victim of paranoid schizophrenia hears God's voice commanding him to kill someone and assuring him that society would applaud him for following a Divine wish. Since, by reason of his mental disorder, he does not know that the act was wrong, he is irresponsible.

The psychiatrist is entitled to consider such behavior as voluntary surrender to the police, statements of repentance and sorrow, and flight from the scene as evidence that the subject knew he was doing something wrong. The doctor may also call the court's attention to the fact that the subject may have known that the act was wrong without realizing how wrong it was. This is especially true with respect to an idiot or an imbecile who may think of an act as being

[5] *Ibid.*

merely naughty (like gleefully pushing his brother out the window)
when it is actually murderous. In this type of case, the defendant
has two possible escapes. It may be argued that he did not know the
quality (harmfulness) of the act or that he did not "realize" how
wrong it was. The decision rests with the jury, not with the psychiatrist, whose function is simply to place his findings before the
jury along with his own expert opinion as to whether the defendant
knew (and to what extent he knew) the nature, quality, and wrongfulness of the act.

Many persons who should know better think that the test of responsibility in criminal law is whether the accused knew the difference between right and wrong. This is not only an oversimplified
answer; it is a misleading one. Knowing the difference between
right and wrong is a matter of abstract philosophic ethics. There was
a time when this really was the test, and an unhappy time it was.
Consider, for instance, the state of affairs in 1818. A twelve-year-
old child was arrested for stealing spoons—at that time a capital
offense. The defense was that he was too young to realize the
enormity of the offense. However, the prosecution called the minister
who testified that the child attended church regularly and that the
pastor often preached sermons on good and evil, and always told his
parishioners to do no evil. On this evidence, it was held that the
child was guilty because he had been taught the difference between
right and wrong. The court said that the test was only that the
defendant should "have sufficient discernment to distinguish good
from evil." And if the "right and wrong" test were in use today
that would indeed be a fair criterion.

It is true that in some states the phrase is "know right from
wrong" (rather than "know that the act was wrong"). But always
it is used in connection with the particular act. For instance, in
military law the formula is given this way: "so free from mental derangement as to be able *concerning the acts charged* . . . to distinguish right from wrong." Thus, while "distinguish right from
wrong" is used, the preliminary clause (my italics) makes it clear
that it must be applied with respect to the specific act, not with respect
to a general ethical philosophy. Many states have similar variants
in the phrasing. In California, for instance, the formula is: ". . . did
not know the nature or quality of the act or that it was wrong to
commit it," the italicized phrase (my italics) serving to delimit the
general right-wrong concept to the specific act, just as does the *concerning the acts charged* in military law. And in Colorado the expression is: ". . . no capacity to understand the nature of the act

and no ability to distinguish between right and wrong *as applied thereto*," the final phrase again removing the test from the realm of the general and ethical to that of the pragmatic and specific.

The psychiatrist, therefore, must focus his attention on the patient's evaluation of the specific act and not on his general philosophy of ethics.

The Appraisal of Insight

Usually, then, the problem facing the psychiatrist is this: at the time he committed the act, did this person know that he was doing something "wrong"—that is, something generally condemned by the community? It can be assumed that a nonpsychotic of ordinary, or even somewhat subnormal, intelligence knows that it is wrong to commit murder, assault, or theft. This is a strong presumption, and the examiner should not discount it unless there is *affirmative* evidence that the offender did not know that he was doing something wrong. A simple way of finding out is to ask the offender whether he now thinks his act is right or wrong. This sounds naïve, yet it has value. If a defendant has pleaded irresponsibility, but tells the examiner that he is sorry for his act, it is a reasonable inference that he knew it was wrong.

The doctor should also consider such acts as efforts to escape or deny responsibility, efforts to prevent identification (such as by erasing fingerprints, wearing a disguise, or using an alias) and the like as evidences that the offender knew that he was doing something wrong.

Consideration is also given to the way in which the accused was apprehended. In general, there are four possible routes of apprehension:

1. He may have gone to the police and demanded punishment.
2. He may have committed the crime so openly that it was obvious that he was not avoiding identification.
3. He may have used every means to avoid arrest.
4. He may have done nothing to lead to his arrest and nothing to avoid apprehension.

The psychiatrist ought to be told of the circumstances of the apprehension, since this may throw considerable light on the offender's general state of mind and on his evaluation of the wrongfulness of his acts. No universal formula will translate these four routes of apprehension into simple interpretations of the defendant's sense of wrongdoing.

Where an offender used every method to avoid detection, he was probably conscious that he was doing something wrong. When, without pressure, a mentally disturbed person proclaims his guilt and demands punishment, this is *prima facie* psychologic evidence that he knew he was doing a legal wrong, but that he considered it morally righteous or that he acted under an irresistible impulse. Some observers say that this behavior (open insistence on punishment) is inconsistent with responsibility. This is tantamount to saying that the only time you can be sure the offender does not know he did something wrong is when he says he did something wrong.

That a person commits a crime in public has no consistent significance. If irresistible impulse is offered as a defense, this does meet the "policeman at the elbow test" (see page 13), but there are two limitations to that. The fact that the crime was committed publicly does not, by itself, *establish* irresistible impulse, though it supports such a contention if there is corroborating evidence. In most jurisdictions, acceptable irresistible impulse must be part of a disorder of thinking or feeling and not part of a disorder of will or character. The meaning-value of public commission of a crime is considerably lessened when the offender never expected to be apprehended. Thus, during World War II, certain traitors broadcast for the enemy. Certainly their acts were public enough. However, this does not prove that they considered their acts legal and right. It proves only that they guessed wrong as to which side was going to win the war. Whether they knew the acts were wrong had to be determined by other evidence. The openness of treason has no probative value.

Another factor to be considered is whether the act was planned or impulsive. That a crime was committed on impulse does not prove that the offender thought he was doing something right. He may have known it was wrong but, because of the power of the impulse, he did not, at the moment, care. Where the act was planned, it is necessary to determine whether :

a) The plan was aimed at certainty that the act would be committed ; or
b) The plan was drawn up to avoid detection.

An offender may, for example, determine to kill a public official because of a psychotic delusion that by doing so he will effect a great public benefit. Knowing that public officials are well guarded, he may draft an elaborate plan to penetrate the guard and overcome all obstacles in order to consummate his mission. Under these circumstances, the elaborateness of the plan does not prove that the offender knew he was doing something wrong. On the other hand, where the plan includes the erasure of fingerprints, successful flight from the state, hiding out under an alias, or the construction of a spurious alibi, then we must assume that the offender knew he was doing something wrong. This assumption may be refuted by the facts in a particular case; but, until refuted, it is a reasonable inference. If a paranoid person buys a revolver, using a forged permit with a false name, the psychiatrist must know whether this precaution was taken to confuse the offender's imaginary persecutors or whether it was designed to escape apprehension. If the former is true, then the planning does not indicate that he knew he was doing something wrong. But if the permit was forged for the purpose of avoiding detection, it is fair to conclude that he knew he was doing something against the law.

Specific Determinants

Intent, Premeditation and Willfulness.—Usually a crime requires an overt act plus a specific intent, generally an intent to do harm. Some crimes also require an element of premeditation. This offers another possibility for psychiatric analysis, since the examiner may find that the defendant knew that the act was wrong, but that, by reason of drunkenness, psychosis, or deficiency, he was unable to form the required intent. For example, the law presumes that murder is in the second degree and imposes on the state the burden of proving the willfulness and premeditation necessary to establish first degree murder. The mental state of the defendant might be such that the prosecution could not prove the premeditation or deliberateness essential to the more serious finding; yet the defense might have to concede that the accused knew the nature, quality and wrongfulness of the homicide. The net result is a sort of "partial responsibility." Indeed, if, as lawyers are prone to do, the word "responsibility" is equated with "sanity," the effect is to establish "partial insanity," an admitted psychiatric absurdity, yet one which is forensically logical.

In this connection, Glueck [6] says: "The courts of at least two states have had sufficient vision to cope with the problem of the semi-irresponsible." The states referred to are Utah and New Jersey. In Utah,[7] a court has said, "A person's mental condition may not be such as to make him irresponsible yet it may be such as to relieve him from the supreme penalty;" while the New Jersey decision [8] reads:

[6] Sheldon Glueck, *Mental Disorder and the Criminal Law* (Boston: Little, Brown & Co., 1925), p. 203.
[7] State v. Anselmo, 148 Pacific 1071.
[8] State v. Shilling, 112 Atlantic 400.

"If the defendant was so feeble-minded as to be incapable of forming the specific intent to kill with its willful and deliberate character, then his offense would be murder in the second degree."

The examiner should understand this concept clearly, since a man's life may depend on it. The psychiatrist is not finished when he decides simply that the accused is or is not psychotic. He must be prepared to say whether the defendant's mental state was such that he was capable of having the degree of intent, willfulness, deliberateness, or premeditation which the law might require for the offense. This is particularly true of crimes committed by psychopaths during rages or by drunkards during periods of acute intoxication.

Drunkenness.—As a general rule, alcoholic intoxication is no defense to a crime committed under that influence, except when the offender was made drunk against his will and by force. Such cases must be very rare. A nice question is presented in chronic alcoholic psychosis. In such a case the prosecution would admit that the crime came out of a psychotic delusion, but would argue that since the psychosis was the result of voluntary indulgence in alcohol, the defendant was fully responsible. Most courts would probably exculpate the defendant, however, on the theory that his insanity is not a natural result (but rather an unusual result) of his drinking and that, in any event, he did not willfully become insane. The psychiatrist's function would be to tell the jury that the accused had a psychosis, that it was due to alcohol, and that it was a form of insanity.

Drunkenness sometimes robs a crime of one of its elements and thus reduces it to a lesser offense. If a drunkard assaults another man and inflicts grievous bodily harm, he may be indicted for assault with intent to kill or assault with intent to commit mayhem. The psychiatrist might be able to point out that the defendant was so befuddled by liquor that he could not form a clear intent to do anything. If the jury accepts that diagnosis, the effect would be to reduce the crime to simple assault.

Particularly difficult questions are raised by a crime committed during a period of pathologic intoxication. The patient has a complete amnesia for his behavior and will never remember having done what he is charged with. But within the framework of his pathologic intoxication he will have acted sanely. He will show premeditation, planning, and an effort to escape—all of which suggests that he has full responsibility even though his amnesia is genuine. In delirium tremens, on the other hand, the patient is clearly in no condition to plan, deliberate, weigh consequences, evaluate the wrongfulness of the act, or understand its quality.

Some offenses are actually aggravated if the defendant is drunk (reckless driving, for instance) while others may be mitigated, provided the psychiatrist satisfies the jury that the intoxication stripped away one of the mental components of the act, such as intent or premeditation. Courts are not prepared, however, to accept the thesis that acute alcoholism is a disease. To the judges and the jurymen, intoxication is a bad habit and alcoholism a character defect. The drunk usually knows he is doing something wrong. At the moment, however, he just doesn't care.

Irresistible Impulse

In most states, irresistible impulse is not a defense. A psychasthenic suffering from pyromania is guilty of arson in spite of what the psychiatrist says. So is a man who "sees red" and flies into a rage during which he commits an assault.

Irresistible impulse, however, is accepted as a defense in about a dozen states. In Delaware, the Supreme Court [9] has spoken of "deprivation of will power to choose whether to do the act or refrain from doing it," and the Supreme Court of Alabama [10] has indicated that a defendant might be irresponsible if "by reason of mental disease he had so far lost the power to choose between right and wrong and avoid doing the act that his *free agency was destroyed*." Both of these, in effect if not in intent, provide a legal basis for pleading irresistible impulse. So does the military law, since the relevant phrase in the *Manual for Courts Martial* reads : ". . . a person is not mentally responsible unless he was so free from mental derangement as to be able concerning the particular acts charged both to distinguish right from wrong and *to adhere to the right*." [11] The last phrase (italics mine) certainly spells out a defense of irresistible impulse. The psychiatrist could testify with clear conscience, if his patient suffered from genuine kleptomania, that the defendant knew that it was not right to steal but that because of his mental derangement (psychasthenia) he could not "adhere to the right"; or, in the language of the Alabama courts, that "his free agency was destroyed"; or (using the Delaware court's criterion) "that he had no power to do the act or refrain from doing it."

Glueck has examined decisions of appellate courts in every state in the Union and cites cases [12] showing that irresistible impulse has

9 State v. Jack, 58 Atlantic 833.
10 Parsons v. State, 2 Southern 854.
11 For an excellent analysis of the "adhere to the right" concept as a form of irresistible impulse, see *Department of the Army Technical Manual,* TM 8-240 (Washington, D. C.: Government Printing Office, 1953), par. 5.
12 Glueck, *op. cit.,* pp. 267-73.

been accepted as a defense (at least once in each state) in Arkansas, Colorado, Connecticut, Indiana, Kentucky, Michigan, Ohio, Pennsylvania, and Virginia, in addition to Delaware and Alabama as already indicated. This means not that the doctrine is firmly established in those states, but simply that in the cases cited the courts felt that the defendant should not be held accountable. Most of the states (certainly at least thirty of them) will not accept the "irresistible impulse" defense and show little disposition to change their doctrine, no matter how persuasive the psychiatric testimony may be in individual cases.

There are three kinds of irresistible impulse pleas, corresponding to three sets of psychiatric syndromes and representing three degrees of juridical generosity. The narrowest concept is the irresistible impulse sometimes generated within insane persons—sudden explosive reactions powered by some urge within the person. A slightly wider concept would include the impulses of the compulsive neurotic. For example, in certain compulsive neuroses there is an impulse to steal, in others an impulse to step on cracks in the sidewalk or to count fence posts or to repeat a certain verbal formula. There is a well-recognized neurosis in which "pyromania" is a symptom—that is, compulsive setting of fires.

Where irresistible impulse is a defense, it is usually broad enough to include both psychotic and psychoneurotic compulsions, though in some jurisdictions only psychotic impulses are grounds for acquittal. The danger is that the concept, once accepted, might be broadened to include the kind of impulse which occurs to normal people from time to time in response to rage or frustration. To be sure, it seems unfair to hold a person accountable for doing that which he could not refrain from doing. But there are good reasons for this procedure. When the doctrine is accepted with reference to psychotic impulses, it is logical for defense counsel to insist that it apply with equal force to neurotic compulsions, for these too are the result of psychiatric disorder. Then comes the plea that it should cover impulsive acts committed during drunkenness, for intoxication is also a form of mental illness. One step further carries us to the point where it furnishes a shield to anyone who commits a crime in a fit of rage, pique, or frustration.

Time was when the chief objection to this defense was that it was hard to prove and easy to malinger. However, any psychiatrist, given sufficient time with the patient and an adequate history, can recognize a psychosis; and if the doctrine be limited to psychotic impulses, there is no serious probative difficulty. If the defense is expanded to include neurotic impulses, psychiatric science can still meet the challenge. The competent psychiatrist knows that a psychoneurosis is a way of life, not a transient reaction, and he looks for a neurotic history. He knows that in true compulsive neuroses, there is a typical pattern of mounting tension, internal conflict, abashed yielding to the impulse, brief relief from tension, subsequent recrimination, and guilt-feeling leading to more tension with a repetition of the cycle. The psychiatrist is suspicious of an irresistible impulse with no past history that began five minutes before the commission of the crime.

One of the chief points of dispute in connection with irresistible impulse is the query: "Would the person have yielded to that impulse had there been a policeman at his elbow?" In true neurotic compulsiveness the patient is ashamed of his impulses and tries to yield to them only in privacy. Thus a person with a genuine kleptomania, rooted in a clear compulsive neurosis, will not steal in the presence of a policeman. This is the chief theoretical objection to the "policeman at the elbow test"—it does not exclude the genuine compulsive neurotic. However, the test is still a practical one because it meets this objection with irrefutable logic. If an impulse can be resisted in the presence of a policeman, then obviously the impulse is not irresistible.

A person with an irresistible impulse to commit a crime is more dangerous to the community than one who purposefully commits a crime after due deliberation. The very force of the irresistible impulse must make our ordinary safeguards against it ineffective. Assume a jurisdiction where neurotic irresistible impulse is a valid defense, and a situation where a defendant escapes a murder conviction because he proves an irresistible neurotic impulse to kill. He cannot be confined in a mental hospital because he has no psychosis. A psychiatrist who is willing to help free such a person by testifying to the reality of the impulse has a duty to call attention to the hazard the defendant presents to the community. This brings into being one of the doctor's basic dilemmas. Can he say that as a doctor his duty is to help his patient in every way? A statement that the patient is a menace to the community would certainly hurt him. The doctor can say that society has its own experts to worry about protecting the community: his duty is to his patient. Most physicians would agree, however, that a doctor's duty to society transcends his obligation to the individual patient. The code of ethics of the American Medical Association makes it clear that a doctor has a primary duty to the community with respect to the reporting of contagious diseases, but it is silent about the situation presented by dangerous mental disorders.

Irresistible impulse is frequently pleaded in cases associated with sexual perversion—most often as a defense in charges of sodomy, or of murder secondary to perverted sex acts. A man with a very powerful sexual urge, which he seeks to gratify through *normal* channels, is held accountable: he is expected to check that urge until he achieves a situation which is both private and mutually agreeable. The same restraint can be expected of a man with a strong sexual urge which he seeks to gratify through *abnormal channels*. He too can be held accountable for restraining himself until he accomplishes a private, adult, and voluntary relationship. If such an individual is to be exculpated, say, on the charge of practicing sodomy on children, then the man with a normally channeled sex urge could be asked to be freed of a rape charge because his biologic urge also mounted to an irresistible impulse.

Other Determinants

Mental Deficiency.—The McNaghten formula applies to mental deficiency, just as to the psychoses. Indeed, lawyers still confuse the two conditions. As recently as 1921, one high court [13] said, ". . . deficiency of intellect is a species of insanity." The chief difficulty in applying the formula to mental defectives comes when the adult has a mental age in the six-to-twelve bracket. Here many psychiatrists reason that an adult with a mental age of, say, ten, ought to be judged with the same liberalness that would be applied to a ten-year-old child. When the accused is a child, the prosecution always has to prove mental capacity to commit the crime. By contrast, if the accused is an adult, the capacity is assumed, and the defense has to prove lack of capacity if this is pleaded.

Glueck [14] contends that "if it were shown that an adult is below the mental age of fourteen, it would seem more in consonance with the law to place the burden of proving mental capacity on the prosecution." The courts have not accepted Glueck's recommendation. Thus, in one case [15] it was held that "when a man reaches maturity, the presumption is that he possess capacity (to commit a crime) and it is for him to overcome that presumption." This is the general rule in all states.

[13] State v. Shilling, 112 Atlantic 400.
[14] *Op. cit.,* p. 196.
[15] State v. Shilling, 112 Atlantic 400.

Psychiatrists often introduce the defendant's mental age into the record. Judges and juries seem unimpressed by the statement that this adult defendant has the mind of a child. "Criminal responsibility does not depend on mental age," said a Massachusetts court [16] bluntly.

Another eastern court [17] expressed irritation with the whole thesis by saying, ". . . the mental age theory is utterly misleading to a layman and practically useless in the administration of justice." An Arkansas judge [18] has this to say: "When an adult has the intelligence of a child of seven, that fact alone cannot be made the test as to whether he is or is not capable of committing a crime."

Intelligence tests, however, are useful in two particulars: (1) in helping determine whether the defendant had sufficient wit to form the required degree of intent or deliberation (see paragraph on *Intent,* page 9), and (2) in assisting the judge to make disposition of a convicted defendant.

Amnesia and Double Personality.—A common defense is: "Everything suddenly went black"; or, perhaps: "I don't remember doing any of those things. If they say I did them, I guess I did, but I have no recollection of it." Then, when it is demonstrated beyond doubt that the accused actually did do "those things," the explanation is that he had a double personality of the Jekyll-Hyde pattern.

With reference to its legal status, the double personality situation seems to be this: concede that the patient had two personalities. One, the "main" personality, was good; the other, the "secondary" personality, was evil. The offense is now judged within the framework of the secondary personality, and the responsibility is then assigned to the "main" personality. For example:

a) A patient habitually developed aggressive or suicidal reactions after he had only "a little" to drink. He invariably had a total (and genuine) amnesia for his actions during this state of pathologic intoxication. In one of these periods he was in a back yard and tried to rape a child. When she screamed, the parents poured out of the house, the assailant jumped a fence and fled. He displayed great ingenuity escaping capture, gained his own home, went to bed. He was awakened by police officers, seemed genuinely puzzled by the charge, and insisted that he had been home all the time. In spite of positive identification, he would not allow his attorney to introduce any defense of intoxication. He kept repeating in a hurt and bewildered tone that he had not been near the scene of the crime.

[16] Commonwealth v. Stewart, 151 Northeastern Reporter 74.
[17] State v. Ehlers, 119 Atlantic 15.
[18] Chriswell v. State, 283 Southwestern 981.

In this case, consider the question of responsibility within the framework of the intoxication, using the McNaghten formula. Since he tried to flee and carefully eluded capture, it is apparent that during that period he was conscious he had done something wrong. The secondary personality thus appears to be criminally responsible. Projecting this responsibility on the "main" personality, we are forced to conclude that that too was responsible.

b) During the middle of the night, a student in a college dormitory awoke and noisily walked to the clothes rack. He walked so carelessly that he aroused several other students in the room. He inserted his hand into the pocket of another man's trousers. Several students restrained him and reported the incident. The accused was confused. He said only that he was asleep all the time. His past conduct record was perfect except for a verified medical history of somnambulism. Apparently the somnambulistic personality had no consciousness of doing anything wrong, since he made no effort to walk silently. His behavior was designed, in effect, to facilitate capture, not to elude it. This secondary personality had no knowledge of doing anything wrong; and this lack of knowledge was associated with a nervous disorder, i.e., somnambulism. Under the McNaghten formula, the secondary personality is irresponsible. Therefore, under the rule enunciated, the "main personality" (i.e., the defendant himself) is not responsible.

Faced with a plea of amnesia or double personality, what does the psychiatrist do? He remembers that there are six possible explanations and explores all six of them. Setting aside some rare or freakish factor, the six explanations for this defense are (1) hysteria, (2) psychosis, (3) alcoholism, (4) head injury, (5) epileptic fugue, or (6) that the defendant is telling a lie.

Hysteria, if present, should be reflected in the total life pattern of the patient. It is also essential to decide whether the sequence of events was (a) first a hysterical fugue, then an offense committed while in this trance, or (b) first the offense, then an hysterical wiping out of any memory of it. In situation (b) the patient would certainly be responsible. In situation (a) the responsibility would have to be adjudged by the McNaghten formula within the framework of the fugue.

Amnesia associated with *alcoholism* takes one of two forms : either ordinary drunkenness or pathologic intoxication. Drunkenness is evaluated as suggested in the paragraph on that subject. Pathologic intoxication is appraised in terms of the McNaghten rule, applying the formula to the secondary personality.

Head injury is an explanation that must not be forgotten. Crimes are often associated with violence to the perpetrator as well as to the victim. An electro-encephalogram may be helpful with respect to behavior during a concussion-induced fugue. The description of the patient's activities should indicate whether he knew what he was doing or whether he really acted automatically; whether he acted as if he felt he were doing something wrong, or whether he acted reflexly.

Epileptic fugues should be diagnosable by the characteristic electro-encephalographic tracing as well as by an authenticated history of previous fugue states, trances, or grand mal attacks.

For a discussion of *malingering,* see Chapter 11.

In all cases in which amnesia or double personality is alleged, the psychiatrist will want to order an electro-encephalogram and will review the past history for evidence of epileptic attacks, head injuries, alcohol habits, and hysterical behavior.

Presumption of Continuity of Psychosis.—Once it has been established that a person has a psychosis, the psychosis is presumed to continue. Discharge from a mental hospital does not automatically adjudicate a return to sanity; it may mean only that the patient no longer needs custodial care or that he cannot profit from further treatment. The ex-inmate of a mental institution is in good position to plead irresponsibility. Such a plea can be refuted, of course, but the prosecution has to carry that burden of proof. The state can show the hospital discharge, the limited nature of the psychosis and the fact that the patient had lately been conducting himself in a normal manner. All of this might well add up to proof of recovered sanity. Thus, in one case,[19] the defendant committed a murder two years after discharge from a state hospital. The trial judge ruled (erroneously as later determined) that the defendant had to prove insanity if that was his plea. Apparently he could not prove it, and he was convicted. The conviction was reversed by the upper court on the theory that his psychosis, established by his original commitment, must be presumed to continue, and, if recovery is alleged, it is up to the prosecution to prove the recovery, not up to the defense to prove the psychosis.

While previous psychosis is presumed to continue, the reverse does not hold, and a present disorder will not be projected backwards. If a defendant develops a psychosis in jail awaiting trial, this fact has no value in proving that he was psychotic at the time of the crime.

19 Davidson v. State, 4 Southwestern (2d) 74.

Where no psychosis is established by past history, the presumption is that the accused is sane, no matter how fantastic the crime. If the defendant alleges irresponsibility, he must prove it. In some states, he must prove it "beyond a reasonable doubt"; in others "by a preponderance of the evidence"; and, in some states simply "to the satisfaction of the jury." The degree of proof has some bearing on psychiatric testimony. For instance, one good psychiatrist says the accused is psychotic and another says that he is sane. The jury might happen to feel that the former practitioner was more of an expert or had had a better opportunity to know the defendant. If "to the satisfaction of the jury" or "by a preponderance of the evidence" is the measure, the defendant would be found not guilty. But if irresponsibility had to be proved "beyond a reasonable doubt," then the proof in this situation would fall short; since, if the two experts are so evenly balanced, the proof is scarcely "beyond a reasonable doubt."

Psychosis.—Psychosis does not automatically acquit a defendant. An offender may be manifestly psychotic, yet still responsible. If, in spite of his psychosis, the accused knew the nature and quality of his act and knew that it was wrong, he can be convicted. The psychiatrist knows that the human mind is not divided into compartments, and that if a person is psychotic his total reasoning is affected. That, however, is not the law. Consider the following case—one which stretches the McNaghten formula to the extreme:

An elderly schizophrenic would assault children, and after a sexual orgy he would kill them. He frequently would strip off the flesh, cook it, and eat it. He derived orgiastic joy out of inflicting pain. He would normally wear overalls over his naked body and hunt for children in slum areas. The purpose of the overalls, he explained, was two-fold. First, people would think he was a janitor or painter and not notice as he prowled around basements and back yards. Second, he could strip himself naked by loosening a few buttons, and thus save time and trouble. He moved constantly, seldom returning to the same area. He usually kidnapped and assaulted colored children because, he said, authorities paid less attention when they were missing. He tried to beat children in a place where their screams would not be overheard, but if other people were near he would gag them first to silence their cries. He said that on one occasion, he miscalculated how near his place was to a highway, so that he had to restrain himself from mutilating the little boy he had with him, because he was afraid some passing motorists would hear the screams. He must have known that he was doing something wrong.

Otherwise, why would he gag children only when he could be overheard? Why did he refrain the time he was too near a highway? Why did he rarely return to the same area? Why did he prefer children whose absence would raise less disturbance? Why did he want to prowl unnoticed? All of these facts indicate that he knew he was doing something wrong; and the court thought so too.

Here is a situation where a manifestly psychotic offender was convicted of murder because (in spite of his psychosis) he knew he was doing something wrong. This conviction was sustained on appeal. The defense psychiatrist argued that, even within the framework of the McNaghten formula, this patient should have been acquitted. He quotes the defendant as once having said: "What I did must have been right or an angel would have stopped me just as he stopped Abraham in the Bible." From this the defense expert concluded that the offender did not realize he was doing something wrong, since he thought his assaults had divine approval. However, the test is one of action, not words. This defendant *acted* as if he knew he was doing something wrong. This is evidenced by his numerous and effective schemes for avoiding detection and identification. To counter this by citing the offender's *words* seems naïve. We have to deal with operational concepts, not with abstractions; with the actual and anticipated deeds of people, not with their words.

In this connection, Judge Cardozo [20] once made the following point: "If there is an insane delusion . . . that God has ordained the commission of a crime, it cannot be said of the offender that he knows the act to be wrong."

However, before a psychotic defendant can be acquitted on this theory, it must be shown—by his *actions,* not by his statements—that he did not consider the act wrong. In the original McNaghten case, for instance, that is exactly what happened. McNaghten perpetrated his murder openly, with no effort at escape, concealment or disguise, and with a good deal of avowed self-satisfaction that he had brought about a great public benefit. Here the offender's *actions* were in conformity with his *statement* that this killing was not wrong. But in the case cited on the previous page, the offender's actions indicated that he knew he was doing something wrong.

Thus psychosis, in theory at least, is not necessarily a bar to conviction. In practice, however, many judges will dismiss an indictment against a psychotic defendant; indeed, many prosecutors will refuse to ask for an indictment if the offender is unquestionably

[20] People v. Schmidt, 110 Northeastern 945.

psychotic. This, however, is a matter of practice depending on individual enlightenment. It is certainly not written into law.

Psychosis may stop a trial simply because the defendant is unable to participate or cooperate in his own defense, or to plead. This has no bearing on the possibility of his being found guilty: it merely delays the trial until he can cooperate in his own defense. If the accused is a deteriorated psychotic, this may mean a permanent abandonment of the trial.

Psychoneurosis.—Ordinarily a psychoneurosis is not considered one of the "diseases of the mind" necessary to establish a defense of irresponsibility. In general, when a psychoneurotic commits a crime, he knows what he is doing. Special problems are presented in (*a*) hysterical fugues, (*b*) compulsive neuroses, and (*c*) sexually immature or sexually deviated psychoneurotics.

a) *In hysterical fugues,* the patient's responsibility is evaluated within the framework of the fugue. The fact that he has no recollection of the crime has no bearing on his responsibility. If, within the fugue period, he acted as if he knew *what* he was doing and as if he knew he was doing something wrong, he is held accountable. If, for example, in an hysterical fugue, a person commits a burglary, carefully wipes away his fingerprints, stealthily finds his way out, and cleverly eludes pursuit, it must be acknowledged that he acted as if he knew he was doing something wrong. Also see page 16.

b) *Compulsive neuroses* will exculpate the defendant in states where irresistible impulse is a defense but will have no effect in other jurisdictions. See page 11 for discussion of irresistible impulse.

c) *Sexually immature* or *sexually deviated neurotics* are held accountable for offenses committed as a result of aberration. See Chapter 8.

Epilepsy.—In itself, epilepsy cannot exculpate an offender. If a crime is committed during a psychomotor equivalent period or during an epileptic fugue, the patient's accountability is measured by determining whether he acted as if he knew he had done something wrong. See page 15, *Amnesia,* for further review of this point. Crimes committed in a postconvulsive confusional state are evaluated in terms of the patient's ability to appraise the wrongfulness of the act. If the confusion is great, it will be obvious that the offender did not know what he was doing. Accidental injuries inflicted to property or to bystanders are not criminally charged to the epileptic if the injury occurred during the acute phase of a convulsion, since obviously there was no intent to do wrong.

Sex Offenses.—See Chapter 8.

Psychopathic Personality.—Psychopathic personality, under whatever name designated, does not impair a defendant's accountability. Once a diagnosis of constitutional psychopathy or psychopathic personality has been made, the defense counsel is certain to exploit the term by telling the jury that the word "psychopath" means "disease of the mind" which—in a literal sense—it does. The inexperienced psychiatrist often has difficulty in extricating himself from the entanglement caused by the word "psychopath." He has to admit that it is a mental disorder, that it is not something which the defendant willfully became, and that, were it not for this disorder, the accused would not have committed the crime. Taken together, these three statements sound as if the offender must be relieved of all responsibility. This, of course, is nonsense, but the problem is how to explain to the court that psychopathy does *not* mean irresponsibility —how to explain it without delivering an unsolicited lecture.

Legally, there is a vast gulf between disorders of thinking and feeling (such as psychoses and mental deficiency), on the one hand, and "disorders of character" on the other. Society assumes that alcoholism, sexual perversion, drug addiction, and psychopathy are disorders of character—and often refers to these as "deviations of moral faculties." The psychiatrist thinks of alcoholism, homosexuality, psychopathy, and the like as "sicknesses" in the same sense that hysteria or schizophrenia is a sickness. However, society, speaking through the law, insists on segregating the two groups of disorders. Nor is this an unreasonable demand. There does seem to be some force corresponding to the "conscience," and patients with character disorders do seem to have a less effective "conscience" than psychoneurotics.[21]

Certainly the psychopath knows that what he is doing is wrong. He seeks to explain, neutralize, or escape from his offenses by evasive explanations, flight, or the piling up of one prevarication on another. These actions do indicate that he knows he has done something wrong. When closely watched, the psychopath rarely commits crimes: a fact which indicates that he *can* adhere to the right; that is, that he is not suffering from irresistible impulse. In evaluating the accountability of the psychopath, the examiner keeps in mind three

[21] It is true that a character defect is not the person's fault—that the psychopath no more elected his weak superego than a tuberculosis victim elected his "weak lungs." This, however, is immaterial. To argue that the psychopath should be exculpated because psychopathy is an illness would be like saying that a blind man should not be penalized by being denied a driver's license, since it was not his fault that he is blind.

basic questions: (*a*) Does the offender have a disease or a character defect? (*b*) Does he know that he has done something wrong? (*c*) Was he capable of doing the right thing—that is, could he have refrained from yielding to the impulse which led to the crime? The last question is answered by analyzing the problem in terms of "irresistible impulse" as detailed on page 11. Usually the psychopath's life history indicates clearly that he knows when he does something wrong. And on the first question, the law has repeatedly made it clear that psychopathic personality is to be classed, for forensic purposes, as a character defect [22] and not as a disease of the mind.

This may be impalatable to the psychiatrist, but society apparently feels that in self-protection it cannot allow a man freedom to commit a crime on the theory that he was the victim of an ungovernable rage. To exculpate the psychopath, or the man who commits a crime in a fit of rage, would be to penalize those who exercise restraint and offer a reward to the ill-tempered and undisciplined. This is how one thoughtful nonpsychiatrist, William Bolitho, puts it:

In its latest form, the theory seems to run that madness is an emotional disorder. Intellect may be unimpaired, though the critical faculties are weakened. But even in deep science, logic has not lost her rights. To say that "this man is mad because we (psychiatrists) think he must have felt mad" is not a tolerable proposition however it is wrapped. Before the shades of meaning of derangement, weak-mindedness, and irresponsibility can be applied confidently, something more than the terribly abstract norm of conduct hitherto set up will have to be devised. Surely ambition, greed, selfishness, and vanity are as normal as their contraries.[23]

[22] See footnote 21.
[23] William Bolitho, *Murder for Profit* (Garden City, N. Y.: Garden City Publishing Co., Inc., 1926), pp. 6-7.

Chapter 2

EXAMINATION OF THE DEFENDANT

Self-Incrimination

Examining a defendant in a criminal case, the psychiatrist must first be certain that he is not "trapping" the patient into making damaging admissions. (The problem is an ethical rather than a legal one, since most courts refuse to consider a psychiatric examination as a form of "compulsory self-incrimination.") If the result of the mental examination is unfavorable to the defense, it might be argued that the psychiatric interview was, in effect, an underhand way of getting the patient to incriminate himself. There is no legal substance to this thesis, but doctors should err on the side of ethical scrupulousness and be sure that there can be no moral basis for it either. On the legal side, the following two dicta are illuminating:

> Testimony showed that the doctor informed the accused that he had been requested by the county attorney to make the examination. He told the accused that he did not have to answer any questions. The accused submitted to the mental tests without objection. Such testimony is admissible when accused submits to an examination if there were no threats, duress, objection, or deceptions. Such an examination is *not subject to the objection that the defendant was compelled to give testimony against himself.*[1]

> An examination of the defendant to ascertain mental condition is not a deprivation of constitutional rights; nor does such an examination require him to give evidence against himself.[2]

While the prosecutor's psychiatrist is thus legally safe in conducting an examination without consent of (or knowledge of) the defense attorney, it is good form to apprise the patient that the doctor is taking notes, that he will submit a report to the court (or prosecutor or probation officer), and that the patient does not have to tell the doctor anything. The experienced examiner usually says, "I'm a doctor, trying to understand how you happened to get into this trouble. You're under no obligation to answer my questions or tell me anything, but I hope that whatever you do tell me will be the

[1] Wenkel v. State, 218 Northwestern Reporter 137.
[2] Blocker v. State, 110 Southern Reporter 547.

truth. If you'd rather not answer a question, just say so, and it will be perfectly all right. I'm making notes and afterwards I'll send in a report." It might be expected that such a warning would dry up the patient's flow of words, but it usually has no such effect. After the defendant "warms up" to the subject, he generally talks freely enough.

It is essential that the doctor take elaborate notes and that large fragments of the patient's remarks be written down verbatim. These remarks may or may not be included in the report; they also serve to enable the examiner to support his conclusions by firsthand evidence. In Britain [3] it is considered unsporting for the doctor to ask the accused whether he has committed the crime, but American psychiatrists often find it impossible to conduct a thorough mental examination without somehow touching on that point. The general technique of the examination differs little from the routine of a psychiatric examination made elsewhere except that the doctor must keep the McNaghten formula [4] clearly in mind. Did he know the nature of the act? The quality of the act? The wrongfulness of the act? And if so, was his not knowing that the act was wrong caused by a mental disorder?

Preliminary Briefing

It is unwise to conduct this kind of mental examination without a preliminary briefing. The psychiatrist obtains the facts from the investigating officer and asks permission to read the statements of the witnesses and of the accused. For instance, a crime may have been committed in a rage. The witnesses' stories of how the patient looked, what he said and how he acted are helpful to the examiner in determining whether this was an epileptic furor, a drunken rage, or a momentary lapse of inhibition in an otherwise normal man.

A guide to the psychiatric examination of defendants will be found on page 29 and also in Appendix C. The following outline of preliminary briefing may be helpful:

1. Consider first the *source* of the request. While this makes no difference in the examiner's final decision, it does affect his approach. The examination may be requested by:

---

[3] For example, Mercier warns the "examiner against questioning a prisoner as to whether he had committed the crime or as to the circumstances of the offense. I have heard caustic comments from the bench on this practice." Apparently the British psychiatrist is not even supposed to review the "surrounding circumstances." Charles Mercier, *Criminal Responsibility* (New York: Physicians and Surgeons Book Co., 1926), p. 233.

[4] See page 3 of Chapter 1.

a) The prosecutor or district attorney;

b) The defense counsel, family, or organization to which the defendant belongs (church, labor union, veterans' organization, and the
like):

c) An impartial source such as the judge, probation office, or social
agency.

2. In accepting the assignment, the psychiatrist makes it clear
that he is *not* undertaking to find the defendant responsible or irresponsible according to the "side" which has engaged him. Thus, in
agreeing to examine an offender on behalf of the defense counsel, the
psychiatrist explains his position this way: "I can't guarantee, even
after what you have just told me, that I'll find this man insane or
irresponsible. I'm going to send you an honest report, and I know
you won't expect me to shade the truth or give an opinion in conflict
with my own conscience." These words sound like pious cant, but
they are necessary to spare subsequent embarrassment. Unless this
position is made plain prior to the examination, the doctor may find
himself in this position: he sends in a report which is so useless to
the lawyer concerned that the doctor will not be called on to testify.
Probably the report itself is destroyed because the attorney does not
want to risk its being found in his file. When the doctor tries to
collect his fee, the counsel refuses to pay it, stating: "We engaged you
to help us in the defense; you turned out to be of no use to us at all;
I can't ask the defendant to pay money to help his own prosecution.
We asked you to render a service. You have not rendered that
service. Therefore we owe you nothing." Where possible, the source
engaging the doctor should be asked to confirm the agreement in a
letter; and the examiner answers the letter, indicating that he is going
to give an accurate report of psychiatric findings, without precon-
ception. The carbon copy of this answer is retained in the psychiatrist's file.

3. If the doctor's report is unfavorable to the party engaging him,
the examiner will not, of course, be asked to testify for that side. It
would be unethical for him to testify for the other side because, in
preparing for the original examination, he had access to the files of
the "opponent." He could be called to court on a *subpoena,* but he
could not, under those circumstances, be compelled to give an opinion.[5] For example, a doctor called by defense counsel found that the
offender was a psychopath, that he was "not insane," and that he
knew he was doing something wrong at the time of the offense. Ob-

[5] See page 242 of Chapter 15.

viously, the defense counsel is neither going to use this report nor ask the doctor to testify. The prosecutor hears that Dr. X examined the defendant and notices that he is not called as a witness. He concludes therefore that Dr. X's findings were unfavorable to the defense and asks him to testify for the state. This the doctor cannot ethically do, since he obtained information from the patient at a time when the latter identified the psychiatrist as being "on his side." He therefore declines to appear as a witness for the prosecution. The district attorney might serve a *subpoena* on the doctor. (In practice, this is not likely to happen. Attorneys have no wish to put hostile witnesses on the stand if they can avoid it.) As a subpoenaed witness the doctor must testify as to facts. Asked *when* he examined the defendant, he must reply. However, unless he has formally written down a diagnosis, he can decline to answer a question such as "What was your diagnosis?" on the grounds that diagnosis is a matter of opinion, and that he is testifying only in response to a *subpoena*. Still more, he can decline to answer questions touching on the defendant's knowledge of the nature, quality or wrongfulness of his acts. See Chapter 15 for a further discussion of this.

4. The examiner's next step is to obtain the *facts* of the case. A psychiatrist will certainly be embarrassed if he examines a defendant in the absence of the whole story. He then has to rely on the patient's own explanation of events, and, as often as not, this explanation is factually incorrect. Many defendants are psychopaths, and many psychopaths tell untruths with glibness and assurance, so that only a naïve examiner accepts as fact the information furnished by the patient. The attorney should turn over to his psychiatrist an extensive summary of all the facts about the offense and all the available data about the offender. If practical, the doctor postpones his examination until after the probation officer has conducted his investigation and then obtains a copy of that report. For instance, it may be material to know something of the schooling, family background, and past medical history of the defendant. The probation office report is the most compact repository of that information.

The experienced examiner does not allow himself to be flattered into giving an offender "a sanity test" until he gets an adequate history. If the examination is being conducted on behalf of the defense, the family are interviewed, and the defendant's statements to his counsel are analyzed. If the examination is being made for the prosecutor, a summary of the complaint, of the statements of preliminary witnesses, and of the findings of the investigating officers should be made available. If the examination is made at the request of the judge or probation office, the files should be furnished to or summarized for the doctor. The physician should insist on the same standards of history-taking and history-verifying at these examinations as in any good mental hygiene clinic.

5. If the defendant is in a cell, it is necessary to obtain an order to enter the jail and examine him. It is the function of the requesting attorney to obtain the necessary order. The doctor should be certain he has this document with him before he leaves for the jail. Otherwise he may find that the jail is harder to get into than out of. Failure to attend to this may mean that the psychiatrist has driven all he way to the jail only to find that he gets no further than the warden's office, and that he has to return, his mission unaccomplished.

Examinations are ordered more often in capital cases than in less serious offenses. And in capital cases bail is generally denied, so that the examination must be conducted in jail. The doctor asks to have the prisoner brought into the jail infirmary for the examination. If this is refused, the interview may take place in the warden's office, in a visiting room, or, if necessary (though this is undesirable), in the cell. A guard or warden will introduce the doctor, who should explain to the patient that he is a physician, that he is going to examine and interview the defendant, that notes will be taken, and a report sent (indicating to whom) and that the prisoner should not tell the doctor anything that he does not want in the report. The warden or guard should be present during this statement, and the examiner's notes should indicate that this statement has been made. This is to prevent any subsequent complaint of compulsory self-incrimination.

After this has been accomplished, the guard or warden should be asked to leave the room. If the rules of the jail require that a third party be present, the examiner should ask that the third party be the jail doctor, nurse, probation officer, or medical orderly. If a third party remains during the examination, this fact should be recorded in the notes and included in the report. It is unwise to conduct the psychiatric interview in the presence of the defense counsel or in the presence of a representative of the prosecutor's office, though sometimes this is made an absolute condition of the examination.

6. In the event that the defendant is out on bail, he should come to the psychiatrist's office for the examination if this is at all possible. If this is not feasible, the interview should be conducted in a clinic, another doctor's office, in the patient's home, or in the probation office—this being the order of decreasing desirability. Since there are emotional implications in the place at which the examination is made, the site of the examination should be mentioned in the record.

Aims of the Examination

The inexperienced examiner will have on the desk a card which lists all the questions which the examination must answer. He checks against this list as he goes along; and before concluding the examination, he reviews the list to be certain that all questions have been answered. Otherwise he may find, when he is dictating his report, that some essential point has been omitted.

The questions to be answered in the report are these:

1. What is the clinical psychiatric diagnosis?
2. What does a physical examination reveal?
3. Is the defendant sane?
4. What is his intelligence level?
5. Is he a chronic alcoholic?
6. Was he drunk when the offense was committed?
7. Is he addicted to marihuana, opiates, or other drugs?
8. Did he know the nature of the act charged?
9. Did he know the quality of the act charged?
10. Did he know that the act was something which the community considers wrong?
11. Does he understand the seriousness of his predicament?
12. Is he mentally and emotionally capable of cooperating in his own defense?
13. Was he capable of forming the degree of intent, willfulness, or premeditation which the act requires?
14. Was he in the grip of an irresistible impulse at the time he committed the act? If so, was this impulse part of (a) a psychosis, (b) a psychoneurosis, (c) the rage reaction of a psychopath, (d) the rage reaction of a normal, but unstable and frustrated person?
15. If amnesia for the offense is alleged, was the offender:
    a) Suffering from a cerebral concussion?
    b) From epilepsy in any form?
    c) From a hysterical amnesia?
    d) From pathologic intoxication or some other form of alcoholism?
16. What is the prognosis in terms of treatability and future danger to society?

These questions are *not* a guide to a psychiatric examination. They simply represent points on which the doctor might be examined or cross-examined in court, and on which he should have a clear and crisp opinion. Before he leaves the interview, the psychiatrist checks each of these questions against his findings and, by extending the interview where necessary, fills out any that have not yet been answered. Replies to the questions above listed will meet almost any relevant query that might be raised as to the criminal responsibility of the defendant.

Physical Examination

A physical examination (with emphasis on a neurologic survey) is done on all defendants. There are three reasons for this: (a) The examiner's relationship with the offender revolves around his status as a doctor, and it is the stethoscope and "look at the tongue" which symbolize the doctor; (b) the judge and jury always assume that an "examination" includes a physical examination and will feel that the physician was negligent (or not a "real doctor") if he admits that he did not do a physical examination; and (c) something relevant might be found at physical or neurologic examination.

Since the technique of the physical examination is the common currency of any doctor of medicine, the methods need not be detailed here. It may, however, be desirable to list some of the commoner syndromes picked up in the examination of defendants. Below is a roster of clues, the finding of which should lead to further medical study. This is *not* a complete table of diagnostic signs.

Alcoholism: Dilatation of peripheral vessels, tremors, liver enlargement, evidences of peripheral neuritis.

Cerebral Arteriosclerosis: Hardened peripheral vessels, tortuous retinal vessels, arcus senilis, blood pressure changes.

Drug addiction: Pallor, emaciation, coated tongue, needle marks, unequal or small pupils, constipation, tremors.

Encephalitis: History of sleeping sickness, of "influenza," slowing down of movements, tremors, facial rigidity, impaired associated movements, impaired ocular accommodation.

Endocrine defects: These often have a marked influence on personality. The examiner notes size, height, weight, body build, hair distribution, and status of genitalia.

Epilepsy: Periods of impaired consciousness, scars on tongue, characteristic electro-encephalographic tracings.

Hearing defects: These are sometimes denied or concealed by the patient. Examination should always include at least a cursory test of hearing acumen to whispered and conversational voice at several distances and tuning fork responses in the Weber and Rinne tests, with audiometry if needed.

Hyperthyroidism: Fast pulse, exophthalmos, sweating, tremors, and increased metabolic rate.

Hypothyroidism: Myxedema, lowered metabolic rate, slow pulse, dry coarse skin, cretinism.

Neurosyphilis: Pupillary changes, tremors, positive Romberg sign, spinal fluid changes, diminished or absent patellar reflexes, and cardiologic evidence of syphilitic heart disease.

Scars: The entire body should be surveyed and every scar or bruise should be charted. Causes to be considered include: head injuries, bullet wounds, needle injections, self-inflicted injuries, syphilis, epileptic injuries, operative incisions, and injuries sustained in brawls, or perpetrated by guards, policemen,[6] attendants, or fellow prisoners.

Senility: Arcus senilis, tremors, prostatic enlargement, arteriosclerosis.

Visual Defects: If standard test types are not available, test for ability to read standard newspaper type at varying distances. Do a rough perimetry if standard equipment is not at hand. Note if defendant needs or wears glasses.

Whether the physical examination should precede, follow or accompany the psychiatric interview depends on the circumstances of the case and the nature of the doctor's relationship to the defendant. If the latter is surly or suspicious it is probably better to begin with the relatively impersonal physical examination and springboard from physical findings into queries about "nervousness," emotional tension, etc. In other situations (particularly when the doctor is examining at the request of defense counsel and the patient has been prepared for the interview) it is practical to start with the psychiatric study.

Mental Examination

The psychiatric examination itself does not follow any rigid or predetermined pattern. It should however be comprehensive enough to assure an answer to the questions listed on page 28. Many standard psychiatric forms are available. As a minimum, each examination should include:

1. Patient's general behavior, attitude toward examiner, cooperativeness.

---

[6] Sometimes the psychiatrist's note on this point may be catapulted into prominence when the offender alleges "third degree" methods by the police. Thus, in fairness to both the police and the patient, scar charting should be scrupulously accomplished.

2. State of consciousness with reference to clarity, "brightness," and general awareness.

3. Psychomotor activity; especially degree of restlessness, speed of thinking, evidence of any motor tics or verbal stereotypy, productivity, articulateness, coherence, and the general pressure of thought, actions, and words.

4. Mood; what it is, how profound it is, how appropriate to the situation, and how stable it appears to be.

5. Orientation and general contact with reality.

6. Memory; remote events, recent events, notation of any alleged memory gaps particularly with reference to the offense and its surrounding circumstances, digit memory span, tests of recall, comparison of these findings with apparent memory gaps.

7. Hallucinations; kind, vividness, and patient's reactions to them. Are the hallucinations volunteered by the patient? Are they readily elicited by the examiner? Brought out reluctantly? Or evidenced only by implications? Does the patient consider these dreams or "imaginations?"

8. Sense of remorse, guilt, recrimination, or shame.

9. Delusions; their nature, profundity, and stability. Does patient volunteer information about delusions? Are delusions inferred by actions? Are they elicited only by questions?

10. Insight; does offender consider himself a "mental case?" Does he justify his actions on the basis of "nervousness?" How does he evaluate his own mental status?

11. Intelligence; compare top school level with age at which he left school. Are intelligence test scores available in the record? Do patient's conversation and vocational career conform to this estimate of mental age? Results of any formal psychometric test done now or previously. Does emotional state make accurate appraisal of intelligence impossible?

12. Personality; curiously enough, many competent psychiatrists write a good formal psychiatric examination, covering all the above points, and then completely forget to paint any personality profile of the patient. Several special guides to personality analysis are on the market, and the examiner should have at least one of these available. In general the personality is gaged by assembling data on points such as these:

—Is the patient seclusive or extroverted?
—Is he normally moody or stable?
—Is he in vigorous health or is he generally "ailing?"

—Is he ambitious or satisfied with his lot in life?

—Is he energetic or lazy?

—Is he amiable, friendly, unfriendly, or sullen?

—Is he mature or immature?

—Does he make good use of his assets?

—What handicaps does he have and how is he meeting them?

—In general, what about his relations with people: with friends, relatives, members of the opposite sex, co-workers, etc.?

—Is he impulsive, deliberate, spontaneous, rigid, or what?

Of course people do not neatly fall into one pole or the other of these dichotomies, and part of the examiner's skill lies in his ability to indicate where the patient falls with the respect to the extremes of range at each level.

13. Review of findings in terms of the basic questions: Analyze the questions listed on page 28 and make additional observations necessary to reply to any unanswered questions in that list.

Stuporous or Comatose Patients.—If the patient is stuporous or comatose, there is little practical point in doing a complete psychiatric examination, except (*a*) to rule out malingering, or (*b*) to determine the cause of, and treatment for, the stupor or coma. A patient in such a state cannot plead, cannot be arraigned, cannot cooperate in his own defense. Legal action would be suspended until his mental state clarified.

Uncooperative Patients.—If the prisoner is alert but uncooperative, it will be necessary first to fine-comb the history and results of the probation office study or other investigations. The examiner will then notice the following:

1. Is the patient uncooperative in the sense of remaining mute, or is he simply refusing to answer any questions because his attorney told him to say nothing? or because he is suspicious of the examiner? or because of delusions? The shrewd examiner can often get much material out of the patient's announced reasons for his unwillingness to cooperate.

2. Is he acting as if he were frightened, hallucinating, or delusional?

3. If he is engaging in bizarre activity, does this look like buffoonery?

4. If he is quiet and motionless, does he display waxy flexibility? How does he react to a pin when he is suddenly pricked on the back? When he sees the pin approaching?

5. Is he violent, noisy, obscene, bellicose, or aggressive?

6. If he is calm, does he seem disinterested and indifferent? or catatonic? or interested but skeptical?
7. If quiet, does he present the picture of a person in psychic pain? Is he depressed?
8. Does he keep repeating any pattern of words or gestures?
9. Describe his posture and physical attitude. Note evidences of tension, tics, spasms, paralyzed limbs, or bizarre postures or attitudes.
10. Does anything said or done by the examiner provoke any overt emotional response? If so, what?
11. Offer him pencil and paper. Does he write or draw? Does he hold the pencil, drop it, or throw it at examiner?
12. Describe his facial expression, noting whether it displays anxiety, fear, laughter, indifference, or what. Does it change during the examination? Look at his eyes. Do they roll? Do they fix on the examiner or on his pen?
13. Do a physical examination. Note moisture, color, and warmth of skin. Test for areas of anesthesia. Test corneal reflexes. Look for abnormal skin reflexes (such as the Babinski sign). Examine eyegrounds if possible. Take patient's temperature and pulse. Listen for heart murmurs and regularity of cardiac sounds.
14. Find out (from guards if patient is a prisoner; from nurses if patient is in hospital; from family if he is at home) whether he is usually uncooperative; if not, obtain best description possible of general behavior. Ask informants to give concrete illustrations. (For instance, if they say he "acted queer," obtain specific instances of such queerness, etc.)

Intelligence.—Intelligence should always be measured—or at least estimated. If it is obvious from casual conversation that intellectual defect is not a factor, a formal psychometric report will be unnecessary. However, the record should show that there is no evidence of such defect. In all patients, and especially in juveniles, it is desirable to know both (a) the general intelligence level, and (b) in what areas intelligence is superior and in what fields it lags. (See Chapter 10.)

If there has been a good probation office investigation or social history, an intelligence score will appear somewhere in the file. Anyone who has been through an American public school will have had at least one psychometric test on record. A defendant who served in the Army or Navy will have a psychometric test score on file, either with the Veterans Administration or in the Adjutant General's office or in the office of the Bureau of Naval Personnel. If these are not available, an estimate of intelligence may be suggested by the school record. Except where "social promotion" is the rule, the highest school grade accomplished will give a rough estimate of the subject's mental age. In most American schools this is based on first grade being set for a mental age of six, and each grade thereafter for a year higher in mental age. Thus the highest school grade plus five gives a rough estimate of mental age. A man who had left school in the seventh grade probably had a mental age of seven plus five, that is, twelve. First year high school counts as ninth grade, second year as tenth grade, etc. An offender who successfully completed second year high school (tenth grade) probably has a mental age of at least fifteen.

Since mental deficiency is not considered a factor unless mental age falls below thirteen or fourteen, it may be taken as a general rule that anyone who was able to do any successful work in any grade in an American high schol is *not* a mental defective. This may have to be modified in four situations:

1. Where "social promotion" is practiced.
2. Where the school system was inferior to average American standards.
3. Where head injury, encephalitis, or other disorders are alleged to have caused mental deficiency in later life.
4. Where a child had to leave grammar school prematurely for economic reasons.

A psychologist should be available to do psychometric tests on all offenders. In practice this desideratum is seldom achieved. Every psychiatrist doing criminal court work should, therefore, be equipped to do his own psychometric tests. What is needed is simply an answer to the question: Does mental defect play a role in this case? For this purpose, exact mental age scores, though interesting, are unnecessary. Any standard psychometric test capable of furnishing a mental age within one year or an intelligence quotient within ten points will be sufficient, although, of course, the examiner will do a better job if he is capable of administering a test which gives the score with some sensitivity.

Repeated Interviews.—Psychiatrists frequently insist that a period of observation is essential to the making of an adequate diagnosis. For this reason, in many places, psychopathic wards are called "observation wards." It may be necessary for the examiner to ask for a second interview. This may be needed if the patient was stuporous, uncooperative, or acutely disturbed at the initial examination. It may be needed if the clinical syndrome is confusing, unclear, or inconsistent. The examiner should, however, make such request as seldom as possible. If he feels he can always see the defendant again, he has an unconscious tendency to postpone a decision. Frequently it is impractical to permit a second or third interview, or it may mean postponing trial or sentence. In practice, experienced examiners reach their diagnosis after a single interview in 90 or 95 per cent of cases. The psychiatrist who consistently demands repeated examinations is therefore soon held up to unfavorable comparison with his more decisive colleagues. On the other hand, where the matter is of grave importance, where the accumulation of new data has made re-examination necessary, or where the first session was clearly unsatisfactory, a second interview should be requested.

Hospital Observation.—The advantages of confining the defendant to a hospital for observation are obvious. In doubtful cases this is a better procedure than asking for a re-examination in jail. But before recommending hospitalization, the examiner must consider the following: Will the hospital staff really study the patient, or will he simply be housed and fed? Is the hospital secure enough to make the defendant's escape unlikely? What will the patient's legal status be? It sounds incredible, but sometimes dangerous defendants have been permitted to enter state hospitals on a voluntary status, so that they could walk out at any time. Will the hospital staff send its report to *both* attorneys and to the judge, or is it available to the state (prosecution) only? Who takes responsibility for the report—the superintendent, the ward officer, the chief of the section, and will he be available for court testimony if necessary?

Special Procedures

It is a temptation for the examiner to request some special laboratory test—such as an X-ray, an electro-encephalogram, or a blood chemistry—before venturing an opinion. While the psychiatrist should practice good medicine, he should think twice before insisting on some special technical procedure. In practice, the yield from such tests is surprisingly meager. It is interesting to know what the defendant will say under barbiturate narcosis; but if such statements are inadmissible as evidence the procedure will contribute nothing to the determination of the defendant's guilt or responsibility. Thus, narcosynthesis is more useful to the prison psychiatrist, or in presentence investigations, than to the examiner who is asked to make a determination of responsibility—except in jurisdictions where the results are admissible in evidence.

It is also necessary to consider the legal standing of these tests in another sense : Can they be forced on the patient against his will? If he consents, will the tests be excluded as "self-serving declarations"? If he refuses, will the results be excluded as "compulsory self-incrimination?" The psychiatrist must also ask himself what he would do if the test result conflicted with his clinical judgment; for example, if he believes that the patient's behavior indicates traumatic constitution, even though X-rays and spinal fluid studies are negative. In that situation, the psychiatrist presumably will adhere to his clinical opinion and ignore the negative test results. That being so, what was the purpose of ordering the tests (and thus consuming time, money and manpower) in the first place? If after weighing all these factors the examiner still believes that special technical procedures are needed, the following may be considered :

Electro-Encephalography. In forensic psychiatry this is useful in determining the nature of the "black-out spells" and periods of amnesia alleged by defendants; and in assaying the results of head injuries.

Skull X-rays. Friends of the defendant frequently alleged that he engaged in delinquent behavior only after he suffered a blow on the head. And sometimes, in a crime of violence, the perpetrator, as well as the victim, sustains a head injury.

Special Psychologic Tests. These are often helpful in giving the psychiatrist a deeper picture of the patient's personality structure; in determining genuine or malingered mental deficiency; in discriminating between neurotic and "psychopathic" reactions; and in helping distinguish between emotional and organic sequelae of head injury. Psychologic tests, of course, do not *make* these distinctions : they assist the clinician in making a decision.

Spinal Fluid Examination. This is often useful in (*a*) confirming a diagnosis of neurosyphilis, (*b*) appraising the extent and effects of head injury, and (*c*) in confirming or measuring alcoholism.

Narcoanalysis and Lie Detectors. These, as well as interviews under scopolamine, have been used to facilitate understanding of the defendant's emotional state and to obtain confessions. They are still imperfect and sometimes even misleading.[7] A neurotic defendant

---

[7] Frederick Redlich, Leonard Ravitz, and George Dession, *American Journal of Psychiatry,* CVII (February, 1951), 586.

carries a burden of guilt feeling anyway, and though completely innocent of the crime charged, he might make a phantasy confession. This
could be due to a combination of guilt-laden anxiety (part of the
neurotic's personality structure) and hypersuggestibility. Because
of the latter, the patient sometimes reproduces words suggested to
him by his interrogators.

This has been demonstrated experimentally by Redlich [7] who
concludes that "only individuals who, for conscious or unconscious
reasons are inclined to confess, will yield to interrogation under
narcoanalysis." Redlich and his co-workers (Ravitz and Dession)
used a group of "normal" persons and another group of neurotics.
All the "normal" persons persisted in their "cover-up" stories even
under the influence of the intravenous barbiturates. This suggests
that narcoanalysis is *not* a reliable lie-detecting instrument. On the
other hand, intravenous barbiturate interviews do satisfy the examiner's curiosity and facilitate psychiatric treatment.

Such missions, however, are beyond the goal of the pre-trial forensic examiner. Even if these methods had a 100 per cent score in
revealing the truth (and they certainly do not) the test would be
futile because its results would also certainly be excluded from the
trial record. If the material is helpful to the defense, then it would
be contended by the prosecutor that it is, after all, only a self-serving
declaration of no more value than the "not guilty" plea. If, on the
other hand, the defendant had indicated guilt in an interview under
narcosis (or hypnosis), defense counsel would try to exclude the
testimony. He can insist to the judge that the statements made by a
person while "drugged" are of no value. If the testimony is admitted
over his objections, he can say to the jury: "Would you want your
life or liberty to depend on something you said when someone had
drugged you?"

This is not to disparage the value of material obtained under
narcosis. It may help the psychiatrist to understand the patient
better and thus may be fully justified. However, the examiner must
first have a clear notion of his function. If he is advising the court
about disposition or advising prison officials about handling the inmate, then he needs all the information about the patient's mind that
he can get. However, if his function is to determine the defendant's
responsibility within the rigid framework of the McNaghten formula,
then it is a waste of time to collect large masses of completely inadmissible evidence.

The usual reaction of judges toward information obtained under
narcosis is not only an attitude of rejection; it is an attitude of scorn.

For example, here is one court's reaction to the admissibility of evidence obtained under narcosis:

In the present state of human knowledge, such a test is unworthy of serious consideration . . . the court was not told from what well this serum was taken, or in what alembic its alleged truth compelling powers were distilled. Its origin was as nebulous as its effect was uncertain. A belief in its potency, if it has any existence, is confined to the modern Cagliostros, who still as Balsamo did of old, cozen the credulous for a quid pro quo by inducing them to believe in the magic powers of philters, potions and cures by faith.[8]

There is a slowly rising tide of acceptance of lie-detectors. Most courts, however, still feel that lie detection apparatus is too experimental to permit human life or liberty to depend on its application. A typical attitude toward mechanical and physiologic lie-detectors is reflected in the following judicial opinion:

Just when a scientific principle or discovery crosses the line between the experimental and demonstrable stages is difficult to define. Somewhere in this twilight zone the evidential force of the principle must be recognized. And while the courts will go a long way in admitting expert testimony deduced from well-recognized scientific principle and discovery, the thing from which the deduction is made must be sufficiently established to have gained general acceptance in the particular field in which it belongs. . . . We think that this deception test has not yet gained such standing and scientific recognition among physiological and psychological authorities as would justify the courts in admitting expert testimony deduced from the discovery, development and experiments thus far made.[9]

Having accumulated all these data, having read the record and examined the defendant, the psychiatrist next has to make up his own mind. Courts are impatient with an examiner whose conclusion is that "in a way he was responsible, yet in another sense he wasn't." True, in most cases, it is not simply a matter of black or white. Still, the courts want help and the psychiatrist is presumably more of an expert of mental states than anyone else. A clean-cut, crisp, concrete opinion is expected. As guideposts to reaching a definite decision, the psychiatrist will review the doctrines with reference to irresistible impulse, alcoholism, mental age, amnesia, and the basic McNaghten formula elaborated in Chapter 1. These provide both a framework around which the examination may be constructed and a battery of criteria on which responsibility may be evaluated.

[8] State v. Hudson, 289 Southwestern Reporter (Missouri) 920. In this case the defense counsel offered the results of the interview as proof of his client's innocence.
[9] Fry v. United States, 293 Federal Reporter 1010.

Actual decision as to the defendant's responsibility is not made by the psychiatrist. It is the function of the jury or, in special cases, the prerogative of the judge of the trial or appellate court. The practitioner does not testify that the defendant was responsible or irresponsible. That would be a usurpation of the jury's function. He testifies as to clinical diagnosis and as to his opinion of the patient's intent and deliberateness, and as to the patient's realization of the nature, quality and wrongfulness of his acts. There the doctor's responsibility ends.

Chapter 3

REPORTING THE CRIMINAL CASE

An examination of a defendant does not necessarily mean that the psychiatrist will appear in court, but it does mean that he will submit a written report. There are many circumstances under which the examiner will not give testimony: his findings might be unfavorable; the defendant may plead guilty; the examination may have been ordered only after conviction. In any case there is no way in which he can escape writing a report.

The report of an examination of a defendant is an immortal and influential document. Words spoken in court may be misunderstood, distorted, forgotten, or, if necessary, denied. But when a psychiatrist dictates a report, he freezes into permanent form his findings, his opinions, his suggestions. He signs his name as token of his approval of the words. The report remains forever in a file cabinet— in a judge's chambers, in a warden's record room, in a probation office. Perhaps ten years later a prisoner is applying for parole, or a previously acquitted defendant has been rearrested. Now the psychiatrist's report of a decade before is unearthed and leaps into new life.

The persons who read these reports are often officials of importance in the community. They are judges, chief probation officers, parole chairmen, district attorneys. They judge the psychiatrist by the report. The document is, in a sense, the doctor's showcase, for in it is displayed in capsule form the examiner's philosophy, his accuracy, his neatness, his skill, and his common sense. Yet it is a showcase which will soon pass beyond control of the doctor, for once the report has been placed in the mail, the writer forever loses it. He cannot rewrite it, correct its errors, or explain its inconsistencies.

The report thus becomes a document that may, for good or bad, materially influence the psychiatrist's position in the community. More than that, it may save or destroy a life. The district attorney may drop charges of murder if he is satisfied with a psychiatrist's report indicating irresponsibility. If the report does not impress him, he may prosecute the case and obtain a judgment of death. In

borderline cases, the trial tactics of both defense counsel and prosecuting attorney may revolve around the reports submitted by their
psychiatrists. A defense counsel may decide whether to plead guilty
or not guilty depending on the psychiatric report. The report therefore is not a piece of correspondence to be dictated casually or offered
lightly.

The report is here considered in terms of its

1. Form
2. Style
3. Scope
4. Content
5. Use

Form

Some reports are prepared in letter style. Others are set up formally as special documents. In some cases an examination form is
used as the report, and a letter of transmittal is attached. Sometimes
a probation office has a blank form on which it wants all examinations
recorded. The exact form of the report is a minor matter, and the
psychiatrist normally accommodates himself in the preferences of the
addressee. If an attorney wants a simple "Dear Sir" letter, the report
can be written that way. If he wants a formal document headed "Examination of John Doe," he should receive it.

If no preference is indicated, the examiner uses whatever seems
"natural" to him. To most doctors this means simply a letter—much
after the fashion of a report to another doctor on a patient submitted
for consultation. It is addressed to the person requesting the examination, or to the judge if thus indicated, and is written as a simple
letter, stating that an examination was accomplished, that these findings were recorded, and that this opinion is expressed. If for any
reason the doctor or the addressee prefers a more standardized or
formal document, the paper can be set up with "Report of Psychiatric
Examination" typed on top, and then with such headings as these:

1. Name of defendant
2. Date of examination
3. Place of examination
4. Examination made by
5. At the request of
6. Case number or docket number
7. Address and age of defendant
8. Similar identifying data

As a minimum, the report is prepared in triplicate. The examiner retains the first clear carbon copy for his own files, and submits the original and the second carbon copy to the addressee. Sometimes several additional copies are advisable. It may be necessary or courteous to send copies to both attorneys and to the judge; or to these officials and also to the chief probation officer. If the material in the report will be of interest to an institution in which the defendant may be confined, it is good to have an additional copy available for that purpose. Thus it may be necessary to have the report typed in original twice or even three times, since few carbon copies after the third or fourth are legible.

Theoretically the addressee should not judge the doctor by the neatness of the report. An examiner may have a tidy mind yet employ a slovenly typist. In practice, however, people do judge by the sloppiness or neatness of a report; and, while such judgments are unconscious, they are often influential. The record may be passed around a jury-box, sent to a state institution, or maybe, if the appeal continues, read by the United States Supreme Court. It seems sensible for the examiner, therefore, to be sure that he will never be ashamed of the physical appearance of his report.

Style [1]

A good report is written in simple English with short words, short sentences, and unpretentious phrases. If the examiner finds himself using elegant language, he should review his letter, cancelling the more elaborate words and clauses, replacing them with simple English. Thus:

> . . . fundamentally, this defendant is an unctuous sycophant largely devoid of the capacity to follow through with consistency. . . .

is an elegant sentence, but it will send the probation officer to the dictionary and will give the judge the impression that the writer must be hiding ignorance behind a screen of words. Such a sentence should be recast into simpler form until it reads something like this:

> . . . this man is a scatterbrain who gets along largely by flattering his superiors. . . .

Again, consider this kind of sentence:

> With such a constellation of attributes, we conclude that the prognostic import of the psychiatric findings is indeed a guarded one. . . .

[1] See Chapter 21 for a more detailed discussion of psychiatric terminology.

This in plain English means (and should be written) :

> With this kind of personality, the outlook is poor.

Since most of the readers of these reports are laymen, it is essential that the psychiatrist avoid technical terms. For example, "flattened and inappropriate affect" is meaningless to the average official. If the phrase has to be expanded to make it clear, better let it take a few more words than run the risk of being misunderstood. So the examiner could write: "His mood was a flat one, expressing neither joy nor interest nor anxiety. He seemed unconcerned about the seriousness of the charge." While this is more wordy than "flattened and inappropriate affect," it is more easily understood—and under the circumstances brevity must be sacrificed for clarity.

The word "psychopath" should be avoided, except in the diagnosis; and even then it should be parenthetically or otherwise explained. When a psychiatrist writes: "He shows the characteristic life pattern of the psychopath," another psychiatrist will know what he means. But judges, lawyers, prison officials, and probation officers may assume that a psychopath is a psychotic. A word like "insight" is not self-explanatory. The word "psychosis" is defined in the dictionary as "any mental derangement." Other words which can be misunderstood by intelligent laymen are : libido, psychasthenia, schizoid, abreaction, unconscious, empathy, psychodynamics, superego,[2] catatonic, traumatic, and autistic. And whatever *can* be misunderstood will be misunderstood. Consequently words like these should either be omitted from the report or explained as they are used. Here, for example, are illustrations of how these words may be avoided or clarified :

> . . . Last year he was seen at the community mental hygiene clinic, where the diagnosis was "schizoid personality." This means that he was a seclusive person who did not feel comfortable in the presence of others and who did a lot of daydreaming. It does *not* mean that he was considered insane by the clinic. And he is certainly not insane now . . .

> . . . Mention has been made of the "weak superego" in this case. For all practical purposes, it means that this man has a weak conscience. For some reason, this defendant never developed that sense of discomfort which normal men feel when they do something wrong. He knows that these acts were wrong; and in the presence of policemen he would refrain —and has refrained—from doing them . . .

[2] Nine out of ten laymen believe that superego means conceit—i.e., a "big ego."

. . . This man believes that all his co-workers at the factory have joined in a conspiracy to deprive him of 'his rights.' This is, of course, a fantasy. It is not true. None the less, Mr. Jones believes it with all his heart. This constitutes a "delusion," that is, a false idea to which a person clings in spite of evidence to the contrary. Because of this delusion, he is unable to reason sanely on anything connected with his his relations to his fellow workers. And because of this delusion he committed the assault on Mr. Smith. A delusion does not necessarily mean insanity. Many sane people suffer from delusions. But in this case the delusional network is so elaborate, its destruction of his ability to reason sanely is so serious, that the delusion here is evidence of insanity. This type of insanity is called a paranoid state, which means a well-organized delusional system that noticeably affects thinking and behavior.

This last example also illustrates the desirability of short sentences ("It is not true," for instance), the wisdom of using homely phrases (". . . believes it with all his heart"), and the slow indoctrination of the reader. The paragraph takes a hundred words to lead up to a simple diagnosis. But, because the reader is taken step by step through the examiner's reasoning, he is prepared to accept the conclusion when it is presented to him.

Perhaps the best general rule about style is this: Let the doctor write naturally, without straining for effect. To some men formal diction is natural. To others an informal style is appropriate. For example, a report might begin with these words, if this is the examiner's "natural style" of writing:

Pursuant to your request, I this day accomplished a psychiatric examination on John Doe. As indicated in detail below, the defendant presents a difficult problem in disposition, because he is dangerous and will probably commit further assaults; yet he is not certifiably psychotic, and he cannot be confined in a hospital through the ordinary processes of commitment.

For most doctors, this style is somewhat stiff. Few of us ordinarily use such phrases as "pursuant to your request" or "accomplished an examination." However, the paragraph is perfectly clear, and if this style of writing comes naturally to the doctor he should use it. An examiner of different temperament might find the following more natural, whereas such writing would appear highly undignified to his more formal colleague:

That was certainly a tough problem you tossed in my lap when you asked me to examine John Doe. The man is so disturbed that he is likely to explode into violence at the slightest provocation. Yet technically he is not insane and there is no way any doctor can commit him to a state hospital. . . .

Either style is adequate, and the selection depends on the taste of the examiner. The dignified doctor who thinks in long periodic sentences cannot write like an advertising copy man without appearing faintly ludicrous. And the informal speaker who always uses colloquial and colorful language will sound pompous if he tries to write a rigidly formal report.

Scope

The scope of the report depends somewhat on the doctor's relationship with the addressee and on his point of entry into the case. If, for example, he examines a defendant after conviction but before sentence, he will probably want to include recommendations for disposition and a prognosis. On the other hand, if he has been called on by the prosecutor to examine a defendant after indictment but before trial, it will be improper for him to recommend disposition unless he finds the patient psychotic. An examiner for the defense, reporting to the defense counsel, might want to outline a nonpenal plan for managing the patient if he thought this proper.

As a maximum, the report could include the following points:

1. A review of the medical and psychiatric history of the defendant
2. The clinical findings
3. A summary of the facts and circumstances of the offense
4. The diagnosis
5. The intelligence level of the offender
6. Whether the defendant was responsible [3] for his acts
7. Whether the defendant could cooperate in his own defense
8. The prognosis and probable success of therapy
9. The type of treatment or other disposition which would be fairest to the patient and would offer safety to the community
10. A simple explanation of the emotional mechanism behind the criminal act

[3] While this must be included in the written report, it may be out of place in actual court testimony, since determining responsibility is the function of the jury or judge, not the psychiatrist. In the report, the examiner indicates whether the defendant knew the nature, quality, and wrongfulness of the act, and then draws a conclusion as to his responsibility. On the witness stand, however, he omits the conclusion, unless specifically asked—and then only if the judge approves the question.

These ten items represent the maximum scope of the report. Item 10 (a psychodynamic explanation of the patient's behavior) is generally omitted unless there is some affirmative reason for including it. It is more appropriate for reports submitted to probation officers and prison officials than for reports sent to either of the attorneys. Item 9 (recommended disposition) is not included if the patient is found to be a psychopath or is diagnosed as having no psychiatric disorder, since under those circumstances disposition is a judicial, not a psychiatric problem. Item 3 (summary of the circumstances of the offense) is included chiefly to provide the examiner with a compact abstract of the case for his own files. It may be omitted if the facts are few and the circumstances simple, and if the record of the offense is already fully available to the addressee.

Content

Every examiner soon develops his own method of writing a report, and it is better to shape the letter flexibly to meet the needs of each case than to adopt a rigid paragraph-by-paragraph form. However, inexperienced examiners may, at the beginning, find a guide useful, and the following is offered. This is not an eternal model to be followed in all cases. It is suggestive only:

Paragraph 1. Date and place of examination. Name, address, and age of the defendant. Person or agency requesting the examination.

Paragraph 2. Brief summary of the facts of the case and circumstances of the crime. While the addressee usually has this information already, it seems wise to include it here because (*a*) the retained carbon copy will complete the psychiatrist's own office record, and (*b*) it will show on what facts the psychiatrist based his conclusions, so that if these prove incorrect or incomplete, the necessary corrections and adjustments may be made.

Paragraph 3. Brief summary of the past medical, vocational, educational, social, and emotional history of the defendant.

Paragraph 4. The clinical findings, including defendant's own explanation of the offense. The guide on page 31 may be used as a basis for this paragraph.

Paragraph 5. The physical endocrine and neurologic findings. (See page 29.)

Remaining paragraphs. Answers to the sixteen questions listed on page 28—or to as many of them as seem relevant to this case. Essentially, this includes—

a) Clinical diagnosis
b) Opinion as to responsibility
c) Appraisal of prognosis
d) Recommendations

Distribution and Use of the Report

Two copies should be sent to the addressee and one retained by the psychiatrist. When the probation office has requested the examination, it will be necessary to send a single copy to the judge, as well as the two copies to the probation office. In some jurisdictions it is a matter of ethics, courtesy, or procedure to send copies to both the prosecuting attorney and the defense counsel. Whether these documents are privileged communications depends on the laws of the state, and on whether the examiner (who does not treat the offender) is legally considered as having a doctor-patient relationship with the defendant. If the psychiatrist has been privately engaged by the defense and is sending a report to the defense counsel, the document becomes, in effect, part of that attorney's file, and as such it enjoys the protection afforded by lawyer-client relationships. Whether the doctor's retained carbon copy could be subpoenaed depends on the practices of the particular state. There is a form of subpoena which requires the doctor (under penalty of contempt of court, which is what the words *sub poena* mean) to bring his records to court, and such a writ would require the examiner to take his carbon copy of the report with him to the court room. That, however, does not automatically expose it to the jury, since it would first be necessary to determine whether the record is considered fact or opinion evidence. If the examiner becomes a reluctant witness, testifying only because of the *subpoena,* he can exclude the carbon copy from the record by simply not referring to it. Once he refers to it, however, whether to refresh his memory or to read from it, the copy becomes, in effect, part of the evidence and may be seized as an exhibit.

If the examiner is a willing witness, it is well for him to bring the carbon copy of the report to court with him and to use it to refresh his memory in giving testimony. The attorney who is examining the doctor will have the original in his own file, and his questions will be based on that original. If the doctor has the carbon copy with him on the witness stand, the questions and answers of the direct examination will proceed more smoothly. If the doctor refers to the report, it may be seized, stamped as an exhibit, and handed to the jury. This is something for the doctor to remember when he dictates his report in the first place—it might be passed around and scrutinized by twelve of his fellow citizens. In practice this rarely happens, but since there is a possibility that it could happen, the alert examiner is careful to have nothing in that carbon copy which he would be ashamed to exhibit to twelve laymen.

Chapter 4

PERSONAL INJURY EVALUATION

The psychiatrist is called in to evaluate the effects of personal injury when:

1. A worker is injured in the course of his employment. He seeks to obtain workmen's compensation benefits, alleging that as a result of the injury he developed an emotional or mental illness. This would be a *workmen's compensation* action.
2. Someone suffers an injury not connected with his employment. He sues the person responsible, alleging that, as a result of the accident, he has developed an emotional or mental disorder. This would be a *tort* action.
3. The employer, defendant, or insurance carrier contends that the effects of an accident are "purely functional" and are not the result of structural or organic damage. This would constitute a *defense* in a tort action, or a *response* in a workmen's compensation action.
4. A subscriber holds an accident insurance policy and claims benefits under it. The company refuses to make any payments because it contends that the disorder is a "nervous" one not covered by the policy; or that the disability was not due exclusively to "accidental and external causes" but is caused, in part at least, by the subscriber's predisposition; or that the patient is not as disabled as he alleges, the excess disability being due to emotional components. The legal procedure here would be a *contract* action and psychiatric testimony would be desired by both parties to the suit.

It makes a difference to the psychiatrist whether he is examining, reporting, and testifying for or against the claimant, and whether the action is a tort, contract, or workmen's compensation procedure. If, for example, he is examining the claimant on behalf of the insurance company, employer, or defendant, he is likely to find the patient more hostile and less cooperative than if he is conducting the examination on the claimant's own behalf. This in turn affects his examination

49

technique as well as the credibility of the history and subjective symptoms. Again, the method of appraising the disability is different in compensation and tort actions. In general, in a *workmen's compensation* case, disability is evaluated in percentages and the compensation paid to the worker is, in theory, replacement for lost earning capacity. In a *tort* action, the money awarded is construed as damages rather than as replacement, and disability and prognosis are given in terms of pain, suffering, and recoverability rather than in percentages of impairment. Furthermore, a tort action is usually tried before a jury, while a workmen's compensation case is heard by a board, commissioner, or referee, so that the climate of the court room is somewhat different in the two situations.

Legal Framework

The psychiatrist will do a more polished job if he understands the fundamental nature of tort and compensation actions and the differences between them.

Tort Actions.—When one person is injured by reason of another's negligence, the victim can sue the other person. He must prove first that the defendant was negligent (and in most states that he himself was not also negligent). Then he must show that he suffered disability, personal injury, pain, or loss of earning capacity. If he does this, he will receive a cash award in dollars and cents. This closes the case, unless there is an appeal. If there is an appeal, a final, fixed award is reached and this ends the matter. (In workmen's compensation cases, on the other hand, the award is usually so many dollars a week for a specified number of weeks and, if the disability becomes greater, the case can be re-opened.)

Automobile accidents are responsible for most personal injury tort actions. If a truck driver, while at work, is involved in an accident because of another driver's negligence, he can take action both in the workmen's compensation tribunal (against his employer) and in the regular court (against the other driver). However, he does not receive the aggregate of both awards, since the employer could recover part of his compensation payment from the monies collected from the other driver.

Some psychiatrists are willing to submit a report but are loath to testify in court. For their comfort, it may be noted that the overwhelming majority of personal injury cases are settled by agreement between the lawyers and never reach a courtroom.[1]

[1] If the injured person is a child, it is usually necessary to have a jury approve the settlement. This is to protect a child from greedy parents who might dispose

In a tort action, the psychiatrist's function is to make a diagnosis, determine whether the condition was causally related to the accident, and give a prognosis. If he finds that pretraumatic personality factors played a role, he should be prepared to indicate whether the accident was a precipitating or aggravating factor or whether the accident had nothing to do with the condition found at examination.

The amount of money damages awarded is limited only by the discretion of the jury, except that where the award is egregiously out of line with the disability, the judge may reduce the award (if it is excessive) or permit a new trial (if it is inadequate). In practice, judges seldom disturb the jury's award, though appellate courts not infrequently reduce the damages. Physicians are seldom in a position to make any advance estimate of the amount that an injury is "worth" (by contrast with workmen's compensation procedures, where the experienced examiner can often estimate the percentage disability with considerable accuracy).

The psychiatrist's fee is fixed by himself, within reasonable limits. It becomes part of the claimant's "medical expenses" and is one of the items figured in computing damages. As a matter of practice, the bill submitted by the psychiatrist is usually agreed on, in advance, by the plaintiff's attorney. The size of the bill (including the frequency and nature of the professional services) becomes, in effect, a public record, as the patient must indicate all his expenses in connection with treating the injury and its aftereffects. It would be unwise for the psychiatrist to submit a bill in excess of the fees he normally charges in private practice, since the bill could be subject to scrutiny in the court room. The fee should be based on the doctor's time and services, including time wasted waiting in the court room, and (if the court house is in a distant city) time spent traveling to and from the court house. If on cross-examination the psychiatrist is asked: "Do you expect to be paid for your testimony in this case?" the answer is: "No, but I expect to be paid for my time and my professional services to the patient."

Workmen's Compensation Cases.—If a worker suffers an injury arising out of, and in the course of, his employment, he can proceed in a special tribunal (industrial accident bureau, workmen's compensation court, etc.) to apply for compensation. He is entitled to this, by law, even if he himself was contributorily negligent, or if a fellow-employee was responsible for the accident. The state usually

---

of a permanent disability claim by accepting a trifling settlement. In these *pro forma* "trials" the medical witness is not usually cross-examined, since the parties have already reached an agreement.

provides machinery for trying to dispose of the case in an amicable and informal manner, and in most jurisdictions the state agency has a medical staff to advise on fair estimates of disability. If an acceptable settlement cannot be reached, the case is docketed for hearing before a more formal tribunal, usually a referee, commissioner, or special board. At this point the worker and the employer can each call on medical experts to testify as to the extent of the disability. The physician who examines and testifies for the worker is paid a fee in accordance with an established schedule, or a fee based on an allowance made by the referee or board. He is usually forbidden to collect any additional amount from the patient. The doctor who testifies for the employer (or for his insurance company) negotiates for his fee directly with the employer or his carrier. In a workmen's compensation action, the doctor's function is to make a diagnosis, determine how this is related to the accident, and estimate the permanent disability in percentage terms. If he believes that pretraumatic personality factors played a role, he should be prepared to indicate whether the accident was a precipitating factor, an aggravating factor, or whether it had nothing to do with the condition.

The method of estimating a "percentage" of disability depends on the local law. In some states, the estimate is based on a determination of how long the patient will be disabled; in others it depends on the extent to which the workman, as a total physiologic unit, is impaired. For example, in a certain state, "total and permanent disability" means that the worker receives his regular salary (subject to a fixed maximum per week) for 400 weeks. Suppose the psychiatrist believes that after six months of treatment the patient should be able to return to work. Six months represent 26 weeks. Then the disability percentage would be $26/400$ or $6\frac{1}{2}$ per cent. In a few states, permanent and total disability means that the worker is paid his regular salary for the rest of his life.[2] Under those circumstances it is customary to use ten years as the base of computation. Ten years represent 520 weeks. If the psychiatrist believes that the patient cannot be expected to return to regular work until he has had a year of treatment, then the disability would be $52/520$ or 10 per cent. Because of extensive state-by-state variation in this formula, the inexperienced psychiatrist should consult with the referring lawyer to determine the basis for compensation in his state.

Where the "physiologic unit" (rather than expected date of return to work) is used as the yardstick, the disability estimate depends on the ratio of vocational impairment which the worker suffered as a

[2] Subject to a fixed maximum per week.

total individual. The psychiatrist would take as his base point the vocational-clinical entity represented by the patient before the accident. If the accident caused a traumatic psychosis with mental deterioration, then obviously there is total (100 per cent) vocational impairment, and the estimate would be 100 per cent. If the accident caused or precipitated a disabling psychoneurosis which reduced the patient's ability (to move around, seek employment, or work steadily) to the point where it was about one third of what it was before, then the impairment is 66⅔ per cent. Some agencies use an arbitrary formula based on the adjective-severity of the psychoneurosis. Thus, 10 per cent might be allotted to a mild, 20 per cent to a moderate, 30 per cent to a moderately severe psychoneurosis. Here, too, the inexperienced physician should ascertain the practice in the community from the referring attorney.

Conversion reactions pose a special problem. Consider, for example, a case of hysterical blindness. The worker would contend that he ought to have the same compensation as for organic blindness (usually 100 per cent), because, whether hysterical or not, he has certainly lost his sight. The employer will retort that the loss of sight is not permanent, that it might clear up overnight, and that it was, to a large extent, due to the worker's pre-existing emotional conflicts and not to the accident. In states where lump-sum payments are the rule, the psychiatrist could estimate a conversion reaction as representing half the disability which the same impairment would get if it had an organic basis. For instance, in one state organic paralysis of the arm from the shoulder down is allowed 40 per cent. A psychiatrist then could, justifiably, estimate a hysterical paralysis of the extremity at 20 per cent, on the theory that there is a fifty-fifty chance of recovery. In states where payment is made by lump sum, this would be a reasonable compromise. On the other hand, where compensation is paid in small weekly amounts, it would be easier to justify making the same estimate as for organic disease. In the example, suppose 40 per cent were allowed for permanent loss of use of the arm, and that 40 per cent means that the regular salary (subject to a fixed maximum per week) is paid for four years. (This would be the case, of course, where 100 per cent equalled ten years.) An estimate of 40 per cent could also be made for hysterical paralysis. If, before the four years (208 weeks) were up, the patient recovered use of his arm, payments could be stopped at once, and the amount of compensation would have corresponded exactly to the period of disability. If, on the other hand, the entire 208 weeks went by without return of function, the patient's benefits would be exhausted at the end of the 208th week. Then if his paralysis continued, he could collect no extra payments. (This might motivate a return of function, of course.) The worker cannot consider this unjust because he would have received no more than this even if he had had an amputation at the shoulder. And the employer cannot complain, since, in fact, the worker was disabled for 208 weeks.

From a mental hygiene viewpoint, a lump sum payment would seem better than weekly indemnification, since the latter puts a premium on remaining sick. However, there are two serious disadvantages to the lump-sum payment principle: (1) the worker often squanders the lump sum on an ill-advised investment and is left indigent, helpless, and hopeless; and (2) if the patient fails to recover after the capital sum has been spent on living expenses, he is without any recourse, since the lump-sum payment is accepted as a release against all future claims for disability arising out of that accident.

Industrial Diseases

In many states workmen's compensation benefits are payable to victims of industrial diseases, as well as to those who suffer gross mechanical injury. Most of these industrial diseases are essentially forms of poisoning, though in some (silicosis, for example) the mechanical effects of the disease are more significant than its chemical effects. Many industrial chemicals can cause neuropsychiatric syndromes,[3] for example:

Manganese is used in mining, smelting, the manufacture of safes, and in ore-separating. Manganese poisoning may cause a paralysis agitans syndrome.[4]

Carbon disulfide is used in the manufacture of artificial silk. Poisoning with this chemical may cause peripheral neuritis or a basal ganglion syndrome.[5]

Formalin is used in the dyeing, drug, tanning, and photographic industries. Formalin intoxication may manifest itself by thalamic symptoms.

Benzol and *benzene* are used in the rubber, leather, linoleum, shellac, and film trades. Poisoning with these drugs may produce a picture simulating, in some respects, chronic alcoholism.

Lead products are used in the manufacture of paint, batteries, bullets, and glass as well as in type foundries. The central and pe-

[3] Henry A. Davidson, "Occupational Disorders," *The Cyclopedia of Medicine* (Philadelphia: F. A. Davis Co., 1932).
[4] J. R. Charles, *Brain*, L (March, 1927), 30.
[5] Audo Gianotti, *Riforma medica*, XLV (September 21, 1929), 1275; and Karl Bonhoeffer, *Monatschrift für Psychiatrie und Neurologie* LXXV (April, 1930), 155.

ripheral nervous systems are both peculiarly sensitive to this metal. While lead encephalopathy is not common, it can be serious. The exact pathology is not known, but there is some evidence that lead causes either a chronic, productive meningitis [6] or actual sclerotic changes within the cerebral cortex itself.[7] Lead poisoning can also produce peripheral nerve involvement, though whether this is due to precipitation of lead acetate in the muscles [8] or to a toxic lesion in the spinal cord [9] is unknown.

Mercury is a well-known central nervous system poison and may be responsible for tremors ("the hatter's shake") and emotional instability. Mercury is used in the manufacture of hats, batteries, glass, explosives, and scientific instruments.

Carbon monoxide exposure occurs among garage employees, in the gas industry, and among any who work near blast furnaces. Carbon monoxide poisoning may cause an anoxemia which, in effect, induces a form of asphyxiation which may lead to a chronic headache and irritability that may suggest an organic or deteriorative disease of the central nervous system.

Beryllium [10] is used in the manufacture of machinery, precision instruments, electric filaments, and ceramics, and is also a source of neutrons. It may produce a degree of fatigue and irritability which leads to an erroneous diagnosis of "neurasthenia."

This is, of course, not an exhaustive list. It is obviously impossible to insert a complete textbook of industrial toxicology within this chapter. Nor is it necessary. The examiner needs only to be alerted to the possibility of industrial disease in the face of chronic neuropsychiatric symptoms. He can then ascertain to what chemicals the patient was consistently exposed, and from standard sources he can discover the clinical picture.

Traumatic Psychosis

Traumatic psychosis is an uncommon reaction. The nomenclature is confused. Many forms of posttraumatic mental disorder and encephalopathies are classed with the psychoses, though clinically they are more akin to neurotic reactions. From 1920 until early in 1952, the American Psychiatric Association used the 1920 terminology

[6] Joseph Aub, *Lead Poisoning* (Baltimore: Williams & Wilkins Co., 1926).
[7] Ruth Tuthill, *Bulletin of the Buffalo (N.Y.) General Hospital*, VII (June, 1929), 15.
[8] Paul Reznikoff, *Archives of Neurology and Psychiatry*, XVII (April, 1927), 444.
[9] G. H. Hyslop, *Archives of Neurology and Psychiatry*, X (October, 1923), 444.
[10] H. S. Martland and H. A. Brodkin, *Journal of the Medical Society of New Jersey*, XLV (January, 1948), 5.

which recognized four types of traumatic psychoses: traumatic delirium, posttraumatic personality disorder, posttraumatic mental deterioration, and miscellaneous posttraumatic reactions. It is probable that many hospitals will adhere to that nomenclature for some years after the 1952 terminology has been made available; and certainly the thousands of physicians who were trained between 1920 and 1952 will continue to use the nosology with which they have become familiar.

The 1952 edition of the *Standard Nomenclature of Diseases and Operations* (published for the American Medical Association by the Blakiston Company, Philadelphia, 1952) uses the 1952 nomenclature of the American Psychiatric Association for mental disorders. In this terminology, traumatic psychoses are called "Chronic Brain Syndromes associated with Trauma with Psychotic Reactions." The nomenclature is flexible enough to permit the affix "with neurotic reaction" or "with behavioral reaction" in lieu of "with psychotic reaction" when appropriate. This system permits the examiner to use a label which is more descriptive and more accurate than was possible under the older terminology.

In the British classification, traumatic psychoses are listed as "insanities with grosser brain lesions" (if such lesions are evidenced) and then subtyped according to the clinical symptomatology. Adolf Meyer [11] in 1904 suggested a five-class terminology: (*a*) traumatic delirium, (*b*) traumatic constitution, (*c*) traumatic defect states, (*d*) other psychosis precipitated or aggravated by trauma, and (*e*) psychosis from injury not involving the head.

Our modern classifications are not much better than this five-fold scheme suggested in 1904. The United States Army (*Field Manual* 8-45) uses the generic term "traumatic psychosis" with subtypes classed as delirium, mental enfeeblement, and "traumatic constitution."

Until April, 1952, the U.S. Veterans Administration used the phrase "Encephalopathy, traumatic, manifested by psychotic reaction" to indicate a traumatic psychosis. The same term could be used for nonpsychotic disorders related to brain injury by simply replacing "psychotic reaction" with "nonpsychotic reaction." However, the Veterans Administration now uses the American Psychiatric Association nomenclature [12] under which such lesions are listed as "Chronic Brain Syndrome associated with Trauma," with an affix

[11] Adolf Meyer, *American Journal of Insanity* (now *American Journal of Psychiatry*), LX (January, 1904), 373.
[12] George N. Raines (ed.), *Guide to Nomenclature* (Washington, D. C.: American Psychiatric Assn., 1952).

indicating "with psychotic reaction," "with neurotic reaction," or "with behavioral reaction."

Classification has, in general, proved so unsatisfactory that practically every psychiatric author conjures up his own nomenclature. One might suppose that the formal classification scheme would not be of much clinical importance since, after all, the essential problems are to recognize that a psychosis exists (or does not exist), to estimate its severity, gage the prognosis, and determine its relationship to the accident. However, when a case is litigated, or when an insurance company is paying benefits, the formal label assumes a disproportionate importance. If, for example, the psychiatrist writes that, as a result of the accident, the patient now has a "traumatic constitution," all sorts of medico-legal problems are immediately raised. Does this mean that the claimant had a constitutional predisposition? Or that the injury altered his basic personality? Or that he now has a genuine psychosis? The claimant's attorney will point to the fact that in the classification suggested by Strecker and Ebaugh [13] "traumatic constitution" is unequivocally listed as *psychosis* and is defined as a "posttraumatic dispositional change in which the patient suffers from headache, fatigues easily, is irritable and emotionally unstable." This description will fit the patient perfectly; and since Strecker and Ebaugh are psychiatrists of unimpeachable authority, the attorney will contend that his client now has a psychosis—that is, a form of "insanity"—and thus merits substantial compensation. The defense attorney, on the other hand, will point out that in most nomenclatures "traumatic constitution" is *not* listed as a psychosis, that the very word "constitution" implies an inborn or early developmental trait, and that the symptoms as described certainly do not spell out anything like "insanity."

Thus, within the framework of the law, the formal nomenclature assumes a vast importance. Perhaps the safest practice for the examiner would be to adhere to the current *Standard Nomenclature of Diseases and Operations,* [14] a copy of which can be found in the record room of any large hospital. This follows the classification of the American Psychiatric Association, identifying the traumatic psychoses as "Chronic Brain Syndromes with Psychotic Reactions." If the "reaction" is neurotic, rather than psychotic, it is listed as "Chronic Brain Syndrome with Neurotic Reaction" (or "with Behavioral Reaction" if appropriate).

[13] E. A. Strecker and F. G. Ebaugh, *Practical Clinical Psychiatry* (Philadelphia: P. Blakiston's Son & Co., Inc., 1925), p. 18.
[14] Published for the American Medical Association by The Blakiston Co., Philadelphia, 1952.

In plain English, the "official" terms for traumatic psychoses have the following implications:

Traumatic delirium embraces both the acute deliria and the more or less protracted states of disorientation and motor excitement. Acute delirium is characterized by hallucinations, confusion, excitement, and overactivity.

Posttraumatic personality disorder is the generic term for the irritability, memory defects, and sensitivity which sometimes occur following brain injury. It corresponds to the "traumatic constitution" of some classifications and may also be described as an "encephalopathy with psychotic reaction." Since it is here included under the rubric of psychoses, the term should not be used for sequels which fall short of the psychotic. Or if this is too strict a gospel, it should be made clear in reports and testimony whether a case of "posttraumatic personality disorder" is in the psychotic or nonpsychotic category.

Posttraumatic mental deterioration is a term reserved for dementia, gross intellectual or emotional deterioration or persistent and marked loss of reality contact. Sometimes an epilepsy or aphasia following head injury is assigned to this classification, but if there is no mental deterioration this would be hard to justify.

Traumatic psychosis is diagnosed when (*a*) there was a substantial head injury, (*b*) there was no overt clinical evidence of psychosis prior to the accident, and (*c*) the syndrome fits into one of the descriptions above detailed. For the role of trauma in the precipitation of other psychoses, see pages 67-72.

While traumatic psychosis is rare, psychoneurosis following injury is exceedingly common, and will be considered below.

Psychoneurosis Following Trauma

Having made a diagnosis of psychoneurosis following trauma, the examiner must next decide the exact role played by the injury. He often neglects this step, either because it is too obvious or because he assumes that "posttraumatic neurosis" is a complete formulation. However, there are two excellent reasons for the doctor's working out the exact relationship between the injury and the psychoneurosis. First, this is essential to the understanding and handling of the case. Second, if he has not thought through the exact relationship, he is likely to be embarrassed on the witness stand. Thus, the doctor may have assumed that the emotion surrounding the injury was the cause of the symptoms. It all seems clear and he mounts the witness stand in complete confidence. Under cross-examination he is asked all sorts of questions about the role of existing emotional conflicts, about the importance of pretraumatic personality factors, about the kinds of personality likely to break down under minor trauma, etc. As a result he may be talked into a complete reversal of the opinion expressed at direct examination, or he may give the court the impression that he has only the foggiest notion of the relationship between the trauma and the neurosis. An insurance company examiner may have reported that the injury was too trivial to have set off such a severe neurotic reaction, and he gives this testimony in court. The claimant's lawyer then hurls at him a series of questions about the emotionally traumatic effect of injury; reminds him that prior to this accident the claimant was emotionally stable; wants to know if the doctor thinks it was just an amazing coincidence that the patient developed symptoms after the accident.

These lines of cross-examination are not especially hard to handle, provided the doctor has in advance thought out the problem and has in his own mind a clear-cut picture of the relationship between the injury and the symptoms.

To assist in this formulation, the examiner might consider the following five-point differentiation worked out by Ebaugh and Benjamin: [15]

1. The trauma was the *cause* of the psychoneurosis. This can be said when there were no signs (manifest or latent) of mental abnormality before the injury; when the disorder would not, to the best of our opinion, have occurred now or later, had there been no injury. These criteria can be met only in head injuries, and not in many of them.

2. The trauma was a *major precipitating factor*. This would be the case in head injuries where the emotional disorder was present in latent or potential form, but where it is reasonable to suppose that, but for the accident, the symptoms would certainly not have occurred at this time.

3. The trauma was an *aggravating factor*. Here some emotional disorder was clinically manifest prior to the accident, but the course of the condition was materially affected by the injury.

4. The trauma was a *minor factor*. Here the emotional disorder was well developed prior to the injury, but the psychologic or mechanical effects of the accident contributed somewhat to the intensity of the present symptoms.

[15] F. G. Ebaugh and J. D. Benjamin, "Trauma and Mental Disorder," *Trauma and Disease,* ed. Leopold Brahdy and Samuel Kahn (Philadelphia: Lea & Febiger, 1937), chap. viii.

5. The trauma is *unrelated* to the emotional disorder. Ebaugh and Benjamin write that "if there was an asymptomatic period of more than 30 to 90 days after the injury, it is extremely unlikely that the trauma was in any way connected with the illness." (I think this is too rigid a criterion, though it has general applicability to *psychoses* following trauma. With *psychoneurosis*, the examiner cannot be so dogmatic.)

It is well for the examiner to review the five possibilities in the Ebaugh-Benjamin scheme above listed, and to classify each case in accordance with this formulation. As a further guide, I suggest the following etiologic classifications : [16]

Fright Neurosis.—This corresponds to the *Schreckneurose* of the German literature [17] and the "terror neurosis" of Strauss and Savitsky.[18] To fall into this class, the psychoneurosis must be clearly traceable to the fright, emotional shock, or terror of witnessing or taking part in an accident. The accident must be one which would produce an overwhelming or benumbing emotional effect. If the patient was a victim, he ought to have thought that he was in immediate danger of death; if he was a witness, the accident must have been one in which there was terrorizing disaster or dreadful mutilation or bleeding. It is typically the acute panic state following earthquakes, ship disasters, mine explosions, or battle. Most of us are too calloused today to be so overwhelmed in "ordinary" automobile or industrial accidents, though a neurotic fright reaction could result if the situation happened to be unusually frightening or sickening. The clinical picture here is that of acute panic followed by chronic and recurrent anxiety attacks or latent anxiety as manifested by dreams. This type of traumatic neurosis is well described by Kardiner and Spiegel [19] in these words :

The traumatic neurosis is the record of the lasting consequences of an abrupt change in the external environment to which the resources of the individual are unequal. It is the record of the disturbances created by the trauma on the previously established adaptations; and of persistent and unrelenting efforts at restitution.

[16] Henry A. Davidson, "Occupational Disorders," *The Cyclopedia of Medicine* (Philadelphia: F. A. Davis Co., 1932).
[17] P. Horn, *Zeitschrift für des Gesampte Neurologie und Psychiatrie,* XXXIV (1916), 206.
[18] I. Strauss and N. Savitsky, *American Journal of Psychiatry,* XCI (1934), 189.
[19] Abraham Kardiner and Herbert Spiegel, *War Stress and Neurotic Illness* (New York: Paul B. Hoeber, Inc., 1947).

Some psychiatrists contend that even in these cases the patient must have had some kind of pre-existing latent psychoneurosis. As a practical matter, however, this is academic hairsplitting. It may be assumed that no man is so rugged that he could withstand any kind of trauma no matter how severe. If a person made a reasonably good emotional adjustment before the accident, and if the experience itself was of such nature as to have panicked any "average" individual, then it seems only reasonable to call this a traumatic psychoneurosis and to indict the accident as the effective precipitant.

Psychoneurosis Due to Suggestion.—A victim may be removed from the scene of an accident with relatively little emotional damage. However, in the hospital emergency room he hears the intern mention that it was surprising (or lucky) that there was no paralysis of the arm. Or in the surgical ward, he discusses his symptoms with other accident victims. Nurses, attorneys, and visitors may quite unconsciously—sometimes only by gesture or inflection—suggest symptoms. Thus a large battery of symptoms may be built up in a suggestible patient.

Latent Psychoneurosis Precipitated by the Accident.—This must be distinguished from "compensation neuroses" and also from pre-existing clinical neuroses which were aggravated by the injury. This takes a little deliberation, but the distinction is usually not too difficult. The picture here is that of a person already troubled by emotional conflict, who had not previously discovered that illness was one way of solving the conflict. As a result of the accident, he gets a degree of personal attention and freedom from responsibility that he had never previously enjoyed. This, and not compensation, represents the secondary gain from his illness. The litigation has little effect on the progress of his neurosis, but the attitudes of his family and the nature of the psychiatric treatment may have considerable influence on the course of his symptoms.

Psychoneurosis Aggravated by the Injury.—The examiner may find—indeed the patient may spell out—a distinct and pre-existing clinical psychoneurosis. The claim is that the accident aggravated the symptoms, and there is a good deal of evidence to support this. Neurotic stuttering, hysterical seizures, various phobias, and the like may have been visibly increased after the accident. In some cases it may even be possible to measure the increment. This would be true, for example, where periodic attacks of headaches, convulsions, or "spells" of some other sort existed before the accident at a known frequency. In most cases such neat mensuration is impossible, but some aggravation can be demonstrated.

Compensation Neuroses.—In some patients the desire for cash compensation may be the major, though usually unconscious, force in keeping the symptoms alive. In workmen's compensation cases, the financial award is usually small and doled out over a long period. In tort actions, the compensation could be large (in the patient's fantasy the sum might amount to tens of thousands of dollars) and is usually paid in one lump sum. Psychologically, there is a considerable difference in the dynamics of the desire for compensation in these two groups of cases. In the workmen's compensation case, the weekly award is usually much less than the claimant had been earning, or could be earning, so that the dollars-and-cents value of the neurosis is negligible. However, the money has potent symbolic value. The weekly compensation check, flowing in steadily regardless of how early the patient arises or how hard he works, is a comforting symbol of security. I know a physician who has been adjudicated as 10 per cent disabled by the Veterans Administration. He thus receives $16 a month for his psychoneurosis. His actual net income is well over a thousand dollars a month. I asked him once why he continued to claim this trifling monthly compensation when it meant that he had to be carried on federal records as a "neurotic." His answer was: "This $16 pays my life insurance. Thus I know no matter what happens to me, my family is fully protected." It was scarcely a rational explanation, but obviously this $16 a month had tremendous symbolic security value—enough to override the traditional stigma of the "neurotic" label.

The insurance company examiner frequently testifies that a desire for compensation is the prime motive. On cross-examination he is asked something like this: "If this worker had no symptoms, he could earn $60 a week at his regular job. His maximum compensation is $25 a week. If, as you say, desire for money is the prime factor here, how do you explain his election to remain ill at $25 a week rather than to earn $60 a week by getting well?" By any rational arithmetic, the decision of course is inexplicable. Actually, however, the patient gets more than $25 a week. He gets sympathy and attention; he avoids a possibly disagreeable job; he has the assurance of a steady income regardless of what happens to him. Furthermore, the motivation is rarely anything as simple as an uncomplicated greed for money. Some claimants derive unconscious satisfaction out of "punishing" the employer. Some had lived for years in fear of losing a job, and the weekly compensation check is satisfyingly independent of employment fluctuations.

In tort actions, the mechanism is somewhat different. Here the possible cash award may look to the patient like a veritable fortune. A $30-a-week laborer dreams of getting, perhaps, $50,000 in damages. That will set him up in his own business. He develops the fantasy of "being his own boss" and of the snowballing earnings which his business will yield. He usually allows, in his own thinking, for the persistence of his disability. If, for example, he has a hysterical paraplegia following the accident, the fantasy includes a picture of himself sitting in a wheel chair as he operates his own business. This concept is essential to preserve his sense of his own honesty. Unless the wheel chair were a permanent part of his future, the large cash award would not be justified. (This differentiates him from the malingerer.)

There is a common idea that, once compensation is paid, the symptoms vanish and the neurosis is cured. This does sometimes happen, but I know of more ex-patients who remained disabled long after the case was closed than ex-patients whose symptoms disappeared when the final check was received. This is worth mentioning because a defendant's doctor is often induced to tell the jury that the payment of damages will cure the patient. This has the effect (if not the intent) of making the jury believe that the claimant is a malingerer. It is difficult for the doctor to justify this statement, and the cross-examining attorney would be well within his rights if he asked the physician to cite a few cases of such complete cures. Unless the doctor in fact knows of such cases, he ought to avoid making such a sweeping prediction.

Pure compensation neuroses are not common because human motivations are rarely simple. A compensation psychoneurosis may be suspected when the patient is resistant to treatment, or even to the suggestion of treatment, and when careful analysis of the anamnesis shows no factors which would put the case into one of the other classes.

Attitudinal Pathosis.—In 1949 Thorne [20] suggested the term "attitudinal pathosis" for the personality disorder brought to light by trauma, in which the basic difficulty is the patient's conscious attitude towards his "rights." A person might have a constellation of attitudes towards his employer, towards insurance companies, towards

[20] Frederick Thorne, "The Attitudinal Pathoses," *Journal of Clinical Psychology,* V (January, 1949), 1.

entitlement to compensation, which formed a sort of central axis in all his thinking about the effects of injury. The condition was presumed to fall somewhere between a psychopathic personality and a traumatic neurosis. Kamman [21] developed the concept to the point where he set up criteria distinguishing three groups of post-accident emotional disorders: (*a*) traumatic neurosis, (*b*) compensation neurosis, and (*c*) attitudinal pathosis.

a) The term "traumatic neurosis" Kamman would reserve for a conventional psychoneurosis lighted up by the accident. In this connection, Kamman refers to an old article of mine [22] in which I suggested that a traumatic neurosis was an effort to solve a conflict between the desire for adventure and the desire for security. The cited sentences are:

> Independent employment is uncertain but adventurous. It carries the seal of community approval and self-respect. But it also stands for uncertainty. Against this is the security which comes with a guaranteed weekly compensation payment. Between the unconscious desire for adventure and community approval and the unconscious desire for security is a genuine conflict. To say that the patient coolly weighs the advantages of being healthy and employed against the advantages of being idle but compensated is to be blind to the complex psychologic factors involved.

Going further into the psychopathology involved, Kamman sees the true traumatic neurosis as a narcissistic regression. However, some authorities (particularly those whose experience has been essentially military) prefer to limit the term still further and to reserve the label "traumatic neurosis" for "the result of severe, acute fear or of repeated chronic fears." [23] In any event, there seems to be general agreement that we ought not to use the label "traumatic neurosis" for superficial emotional disturbances following an accident, but that we ought rather to limit it to basic conflicts in which the trauma simply pulled the trigger. It corresponds essentially to "latent psychoneurosis precipitated by the accident."

b) The second category would embrace the "compensation neurosis" already described above. Kamman [24] suggests that an expertly administered Rorschach test might be a useful tool for distinguishing the traumatic neurosis from the compensation neurosis, because it

[21] Gordon R. Kamman, "Traumatic Neurosis or Attitudinal Pathosis?" *Archives of Neurology and Psychiatry*, LXV (May, 1951), 593.
[22] Henry A. Davidson, "Neurosis and Malingering," *American Journal of Medical Jurisprudence*, II (February, 1939), 94.
[23] George N. Raines, in discussion of Kamman's paper (footnote 20), *Archives of Neurology and Psychiatry*, LXV (May, 1951), 601.
[24] *Ob. cit.*

could measure the degree of regression, and the greater the regression the more likely that the condition is a true psychoneurosis. In fact, Kamman tells us that "in some courts, the testimony regarding Rorschach findings was given considerable weight." The essential feature of a compensation neurosis, he continues, is that the syndrome is "created in part by a subjective conviction on the part of the patient that he has been in a compensative accident. The disorder is precipitated by environmental factors. One of these factors is the prospect of indemnification." This can be simply paraphrased: "The desire for cash compensation may be the major, though usually unconscious, force in keeping the symptoms alive." While the volitional factor is certainly operative here, it must not be forgotten that it is essentially unconscious, and it is very different from fraudulent assumption of symptoms. Since, by definition, compensation neurosis is caused by the accident, it is obviously compensable.

c) Kamman's third category—the attitudinal pathosis—is a fairly new concept in forensic psychiatry. Here is the way he summarizes it:

An attitudinal pathosis is a global disorder which involves not only the primary pathologic attitudes, but also secondary personality and environmental reactions. It thus differs from a "pathologic attitude" which is merely one of the basic elements. Given the core attitude "I have been injured and cannot work" one accepts accretions to this central attitude. . . . If he adopts as his nuclear attitude the idea that because he has been injured he is unable to work, he is going to interpret reality according only to attitudes consistent with his basic attitude. This is not a true neurosis nor does the question of indemnification necessarily enter. Suppose an injured worker has a nuclear attitude that, because he was injured at work, he is entitled to special consideration. He refuses to go back to his old job, insists on being given lighter work or shorter hours. It cannot be said that he is a malingerer. Neither was he suffering from any kind of neurosis, traumatic or compensation. He was suffering from an attitudinal pathosis.[25]

This concept does have the advantage of describing, though only on a quasi-dynamic basis,[26] something that actually does take place in the mind of the injured patient. It delineates a large group of persons who fall between the psychoneurotic and psychopath. Thorne [27] distinguishes the attitudinal pathosis from the psychoneurosis in these respects:

[25] *Ibid.*
[26] Not truly dynamic, because it does not explain *why* it happens, nor does it make any effort to relate this thinking to deeper psychopathology.
[27] *Op. cit.*

The neurosis cuts more into the total (and deeper layers of the) personality. The neurosis is rooted in unconscious processes, even when compensation is one of the motives. In the pathosis, the process is "conscious, voluntary, and intellectual." By "intellectual" Thorne and Kamman mean that it is the result of "learning" in an intellectual or educational sense, rather than a result of feeling or experiencing in an emotional sense. In some respects it is strikingly analogous to prejudice. While prejudice has strong emotional roots,[28] it is, in its operational manifestations, largely the result of teaching and learning. No one is born with a prejudice against Negroes or Catholics, for instance. It is learned. Similarly, the attitude that an injured workman is "entitled" to certain perquisites is the fruit of learning. Related ideas include such concepts as the thought that the company doctor will minimize the disability, the insurance company will try to effect a pitifully small settlement, and the employer will ever afterwards be prejudiced against the compensated worker. All of these are "learned" attitudes. "The person with an attitudinal pathosis behaves in a certain way because he believes he is right; the neurotic behaves that way because of complexes which he is unable to control even though he realizes his behavior is illogical. The sufferer from an attitudinal pathosis is motivated by ideas which he thinks are logical." [29]

The entire concept comes close to that of psychopathic personality. This is scarcely surprising, since the "attitudinal pathosis" is classified by its baptizer (Thorne) as a personality disorder. In speaking of the forensic implications of the concept, Kamman [30] questions whether the victim of an attitudinal pathosis should be entitled to indemnity: "Although the sufferer from an attitudinal pathosis is honest and sincere in his convictions, and although he has no conscious intent to fake or commit fraud, the factor of volition is so much more dominant in attitudinal pathoses that the legal philosophy should be modified with this in mind."

I doubt if any psychiatrist would have a comfortable time on the witness stand if he classified a plaintiff or claimant as having an "attitudinal pathosis." The term has no official medico-legal standing. The witness would be subject to severe cross-examination both as to the propriety of his diagnostic term and as to the meaning of his testimony in any medico-legal sense. If he testified for the claimant, the cross-examining attorney would certainly bring out that the pa-

[28] Henry A. Davidson, "The Anatomy of Prejudice," *Common Ground* (New York: Common Council for American Unity), I:2 (November, 1941), 3.
[29] Thorne, *op. cit.*
[30] *Op. cit.*

tient's condition was *not* a psychoneurosis, and that in this case volitional and conscious factors were strong. If he testified for the defendant, the cross-examiner would surely get the doctor to admit that the claimant was sincere and honest and that he had no conscious intent to malinger or exaggerate. Under the circumstances, the entire concept of "attitudinal pathosis" is better for presentation to a seminar than to a jury.

Trauma and Other Psychiatric Disorders

If after an accident a patient shows symptoms that he never had before, the chances are that courts will find a relationship between the symptoms and the injury. For example, Parker and Kernohan [31] report instances where brain tumors were ascribed to head injury. The doctor may know that the patient stumbled because of incoordination due to the brain tumor. But the court finds that, before the stumble, the patient never had symptoms and concludes that the stumble caused the head injury and that the head injury caused the symptoms. These decisions are not so unscientific as they sound. A head injury may cause bleeding into a previously slow-growing brain tumor and thus accelerate it into much greater clinical activity than before. In diseases of obscure etiology, like multiple sclerosis and most psychoses, it is hard for the physician to demonstrate that trauma plays no role, or to assert that the occurrence of symptoms following an injury is pure coincidence. Head injury may result in minute, scattered, and silent hemorrhages into various areas of the brain, and this may cause acute psychiatric symptoms; while the subsequent cerebral scars, even if very small, could cause chronic mental and emotional symptoms.

Neurosyphilis.—Trauma has long been held accountable for the exacerbation of, or the first precipitation of, the symptoms of neurosyphilis, including general paresis. There is a vast literature on this, well reviewed by Solomon.[32] In general it indicates that there is some medical basis and considerable legal support for the thesis that injury can light up a latent paresis and bring it into clinical activity. Nor need this be a head trauma. In the famous case of *Finkelday v. Heide* [33] it was held that the employer had to pay compensation for paresis following a fracture of the wrist. In this connection, the court said:

[31] H. Parker and J. Kernohan, *Journal of the American Medical Association,* XCVII (1931), 535.
[32] Harry Solomon, "Trauma and Neurosyphilis," *Trauma and Disease,* ed. Leopold Brahdy and Samuel Kahn (Philadelphia: Lea & Febiger, 1937), chap. ix.
[33] 230 New York 598, and 193 N. Y. Appellate Division 338.

It was testified that paresis was due to syphilis and that any injury, even an emotional injury, in a syphilitic person may be an activating factor in the development of paresis. Although at the time of the accident, the claimant had the syphilitic disease, it had not at that time developed itself and did not interfere with his ability to work. But about a week after the injury to the wrist he went to the (state) hospital where he has remained since. That the disease has been accelerated by the accident is clearly a legitimate inference. It is no answer to argue that the infection (syphilis) did not result from the injury. It is sufficient if the disease existed at the time of the injury and was thereby accelerated to such an extent as to impair the claimant's earning capacity.

This is, in general, the way most courts look at it. And if a disease of known origin, like paresis, can be charged to an injury to the wrist, then diseases of unknown origin (including "functional psychoses") will certainly be ascribed to head injuries.

Epilepsy.—In convulsions following trauma, the defense will take the position that prior to the accident the patient must have had petit mal or psychomotor equivalents; that the accident in fact was due to this disease (rather than vice versa); and that the subsequent seizures were simply the natural progress of the pre-existing epilepsy. The claimant's attorney will argue that (*a*) the patient had no major spells before the accident, (*b*) head injury *can* cause epilepsy, and (*c*) in this case the head injury did cause the grand mal attacks. If, in fact, no grand mal seizures were demonstrated prior to the injury, the courts will almost always consider this a case of traumatic epilepsy. We know, from war experience, that even severe head injuries are seldom followed by epilepsy. However, even if only one per cent of severe head injuries were followed by epilepsy, that incidence would be high enough to justify a legal finding in a specific case.

Theoretically, a posttraumatic epilepsy should show some focalization as evidenced by the electro-encephalogram or by a characteristic "march" in the pattern of the convulsive movement throughout the body. In practice, however, if it is established that the claimant had a head injury, and that he did not have seizures before the accident, it is almost certain that he will receive a judgment in his favor regardless of the absence of focalizing evidence.

Manic-Depressive Psychosis.—It is a convention of psychiatry that whereas schizophrenia is an endogenous disease, manic-depressive psychoses often seem to be precipitated by external factors. Since we do not know any specific cause for the psychosis, it is hard for us to deny that external trauma could be a precipitating factor. On the other hand, most manic-depressive attacks are certainly not related to any antecedent mechanical injury, so that head trauma can scarcely be postulated as a common cause. This illustrates the difference between the medical and legal approaches to the problem. A medical scientist has to deny the importance of injury because (a) autopsy studies do not show brain lesions consistent with injury, (b) men are more exposed to head injury than women but women suffer manic-depressive attacks more often than men, (c) most attacks occur in the absence of any history or injury, (d) the psychosis is a nondeteriorating disease, whereas structural brain damage, if it causes extensive mental symptoms at all, usually leads to some deterioration.[34] At the most, the medical scientist would say that an injury might be responsible for an acute attack, or for the aggravation of an existing attack, in a patient already in somewhat precarious manic-depressive balance.

The attorney, on the other hand, would argue as follows: given a situation in which a patient previously showed no psychotic ideation, and in which a manic-depressive attack followed a head injury, one would have to assume a relationship since the only alternative would be an astonishing coincidence. The fact that other manic-depressive patients have had no head injury is immaterial. We are not interested in the other cases. This patient, male or female, developed a psychosis after head injury. No doctor can swear that trauma is *not* the cause, because no doctor really knows the cause. From this it follows that, if he does not know what did cause the disease, he cannot know what did not cause it. (The scientist would see at once the philosophic absurdity of that line of reasoning, but juristically it is sound because of the legal concept of "burden of proof.") The legal reasoning would then be: the claimant has the burden of proof. He meets this initially by showing (a) previously good mental health, (b) a head injury, (c) evidence that the brain is the organ of the mind and the brain lies within the head which was injured, and (d) a subsequent disease of the mind.

The burden of going forward with the proof now shifts to the defense. To meet this *prima facie* case, the defense must show that the injury did not cause the psychosis. This can be done only by proving either (a) that something else caused the disorder, or (b) that it would be a clear breach of all medical principles to assume that the head injury could have been the cause. This challenge the defense cannot meet, and it leaves the *prima facie* claim unanswered.

---

[34] This is because central nervous system tissue never regenerates. If, by reason of scarification or other lesion, the head injury causes some destruction of nerve cells, these will forever remain lost.

Sometimes a state of euphoria or of reactive depression following a head injury is mistakenly diagnosed as manic-depressive psychosis. Even a traumatic delirium may, at first sight, give the picture of a manic state. If the victim suffered from the death of, or serious injury to other members of the family at the same accident, this may precipitate a secondary depression, clinically indistinguishable from a melancholia. If a patient has had several previous attacks, the entire emotional constellation surrounding an accident may pull the trigger producing the current episode. In this case, the trauma was a major etiologic factor of the attack, but it was mediated through the emotional, not the mechanical, effects of the injury.

Mental Deficiency.—The layman believes that a fall from the cradle is the commonest cause of mental deficiency. Judges, referees, and jurors are, in this sense, laymen, and share that belief. The problem is presented to the psychiatrist under two sets of circumstances. The following cases are paradigms of those circumstances:

1. A piece of plaster falls from the ceiling, striking a child on the head. A laceration is produced, possibly some unconsciousness. Subsequent study shows the child to be a mental defective. The parents sue the landlord, contending either (*a*) that the child was normal before the accident, or (*b*) that the child became more retarded after the accident, admitting some mental retardation prior to it.
2. After a head injury, an adult shows increasing mental deterioration, until, when tested, he shows marked enfeeblement of intelligence.

In situations like the first, the problem is to obtain and evaluate the evidence of the child's mental state before the accident. If the child was more than six years old at the time of the accident, the school record will be the most accessible evidence. Thus, if he had never gone to school, why not? Was he denied admission because of mental retardation? The records should show. If he did go to school, there will be records of his mental age, and possibly of his achievement and aptitudes which will promptly dispose of the question of his pretraumatic intelligence. If the child was under age six, it will be helpful to obtain the hospital record of his birth, showing duration of labor, type of delivery, instrumentation, and the infant's early development. Of course, in the overwhelming majority of cases, mental deficiency is *not* due to head injury, but it would be poor practice to dismiss the possibility categorically in any particular case.

The testing necessary to determine the exact mental level is best done by a clinical psychologist. In some states, if the psychiatrist ordered and interpreted the test, he is competent to testify about it. In other jurisdictions, the psychologist will have to testify first, and then the psychiatrist could be given the test results in the form of a hypothetical question. He could then give his opinion, based on the acceptance of the test results. (See Chapter 20 for explanation of the hypothetical question.)

A careful developmental level, age by age, has to be obtained in these cases. The best known of the developmental yardsticks is the scale formulated by Gesell and Amatruda.[35] If the mother or other reliable informant can tell the doctor at what age the child first walked, talked, had bladder control, could sit up, could use a spoon, follow light, etc., the pretraumatic development can be worked out. The doctor would compare these ages with the Gesell-Amatruda norms and thus formulate a reasonably accurate picture of the child's pre-traumatic mental level. This could then be compared with the psychologic test findings after the injury. Like all tests neither the Gesell-Amatruda norms nor the results of current testing are automatic and self-interpreting. The results must be filtered through the screen of clinical judgment. That, however, is part of the daily function of the competent psychiatrist.

·In situations like the second (concerning an adult), the problem is much simpler. By now practically every American adult has somewhere on record a report showing his mental level. Any adult who ever attended an American public school, for example, has a folder somewhere in the school system, showing a mental age, an achievement level, or some similar score. Any adult who ever served in the Army had a classification test. In most large industries personnel have been subjected (usually when applying for jobs) to various psychological tests. If the patient or his attorney will consent, this information is usually obtainable and it gives the doctor a base of reference. The educational record alone will give a rough gage of the subject's basic intellectual level. Determine the highest school grade which the claimant successfully completed. Equate this to the public school grading system, so that, for example, third-year high school is translated to eleventh grade (because it is three years beyond the top grammar school grade). Add five to the grade number,[36]

[35] Arnold Gesell and Catherine Amatruda, *Developmental Diagnosis* (New York: Paul B. Hoeber, Inc., 1941).
[36] The average American public school is geared so that first-grade work requires a mental age of six, second-grade work that of seven, etc.; therefore, grade plus five equals required mental age.

and this gives a rough basic mental age. Thus, if the worker left school in the seventh grade after successful completion of sixth grade, the doctor adds 6 (for sixth grade) to the constant number (5), for a total of 11. The worker then must have a mental age of at least eleven, because he could not have accomplished sixth-grade work with any lower mental age. If now, after the accident, testing shows a mental age of, say, 11½, it is obvious that there has been no intellectual impairment.

This formulation is admittedly rough, but its error is consistently in the direction of underestimating rather than overestimating the mental level. This is because a pupil may have left school for financial or other nonscholastic reasons, and thus it cannot always be inferred that he had reached his intellectual ceiling when he left school. For example, a bright boy might have gone to work instead of to high school simply because his family needed the money. By this formula, his mental age would be adjudged to be 13 (eighth grade plus 5), whereas he may have superior intelligence. The reverse error is rare, because (unless he was unconscionably "pushed" by the teacher) he could not have successfully completed a grade with a mental age below the level needed.

Most cases of apparently traumatic mental deficiency in adults turn out to be instances of posttraumatic mental enfeeblement or deterioration, rather than mental deficiency. See page 58 for a consideration of this.

Schizophrenia.—The cause of dementia precox is the Number one mystery of modern psychiatry. Although millions of dollars have been spent in research on the subject, although dozens of etiologic theories have been advanced, we simply do not know what causes this psychosis. From the jurist's viewpoint, this means that we cannot deny that head injury could be a cause. From the scientist's viewpoint, this means that we cannot assert that trauma is a cause.

Schizophrenia is a tragically common psychosis. Very few of the patients suffering from it have a history of head injury; obviously, therefore, trauma cannot often play a role in the diagnosis. On the other hand, every once in a while the psychiatrist will be presented with a case in which the symptoms appeared only after a head injury. Unless he has evidence of an actual traumatic psychosis (see page 55) he cannot in clear conscience testify that trauma caused the schizophrenia. And if he does have such evidence, he should classify the case as a traumatic psychosis, not as a dementia precox.

Some of the schizoid pictures seen after head injury are toxic or organic psychoses. In a young patient, the early clinical picture of a traumatic mental enfeeblement or a toxic psychosis will closely simulate schizophrenia. Toxic psychoses may be accompanied by confusion, and traumatic psychoses by deterioration, so that the differential diagnosis becomes obscure. True schizophrenia is, according to most textbooks, a disease of insidious onset. However, acute schizophrenias were seen by Army psychiatrists all over the world during the Second World War. In the early days of the war, there was a reluctance to label such patients as schizophrenics because of the firm tradition that dementia precox was a disease of slow onset. Hence it was assumed that they must have been suffering from toxic, infectious, or hysterical states. And many of them in fact were. However, by the end of the war a residue of these "acute" cases had accumulated and were clearly and typically schizophrenics. It seems reasonable, by now, to accept the fact that schizophrenia *can* have an acute onset.

When a true schizophrenia develops swiftly after a head injury, the psychiatrist will be unable to ignore the precipitating role of the trauma. He will point out that such a psychosis would have developed anyway, head injury or not. This, however, remains a speculation. The precipitating (but certainly not the causative) role of the injury can hardly be denied except by assuming an amazing coincidence. No one knows whether the brain damage produced the acute psychosis by way of structural cerebral injury, or whether the emotional content of the injury was the precipitating mechanism. All of this assumes a reasonably close time relationship between the trauma and the symptoms. Where symptoms of a typical schizophrenia first appear some months (or longer) after a head injury, the relationship is very doubtful.

Psychiatric Factors in Death Claims

If a claimant dies as a result of an injury or industrial illness, one might suppose that the psychiatrist could not assist the court in determining the cause of death. However, from time to time claims are made that emotional factors were major precipitants of the death. For example, it might be alleged that an emotional sequel of an accident caused the patient to be hypertensive and that this, in turn, led to his death. In one case, a court awarded a widow a claim based on the rupture of a syphilitic aneurysm on the theory that the emotion associated with the accident caused a sudden rise in blood pressure which, in turn, caused the aneurysm to rupture. It was agreed that this claimant was doomed to death in any event. But the referee accepted the brief of the petitioner which stated in effect that, had it not been for this emotional experience, the worker might have lived for some years and then died quietly at home some night.

I have elsewhere [37] analyzed emotional components as a cause or precipitant of death. In the legal arena most of these problems center around emotional factors in cardio-vascular disease. There is also, however, evidence to show that emotions may account for the perforation of a peptic ulcer,[38] for serious changes in the blood clotting time,[39] and sometimes for deaths in apparently healthy persons [40] who simply expected to or wanted to die.

Personal Orientation

A psychiatrist who does much medico-legal work soon acquires a personal philosophy with respect to psychoneuroses following injury. He believes either (a) that most of these patients are motivated primarily by greed, or (b) that they have a genuine illness in which the money-motivation factor is of minor importance. Sometimes the psychiatrist's personal doctrine results from long identification with insurance companies on the one hand, or with plaintiffs on the other. Sometimes it works the other way: The doctor first develops a consistent attitude towards traumatic neurotics, and as a result he becomes useful to attorneys on one side and useless to attorneys on the other side of the litigation. This in turn leads to his being called in with increasing frequency by plaintiffs or by carriers, as the case may be. Here, for example is a point of view reflecting one orientation:

> The predisposing conditions of traumatic neurosis are compensation which the patient knows he may obtain, and the idea, common in our business culture, of getting something for nothing; desire for escape from dreary work, desire to spite someone or desire to punish a wife or employer; the patient's anxiety over his condition, or castration fears aroused by the accident. Also, it has been found that workers on temporary jobs are more likely to develop traumatic neurosis than regular workers. On occasions patients are motivated by a desire to get even, as in the German idea of a justice neurosis. Other patients seem to be more susceptible because of a lack of pivotal values.[41]

[37] Henry A. Davidson, *Journal of The Medical Society of New Jersey,* XLVI (July, 1949), 350.
[38] D. N. Stewart, *Lancet,* I (February 28, 1942), 259.
[39] G. DeTakats, *Archives of Surgery,* XLVIII (February, 1944), 105.
[40] See, for example, cases reported by Russel G. MacRobert, *Journal of Insurance Medicine,* IV (April, 1949), 2, and by Paul R. Hawley, *American Journal of Psychiatry,* CIV (June, 1948), 753.
[41] Simon Olshansky, *American Journal of Occupational Therapy,* IV (February, 1950), 12.

A psychiatrist who accepts this doctrine must find it difficult to testify for a claimant. If he believes that a more or less conscious idea of "getting something for nothing" is behind the symptoms, it will be hard for him not to indicate this during cross-examination. If he says, on direct examination, that the claimant's symptoms were caused by the accident, his heart will not be in the statement. As a matter of fact, it is unlikely he would testify for a plaintiff at all, since his report to the lawyer is bound to reflect this attitude. Receiving such a report the attorney would, in all likelihood, either settle the case for what he could get, or refer the claimant to another psychiatrist and discard the unfavorable report submitted by the first doctor.

Contrast this attitude with the one reflected in the following quotation:

When the words "hysterical" or "functional" are used to characterize a neurosis its social meaning is that the subject is a predatory individual trying to get something for nothing. The victim of such a neurosis may be without sympathy in court, and without sympathy from some physicians who may take the words "functional" or "hysterical" to mean that the individual is suffering from some form of wickedness, perversity or weakness of will.[42]

This reflects, of course, a warm empathy with the patient. Such empathy is totally missing from the previous quotation which emphasizes compensation as one of the major factors, and which hints at "lack of pivotal values" with an implication of character defect. No one can say which point of view is closer to the truth. But it can be said that the view adopted by the doctor will mould his diagnoses, his evaluations, and even, sometimes, his findings.

[42] Abram Kardiner and Herbert Spiegel, *War Stress and Neurotic Illness* (New York: Paul B. Hoeber, Inc., 1947), p. 406.

Chapter 5

MARRIAGE, DIVORCE, AND ANNULMENT

While there are many causes for annulling a marriage, only two of them concern the psychiatrist. These are: annulment on the basis of lack of mental capacity, and annulment on the basis of fraudulent concealment of prior nervous or mental disease.

Annulment for Lack of Mental Capacity

"The contract to marry is extremely simple. It does not require a high degree of intelligence to comprehend it." [1] That appears to be the opinion of the courts. Thus a man may be too defective mentally to be permitted to buy a frankfurter stand, yet bright enough to make a legally valid marriage contract. While the standard of mental capacity required for marriage is very low, it is still necessary that the partner be free of any mental disorder (at the time of marriage) which would render him incapable of giving his free consent or which would rob him of his ability to understand the "implications" of marriage. If it appears that the person was insane at the time of marriage, he can apply to have the marriage annulled. The case is the same with a person who married while drunk.

Many states have laws which forbid ex-inmates of mental hospitals to marry without clearance from the authorities of the hospital. However, violation of such a law will not nullify the marriage; it merely lays the violator open to criminal penalties.

The Criterion of Capacity.—The question which the psychiatrist must answer is: "Did the party understand the nature of the marriage relationship and the obligations assumed under it?" [2] Generally courts are reluctant to void a marriage. The evidence must be clear and it must apply to the petitioner's mental state at the time of the marriage. If the evidence is evenly balanced in both directions, courts

---

[1] H. D. Singer and W. O. Krohn, *Insanity and the Law* (Philadelphia: The Blakiston Co., 1924), p. 265.

[2] Storf v. Papalia, 24 New Jersey Miscellaneous 146; Adams v. Scott, 93 Nebraska 537; Hagenson v. Hagenson, 258 Illinois 197; and many other cases.

tend to let the marriage stand. On the other hand, if it is clear that the party was psychotic or so drunk or defective at the time as not to understand the obligations, nature, and implications of marriage, the annulment will usually be decreed.

Initiation of Action.—An interesting and important question concerns the right of the competent partner to take action under this doctrine. There is no doubt that a person who finds that he married while he was drunk or psychotic can have it annulled. But can the other partner institute such action? For example, a woman marries a man who impresses her with his quiet shyness, his seriousness of purpose, and freedom from vices. Later it appears that the man was a victim of hebephrenic schizophrenia. He does not want to annul the marriage. She does. Can she institute action? In most states, she cannot.[3] However, the New Jersey statute [4] has the following reference to a suit for annulment based on lack of mental capacity: "Where the competent party is the applicant, such applicant shall have been ignorant of the other's incapacity." Presumably this means that the sane spouse can initiate action. In one case,[5] an annulment was granted with the following dictum: "Where defendant lacked capacity to marry and petitioner was ignorant of that, and did not ratify marriage [6] after knowledge of that lack of capacity, he is entitled to a decree of nullity." A similar doctrine seems to prevail in Missouri where, at the petition of a husband who had lived with his wife almost twenty years, a marriage was annulled when it was shown that she never had had sufficient mental capacity to make a marriage contract.[7] Similarly, in New Hampshire a marriage had been annulled at the petition of the competent spouse when it appeared that he had been kept in ignorance of the mental status of his fiancee until after the ceremony.[8] Although the apparent grounds in this case were fraud, the legal implication is certainly that it was the lack of capacity which nullified the marriage, since a psychotic person could hardly have engaged in willful deception.

The law on the right of the competent spouse to institute suit seems to be in a state of flux. Originally the same rule applied to marriage as to all contracts attacked on the basis of lack of capacity;

[3] Such were the rulings, for example, in Hoadley v. Hoadley, 155 Northeastern Reporter 728; and in Sleicher v. Sleicher, 228 New York Supplement 711.
[4] *Revised Statutes of New Jersey,* 2:50-1. Many state codes have similar clauses.
[5] Storf v. Papalia, 24 New Jersey miscellaneous 146.
[6] Here the word "ratify" means "to continue to live together as man and wife."
[7] Chapline v. Stone, 77 Missouri Appeals 523.
[8] Keyes v. Keyes, 22 New Hampshire 553.

namely, that only the incompetent party could start suit. However, there appears to be a growing liberalization, the effect of which eventually may be to allow either spouse to open the question.

Drunkenness.—If one party was drunk during a marriage ceremony, the marriage is voidable at petition of the spouse who was drunk provided that the intoxication was enough to rob him (or her) of the required degree of understanding. If the participant is simply "a bit high" this will not be sufficient to void the marriage.[9] At present there appears to be no way in which the sober spouse can void such a marriage at his own petition. Even if the decision in *Storf v. Papalia,* cited above, is sustained, it would not open the door to such actions. The essential feature in that case was the husband's ignorance of his wife's mental capacity, whereas it is unlikely that a sober man would not realize that his marriage partner was drunk. If a couple marry while one is drunk but continue to live together after the return of sobriety, this is considered ratification, and no suit for annulment on that basis may subsequently be initiated.

Senility.—The psychiatrist is sometimes asked to pass on the mental state of an old man who has entered into a marriage which, his family suspects, was prompted more by the irritations of a large prostate than by the promptings of true love. The same rules apply. If a senile psychosis was present, the marriage is voidable. If the mental state was one of simple, nonpsychotic senility, the doctor must determine whether he was "capable of understanding the nature of the marriage contract and the duties and obligations such a contract entails."

Psychoneurosis.—Since a psychoneurosis does not deprive a person of mental capacity, a suit to annul a marriage on that basis cannot be initiated by either party.

Impotence.—One other type of lack of capacity may interest the psychiatrist. That is impotence on an emotional basis. The capacity to marry implies a capacity to perform sexual intercourse. A permanently impotent single man is legally incapable of contracting a valid marriage (except possibly if he had explained that incapacity to his prospective wife and if she accepted him in spite of it). If a woman does not know of the existence of a permanent impotence in her fiance, she can ask to have the marriage annulled after she discovers the defect. The impotence may have an emotional basis. However, since it is a simple question of lack of capacity, not a matter of mis-

9 Prine v. Prine, 36 Florida 676.

conduct or willfulness, the impotence invalidates the marriage regardless of its cause. In a divorce action for constructive desertion (see below) the emotional nature of the impotence may be a material factor; but not in an action for annulment, where it is relevant only in so far as it touches on the question of the permanence of the defect.

Annulment for Fraudulent Concealment of Nervous or Mental Disease

Fraud implies a willful intent to deceive. If a spouse deliberately perpetrates a fraud, if the fraud goes to the "essence" of the marriage, and if the other partner relied on the misrepresentation, the marriage will usually be annulled. Misrepresenting vocational, social, or financial status is not such a fraud to the "essence" of a marriage. Consequently this kind of misrepresentation is not a valid basis for annulment once the marriage has been consummated. On the other hand, willful concealment of serious ill health is a fraud that goes to the "essence" of a marriage. Generally the concealment of prior mental disease is *not* considered a fraud because the mental disorder itself makes the partner incapable of "guilty" deception. Even if a person has recovered from a psychosis prior to marriage, silence about this is not a fraud because a recovered psychotic rarely considers that he was insane. If he does not think he was ever insane, then it is scarcely deliberate fraud if he does not say so. The result of this doctrine is to make it almost impossible to get an annulment on the grounds of fraud if a concealment of mental disease is the basis of the charge.

An excellent illustration is the following: In 1906 a young woman spent seven months as a patient at a mental institution. She was discharged as "cured." In 1925 she married. In 1926 she developed an involutional psychosis. Now for the first time the husband learned of her previous mental hospital experience. He contended that his wife's concealment of that was a fraud. The court refused to annul the marriage, using the following informative language:

The defendant had made no affirmative representation as to her condition. Silence resting on honest belief even in things false, is not actionable. The defendant was not aware that her nervous breakdown was an attack of insanity. By the time she was married, 20 years later, the breakdown of 1906 was an unpleasant episode and the commitment an accident in the drama of life which she had long since put aside without thought or suspicion of recurrence. When she omitted to recount that experience, it was not a conscious concealment. She did not simulate health, she felt it.[10]

[10] Buechler v. Simon, 146 Atlantic Reporter 420.

The touchstone of this case can be applied in almost any action to annul on this basis. Still undecided is what would happen if a psychiatrist told a patient that she had recovered from a psychosis and that she should not marry without apprising her fiance of that fact. If the woman married and, in contravention of the doctor's advice, concealed her psychiatric history, then it is possible that an annulment might be granted because the factor of honest error (so prominent in the Buechler-Simon case) would be absent. On the other hand, if she was psychotic when she married, a fraud action could not be maintained because she would not have mental capacity to perpetrate a willful fraud.

Willful concealment of a seriously disabling or potentially hereditary nervous disorder would be a fraud if the patient were sane. This is illustrated in another case. An epileptic, under constant medical treatment, concealed the epilepsy and affirmatively assured his fiancee that he was in good health. Indeed he boasted that he had never had occasion to visit a physician. After marriage, the wife saw him in a fit, learned of the epilepsy and left him. Had she remained with him, she would have "ratified" the marriage and barred an action to annul. As it was, the court said: "When a man has been suffering from epilepsy but represents that he has never been sick and when after the marriage the wife discovers the disease and straightaway leaves him, she is entitled to have the marriage annulled for fraud notwithstanding consummation." [11]

Concealment of previous commitment to a mental hospital is not in itself a fraud except (a) when at the time of the marriage the person was sane, and (b) when he had affirmatively stated that he was never at a mental hospital. Mere silence in such a case would not be fraud, because normally the recovered patient does not believe that he was insane and would have no more reason for telling of his stay at a mental hospital than for cataloging to his fiancee his entire past medical record.

Divorce

Divorce from Psychotic Spouse.—In most states insanity is a bar to any divorce action Since a psychosis is a disease, the other partner has no more basis for asking for a divorce for mental disease than for expecting pneumonia or a fractured leg to be grounds for divorce. In a few states "insanity" is a statutory basis for divorce, but over most of the country this is certainly not true. As a matter of fact, desertion, adultery, and cruelty are not grounds for divorce either,

[11] Busch v. Gruber, 131 Atlantic Reporter 101.

if the misconduct is committed by a psychotic spouse.[12] As the court said in one such case,[13] "Since insanity is no cause for divorce, nothing which is a consequence of it can be."

Constructive Desertion.[14]—Refusal to submit to or engage in sexual intercourse is considered as "desertion" in most states. Hence, if desertion is a ground for divorce, failure to engage in copulation is also a ground for divorce. The question facing the psychiatrist is whether this is willful, since only "willful" desertion is grounds for divorce. If a man develops an emotional state in which he is unable to have or maintain an erection, his wife may (after the requisite time period) sue for divorce alleging constructive desertion. The husband could defend on the grounds that his impotence is certainly not "willful." The wife may retort that, since it is not due to "organic" disease, it is a mental phenomenon, related to lack of motivation, hence to "will." The psychiatrist is asked to give an expert opinion. Most psychiatrists would state that a psychoneurosis is a "disease" which the patient does not acquire voluntarily. Yet on cross-examination many experts would be jockeyed into admitting that such factors as lack of motivation, secondary gain, and the like place psychoneurosis in a somewhat different category from a disease accidentally incurred, like typhoid fever.

The situation is even more ambiguous in the case of a wife's refusal to submit to sexual intercourse because of emotional blocking. Here the courts are prone to decide that since the wife's role could be passive, she could submit if she wanted to, and therefore her refusal is willful. It takes exceptional eloquence on the part of the psychiatrist to persuade the court that this kind of behavior is a "sickness" not under control of the will.

Adultery.—In all states, adultery is grounds for divorce. The psychiatrist comes into the picture when the culpable spouse alleges that he is psychotic or that he (or she) is impelled to promiscuous sexual behavior by reason of neurotic personality, alcoholism, or constitutional psychopathy. Where psychosis is established, the spouse is not "responsible" for the adultery and divorce will not be granted. Such defenses as "nymphomania" or "psychopathic personality" rarely impress the courts, though if they are genuine, the

---

[12] Tiffany v. Tiffany, 84 Iowa 122; Wray v. Wray, 19 Alabama 522; Broadstreet v. Broadstreet, 7 Massachusetts 474; and many other cases.

[13] Kunz v. Kunz, 213 Northwestern Reporter 906.

[14] This section and much of the other material in this chapter represent expansions of the author's monograph, "Orientation to Forensic Psychiatry," *Archives of Neurology and Psychiatry*, LVII (June, 1947), 730.

psychiatrist is certainly entitled to call the court's attention to modern scientific opinion as to the factor of "willfulness" in these cases. Sometimes psychiatric examinations of the defendant reveal a clear hypomanic state, which, being technically a psychosis, should serve as an adequate defense.

Cruelty.—Psychiatrists are sometimes asked to testify that the defendant's behavior caused a "nervous breakdown," a psychoneurosis, or even a psychotic reaction in the other spouse. The difficulty is that the defense will cite evidence to show that the complainant always had "tendencies" towards nervousness, or even, indeed, that it was the petitioner's own neurotic personality which caused the defendant's cruelty in the first place. There is a growing tendency to liberalize the concept of "cruelty" so that, in most states, an emotional trauma is considered as valid a basis for a divorce suit as a physical injury. (Thus, adultery is only one fourth as common on the divorce court docket as it was in 1870; cruelty is four times as common. We are not becoming more cruel to our wives; we are merely defining cruelty more liberally.)

Chapter 6

PLACEMENT AND CUSTODY
OF CHILDREN

The psychiatrist is often called to advise courts, social agencies, and attorneys on the mental hygiene problems associated with the custody, adoption, and placement of children. Specifically, the situations where psychiatric opinion may be sought include:

1. The suitability of an infant for adoption.
2. The emotional stability of a mother or of a couple seeking to adopt children.
3. The wisdom of permitting a divorced father to visit children in custody of their mother.
4. Conflicts between parents, or between parents and grandparents, or between natural and adopting parents, as to the custody of a child.
5. The contention of a mother that she did not know what she was doing when she signed a surrender of her child.
6. The proper placement of a child whose mother is mentally ill.
7. The noninstitutional placement of a juvenile delinquent.
8. Conflicting interests of mother and baby.

Social and Legal Framework

Requests may come from a judge who wants to make whatever decision is best for the welfare of the child and who is in doubt as to the mental hygiene implications of the several possible dispositions. The judge may ask the psychiatrist formally to make a study of the situation and submit a written report; or he may want the doctor to testify privately in his chambers or openly in court. Social agencies often ask psychiatrists to render advisory opinions as to the wisdom of a proposed placement, the competency of a mother, the suitability of an adopting parent, or the mental health of a child who is being considered for a foster or adopting home. Attorneys may ask psychiatrists to testify on behalf of a natural parent, adopting parent, grandparent, or child welfare agency; or on behalf of an institution resisting removal of a child.

The statutes governing child placement vary so much from state to state that it is impossible here to set down any specific law on the subject.[1] In some jurisdictions, adoptions may be arranged privately between the parents of the baby and the adopting parents. In the more progressive states, all adoptions are channeled through a state tribunal or at least through a reputable private agency. Laws also vary as to the absoluteness of the surrender signed by the mother, the jurisdiction of courts to intervene in these cases, the parental rights of the unacknowledged father of a child born out of wedlock, the disposition of the child of an incompetent unmarried mother, the need for preplacement social study of an adopting home,[2] the right to license and inspect children's institutions, the right of institutions to make private placements, the calling of hearings on placement questions, the confidential nature of the records, and the use of trial residence in a proposed adoption home.[3] Where any of these points is material to the issue, the doctor should obtain from the attorney concerned a briefing as to the applicable law.

Although many states legally allow private adoption arrangements, the ethical physician avoids participation in any such plan. The psychiatrist finds himself involved under circumstances like these: An obstetrician knows of a sterile couple anxious to adopt a baby. He delivers a psychotic, defective, grossly underprivileged, or unmarried mother and persuades her (or her family) that the baby would be better off in another home. He arranges for the adoption by having the new parents call at the hospital and go home with the baby after the natural mother has signed some kind of consent form drafted by the family lawyer. He asks the psychiatrist to participate either (a) by certifying that the baby is not a mental defective—particularly when the mother is; or (b) by certifying that the natural mother is too unstable emotionally to provide a healthy home for the baby. At first, this looks like a reasonable and professionally justified activity on the part of the psychiatrist. However, it comes close to taking part in a black market on babies, or even to baby peddling. Where the law does not require that adoptions be processed through courts or social agencies, the conscience of the doctor should require it.

---

[1] For fifteen cents, any reader can buy the excellent pamphlet, *Essentials of Adoption Law and Procedure,* Children's Bureau Publication No. 331, issued by the U. S. Federal Security Agency and purchasable from the Government Printing Office in Washington.

[2] Social investigation of the proposed adopting home is required in thirty-eight states according to I. Evlyn Smith, "Adoption," *Social Work Year Book for 1947,* ed. Russel Kurtz (New York: Russell Sage Foundation, 1948).

[3] The period of trial residence varies from three to twelve months. According to Miss Smith, some trial residence is required in 32 states. *Ibid.*

Out-of-wedlock babies are not the only source of adoptions. In fact, the U. S. Children's Bureau reports that "approximately one half of all adoptions concern children born out of wedlock." [4] This means, of course, that in about fifty per cent of adoption cases, petitions are filed for "legitimate" children.

The psychiatrist should know the state agency concerned with child placement. This may be the state's Welfare Department, Board of Children's Guardians, Department of Mental Hygiene, Youth Authority, Children's Authority, Board of Child Welfare, or any of a number of other diversely named agencies. Since few psychiatrists limit themselves to work with adults, it would seem wise for the specialist to apprise himself in advance of his state's resources in the child-welfare field.

Faced with a specific placement problem, the psychiatrist should obtain, from the lawyer or agency concerned, the locally applicable answers to the following questions:

> Are the records of the examination and hearing subject to public inspection or are they confidential documents?
>
> Is the child permitted to express any choice with respect to his placement? And if so, from what age?
>
> Will a hearing be held on the matter? If so, in what tribunal? Is the hearing private or open to the public? Is the child present at the hearing?
>
> In an adoption proceeding, is there any provision for a "trial residency"? That is, does the child live temporarily at the home of his adopting parents and, if so, for how long, before the adoption is made permanent?
>
> May a mother make private arrangements for offering her child for adoption, or must this be done through an agency?
>
> Is a mother's signed relinquishment of custody irrevocable?
>
> If the mother is unmarried, is the father's consent required to process an adoption?
>
> Does the law provide that a social study be made of the proposed adopting home? If so, does this include psychiatric study of both adopting parents? Would a placement made in the absence of such a study be valid?

A rereading of these questions will show that, in an adoption proceeding, the psychiatrist cannot make an intelligent recommendation without having the answers.

---

[4] U. S. Children's Bureau, *Publication No. 331* (Washington, D. C., 1949), p. 5.

Child's Suitability for Adoption

A couple seeking to adopt a child generally impose two requirements. They want a very young baby, and they want to be sure that the infant is not a mental defective. In some respects, these desiderata exclude each other, because the younger the baby the harder it is to tell whether he is of normal intelligence. Except in cases of obvious mental deficiency, the psychiatrist generally shifts this burden to the child psychologist. The scale worked out by Gesell and Amatruda [5] does provide a series of developmental norms against which any baby (beyond, perhaps, the age of three months) can be measured. The prognostic value of the scale is not too exact for very young babies. Unless an experienced psychologist is available for testing, the best the psychiatrist can do is to give a cautious opinion (without any guarantees) that the baby does or does not have the average motor, sensory, and adaptive behavior for its age level.

Suitability of Adopting Parents

A couple who want to adopt a baby do so to satisfy their own emotional needs, not the baby's. Since this is universally true it does not, by itself, justify rejection of the petition. On the other hand, no psychiatrist will want to place his approval on adoption by a family in which there is a psychotic or seriously psychoneurotic member.

For some reason, few psychiatrists have given much attention to this branch of practice. In fact, appraisal of adopting parents has been left largely to case workers from the social agencies concerned. There is a vast literature [6] on child welfare problems, and much has

[5] Arnold Gesell and Catherine Amatruda, *Developmental Diagnosis* (New York: Paul B. Hoeber, Inc., 1941). Two other works by Dr. Gesell are also useful in gaging a child's developmental level: *Mental Growth of the Preschool Child* (New York: The Macmillan Co., 1930) ; and, in collaboration with Frances Ilg, Louise Ames, and Janet Learned, *Infant and Child in the Culture of Today* (New York: Harper & Bros., 1943). In connection with these texts, Dr. Gesell repeatedly warns that "the age norms are not set up as standards and are designed only for orientation and interpretive purposes."

[6] Some of the books which touch on this are: Mary Buell Snyder, *Substitute Parents* (New York: Commonwealth Fund, 1936) ; Bronson Crothers, *A Pediatrician in Search of Mental Hygiene* (New York: Commonwealth Fund, 1937) ; Harry J. Baker and Virginia Traphagen, *Diagnosis and Treatment of Behavior Problem Children* (New York: The Macmillan Co., 1935) ; Ruth Strang, *An Introduction to Child Study* (New York: The Macmillan Co., 1938) ; Hale Shirley, *Psychiatry for the Pediatrician* (New York: Commonwealth Fund, 1948) ; Susan Isaacs, *Social Development in Young Children* (New York: Harcourt Brace & Co., Inc., 1937) ; James S. Plant, *Personality and the Culture Pattern* (New York: Commonwealth Fund, 1937) ; James S. Plant, *The Envelope* (New York: Commonwealth Fund, 1950) ; L. M. Brooks, *Adventures in Adoption* (Chapel Hill: University of

been written about the assay of motivation and criteria for good adopting parents. Little of this material has been written by, and less of it appears to be read by, psychiatrists.

In evaluating prospective adoptive parents, the psychiatrist, after he has familiarized himself with the literature of the subject, will first insist on a social service survey of the home. Having read this, he interviews each parent separately, and tries to answer these questions: Are they mature people? Do they seek a child to replace a lost one of their own, to neutralize the stigma of sterility, to keep up with the Joneses, to occupy some of the wife's free time, to fill a large and empty house, or to furnish a playmate for their own child? Is the neighborhood wholesome? Is either member of the couple a food faddist, an eccentric, a heavy drinker, or a social, religious, or political fanatic? Knowing the unpredictability of human behavior, the experienced psychiatrist does not, in a report or in testimony, give any petitioner an affirmative certificate of parental perfection. If favorably impressed, he says, or writes, simply that at this time he sees no psychiatric reason for denying the application.

Conflicts as to Visitation

Before filing for divorce, most couples reach agreement as to custody of the children. Sometimes, however, they quarrel about this, and the matter is left to the discretion of the court. The usual decree provides for the mother to retain custody of female children and of young boys, while the father is ordinarily awarded custody of older boys. The parent who does not have custody (the "nonresident" parent) usually asks for and receives certain "rights of visitation." For example, the court may decree that the father be permitted to visit his children at their mother's home on alternate week-ends; or that the children spend a specified part of each summer vacation with the father. Where the mother intends to remarry, or where her living conditions are unsuitable, the court may award custody to the resident parents of, or siblings of, the father, and give the mother a right of visitation.

North Carolina Press, 1940) ; *Role of the Baby in the Placement Process* (Philadelphia: Pennsylvania School of Social Work, 1946) ; Marie Skodak, *Children in Foster Homes* (Iowa City: University of Iowa Press, 1939), and dozens of others. I know of no volume which has any chapter specifically pointed at the appraisal of adopting or foster parents. But all of these works offer either (*a*) concepts of motivations in adoption and foster-home work, or (*b*) concepts as to the emotional needs of the deprived child, or (*c*) information on the social, legal, and administrative aspects of child placement. In the aggregate they offer the reader the foundation for a philosophy of the subject. What he erects on that platform depends on the doctor's own experience, ingenuity, and sensitivity.

The psychiatrist becomes involved when the child shows emotional disturbance at the visit of the nonresident parent. The custodial parent says that this is not her (or his) fault, and that it is simply due to the fact that the child does not like the other parent. The latter retorts that his (her) ex-spouse has influenced the children against their father (mother). For example, the children may be living with their divorced mother and exhibit terror whenever the father visits. The father will say that when she is alone with the children the mother tells them what a "bad" man their father is. The mother, of course, vigorously denies this. Usually the mother is sincere in her denial. What has happened has been that the children were given an unfavorable picture of their father, not so much by what the mother has said, as by her manner and attitude. In this difficult situation, the psychiatrist's help is sometimes solicited. Often there is a pathetic hope that the psychiatrist can say something to the mother or to the children which will ease the problem. Of course this is a vain expectation. The doctor has no control over what the mother says in privacy to her children; and since she is not even conscious of disparaging the father, it will do no good to preach to her about the evil of damaging her ex-husband's standing in the eyes of his children.

A point may be reached where the mental health of the child will require a complete severance from the nonresident parent. If any blame is to be distributed, the "fault" would be that of the custodial parent, not that of the visiting parent. None the less, it may be necessary to deprive the visiting parent of the right to see his own children if it appears that such visits are emotionally disturbing—even though the visiting parent is entirely "innocent." This is an unpalatable decision for any court to make, and for any psychiatrist to recommend; yet, in the interests of the child, it may be the only possible solution.

Conflicts as to Custody

If the children are young and the custodial parent has remarried, it may be better for the child to accept its position in the new home and to establish a filial emotional relationship with the stepparent. Having two fathers or two mothers is disturbing; particularly so if the child has taken the stepparent's name. This is an item to be considered by the psychiatrist in making a recommendation. Older children generally retain their name, and thus symbolically retain identification with the natural father although living with their mother and stepfather. Because of this, and because of their greater maturity, the double-father prospect may be less threatening.

Conflicts also sometimes develop when a mother who has relinquished her child changes her mind. Sometimes the basis of her claim is that she did not know what she was doing when she signed the renunciation. This is discussed in the following section. Sometimes it is simply that she has thought it over and decided that the placement was a mistake and that now she wants her child back. She may or may not know the name of the adopting parents. If she does not know who they are, she may seek to compel the court, institution, or social agency to reveal the name and address. The mother in that situation could disrupt the child's new life very badly once she discovered where he was living. Mothers sometimes "kidnap" their own children from foster or adopting parents; sometimes they haunt the house and create conflict and trauma for the child. Except under unusual circumstances, the psychiatrist would feel that, once the child has adapted himself to his new family, his pattern of life should not be torn apart and serious loyalty conflicts engendered by permitting the natural mother to identify herself to the child.

In most states lawfully processed adoptions are irrevocable. The mental hygiene wisdom of such legislation is obvious. If the child could at any time be taken from his home and thrust among strangers (and his natural parents would be strangers to him), the child's lot would be a most unhappy one.

It is, indeed, largely because of this need for stability in the emotional environment that the law makes adoptions irrevocable. However, some attorneys contend that parental right to the custody of children is so absolute that no law can constitutionally extinguish it. This is argued under two somewhat different circumstances: (1) where the parents had consented to the placement, and (2) where a court had ordered a placement over the resistance of the available parents, usually the mother.

With respect to the first point, it is generally held that such adoptions are permanent. For example, the following quotation shows the legal disposition of one effort to regain custody. Here it was unsuccessfully argued that the placement was itself illegal because it failed to comply with one detail of the law.

The law provides that adopting parents shall be approved for that purpose prior to placement and that any person who receives such child without such preplacement investigation, shall be guilty of a misdemeanor.

The court made the observation that these statutes were enacted to eliminate the exploitation of the placement of infants for adoption by unauthorized persons, for monetary gain, without regard to the welfare of the children.

The court stated that the law was not intended to prevent natural parents from voluntarily placing their children for adoption with some fit persons as adopting parents.

In the situation under review, the natural parents voluntarily signed a consent for the adoption of their child and surrendered its custody to the proposed adoption parents. Although they were present at the same time in the hospital when the child was delivered, the natural parents disclosed that they had no desire to meet the adopting parents.

About a year thereafter, the natural mother inquired as to the possibility of regaining custody of her child and was told that it was impossible.

The natural parents thereafter sought to secure the return of the child and alleged a violation of the preplacement statute and contended that the adoption proceedings were a nullity.

On this stated set of facts, the court found that even had there been noncompliance with the preplacement feature of the law, this would not render the adoption proceedings void. The court observed that the agency that subsequently investigated the adopting parents found them to be responsible persons and that the child had been given excellent care. It was admitted that they were fit persons to whom to commit the rearing of the child.

Accordingly, the court refused to set aside the adoption proceeding, and application on behalf of the natural parents for return of custody was denied.[7]

Competency to Sign a Surrender

Unless the courts have extinguished the parents' rights, an adoption cannot be effected until the available parent or parents sign a "relinquishment" or "surrender." If the mother is unmarried, the father's written consent is usually unnecessary unless he has formally acknowledged paternity. Ordinarily these relinquishments are signed soon after the baby's birth. In fact, it is not at all uncommon to have a pregnant woman sign *before* the baby is born. Thus many of these surrenders are signed when the mother is in a late stage of pregnancy, or in the puerperal period. (Some hasty doctors and lawyers even obtain the signature while the woman is in labor.) This is likely to be a period when the mother is emotionally disturbed. If she is unmarried (and in about one half of adoption cases this *is* the situation) the physical strain of the pregnancy is compounded by the guilt feelings and other emotional aspects of "illegitimacy." Having decided to relinquish her own baby she has, whether married or single, an added burden of guilt. Thus the mother is signing an important document of lifelong effect at a time when, in all likelihood, her mental and emotional state is not at optimum. It is thus possible that, at the time of signing, she did not realize the implications of the relinquishment.

[7] Eugene Urbaniak, *New Jersey Welfare Reporter* (Trenton, N. J.), IV (December, 1949), 14.

It is necessary, both legally and medically, to distinguish between: (*a*) a surrender signed by a parent who was suffering a mental disturbance of such degree that she did not realize the nature of the document, and (*b*) a signature knowingly applied—albeit under considerable pressure—by a mother who knew what she was doing, who wanted to (or had been persuaded to) do it, but who later changed her mind. If the processing was otherwise correct, the law provides no relief in situation (*b*): a surrender signed under those circumstances is irrevocable.

Ideally the doctor, social worker, or lawyer who arranges for the adoption should have a psychiatrist interview the mother just prior to her signing of the surrender. This would afford protection to the adopting parents because, as indicated, it is so easy later to raise a question as to lack of capacity to understand.

At such an interview the psychiatrist would focus his examination on seeking to determine whether the parent knew what she was doing. He would also assay her intelligence, note whether she was sane and rational, and look for any evidences of psychoneurosis or emotional instability. In all likelihood he would find her depressed, and he would determine whether this was a simple reactive depression, part of a manic-depressive psychosis (perhaps precipitated by the puerperium), or whether it was part of a chronic psychoneurosis. He would review the parent's past psychiatric history too, since often the entire problem turns on whether her mental state was transient or part of a lifelong pattern.

This opportunity is rarely afforded to the psychiatrist. Instead he is asked to advise the court or social agency or to testify on the basis of a description furnished to him. He will examine the parent when she is seeking to withdraw her relinquishment, but by itself this will not tell him much about her mental or emotional state at the time she signed the surrender. He has to depend on a hypothesis furnished to him (see Chapter 20) which purports to describe her mental state with sufficient vividness so that the psychiatrist can make a diagnosis in restrospect. Obviously this will depend on the accuracy of the observer. Thus, the doctor who arranged the adoption, now very defensive about it, will testify that the mother was calm, spoke rationally, and was mildly depressed. He will add that this was a "natural" and transient depression, and that it did not affect the clarity of her thought. The husband, on the contrary, having regretted his decision, will testify that the wife was plunged into tears, that she was wild with grief, and that the people who wanted to take the baby said it was only a foster home placement until the mother regained her strength. The psychiatrist's answer will depend, in large measure, on which hypothesis is furnished to him.

Here, for example, is an Associated Press dispatch datelined New York, August 18, 1950. It is typical of many stories heard in courts with surprising frequency. In this quotation, names have been replaced with initials, but otherwise it is a verbatim transcript of the item as it appeared in a New Jersey newspaper. The headline is: " 'Persuaded' to Yield Baby says Unwed Ma"—note that the word Persuaded is in quotation marks.

New York (*P*)—An unwed New Jersey mother testified yesterday that she was "persuaded" to sign adoption papers for her son, now 18 months old, at a time when she was physically ill and emotionally upset. She made the statement at a hearing before Supreme Court Justice P.—

In a suit against the adopting father, F.C. of New York, auburn-haired A.F., 23, is seeking to recover the child, B—, born to her (date and hospital given).

During the hearing, J.K., attorney for F.C., said that Miss F. had signed an affidavit consenting to the adoption of B—, by the C's. Under questioning by Justice P—, Miss F. admitted signing "something to that effect" but explained that she was physically ill, exhausted from the strain of child-birth, and emotionally upset. She said that she had been told by an attorney, whose name she did not know, that the affidavit "didn't mean a thing," that it was just a "temporary" placement until she recovered her strength and that she could have the baby back at any time. Justice P. reserved decision.

The yardstick of mental capacity in these cases is a simple one. At least it sounds simple. It reduces itself to one query: Did she know what she was doing when she signed the surrender? The formula here is the same as that applied to determining competency to handle affairs generally. This is developed in detail in Chapter 13.

From information furnished or garnered firsthand the psychiatrist must decide whether the mother had a specific mental or emotional disorder; or whether she was a more or less normal person subjected to so much pressure that she signed the surrender against her own desires. In particular, evidence should be reviewed for manifestations of: (1) psychosis, (2) mental deficiency, (3) psychoneurosis, (4) alcoholism, (5) physical exhaustion, (6) toxemia with or without fever or delirium, (7) depression, or (8) unusual pressure or duress by members of the family.

1. A psychosis often, but not always, invalidates the surrender. A woman may have a paranoid condition not touching on her relationship to the baby. This psychotic state would not impair her ability

to understand the implications of the relinquishment of the child. And in a depressive psychosis there might be preservation of competency. Suppose, for example, by reason of a manic-depressive reaction, she felt that she had committed a sin in becoming pregnant, and that losing the baby was just punishment for her sin. In such a situation, it cannot be said that she did not know what she was doing. She knew exactly what she was doing in giving up the baby to an adopting parent. And she intended to do just that. There was no fraud or force involved. On the other hand, she surrendered the baby only because of a psychotic delusion. The psychiatrist can thus clearly define the issue, and the court will determine whether the surrender document should be nullified. In general, it is traumatizing to the baby to take him away from an adoptive home after he has adjusted himself to it. And for that reason, the one who testifies in favor of the validity of the surrender is generally on the side of the angels. The proper procedure would have been the appointment of a guardian during the mother's psychosis, and the authenticating of the adoption by both the guardian and the court, with full information about the mother's mental state being made available to the court. If this is not done, courts generally frown on surrenders signed by psychotic mothers.

2. Mental deficiency presents a serious and common problem. For obvious reasons, a defective unmarried girl is more likely to become pregnant than one of normal intelligence.[8] In this situation, the psychiatrist is on surer ground (than with neurotics and psychotics) in gaging the mother's mental state at the time of the signing. This is because intelligence (unlike psychotic and neurotic symptoms) does not vary much over the years, and a finding of imbecility in an adult today usually means that the patient was also an imbecile a year ago. The question of intelligence and ability to understand contracts is discussed in Chapter 13. As a rough rule of the thumb, a girl with a mental age under nine or ten probably does not understand the implications of relinquishing her baby; one with a mental age over thirteen may, tentatively at least, be assumed to understand it; and if the mental age is between ten and thirteen, judgment must be based on evidences of her general capacity as found at examination.

[8] But most unmarried mothers probably have normal intelligence. For some years I served as psychiatrist to an institution for unmarried mothers which accepted both paying guests and welfare clients. The distribution of intelligence among the mothers was substantially average. The actual average I.Q. of the group was 85, which is a shade below the floor of the theoretically normal range (90 to 110). I do not believe the difference is significant.

3. Psychoneurosis would not, by itself, invalidate the mother's signature. If the psychoneurosis is severe enough to raise any question of the mother's competency to sign, it also raises the serious question of her ability to take care of the baby. Thus, socially (though not legally) one cancels the other. Psychoneurosis might have meaning in terms of indicating her susceptibility to pressure (see 8 below) or in terms of reflecting impulsiveness, but these do not invalidate the renunciation of the baby.

4. Alcoholism is rarely a factor. No honest lawyer, doctor, or social agency would ask a woman to sign a paper while she was drunk. Chronic alcoholism would not invalidate a signature; in fact it would only underline the desirability of the adoption. A black-market baby-peddler might present the surrender to a woman when she was drunk (might, indeed, make her drunk in order to be assured of her signature). The test of the validity of such a document would then be whether she was too drunk to understand the implications of relinquishing the baby.

5. Marked physical exhaustion may impair the intellectual faculties, but the burden of proof would have to be on the mother. A woman might by reason of loss of blood, protracted or difficult labor, or other physical complication be so sick that she did not know or did not care what she was doing. The question would be: Did she not know, or, knowing, did she not care? If the second condition prevails, the surrender would be valid. If it could be shown—and this is difficult to prove—that she was really so exhausted or so ill that she just scrawled her name on a piece of paper without knowing what was written on it, then the renunciation would be invalid.

6. Toxemia may blur a woman's intellectual clarity, may indeed cause delirium. If she was in an actual delirium (as defined psychiatrically) she could not realize the implications of any paper she was asked to sign. But it would have to be shown, if this is alleged, that she was excited, hallucinating, and confused. If she simply had a high fever, without delirium, the courts might look askance at the agency which asked a woman to sign an important document while she was in such a state; but it is not likely that they would invalidate the surrender.

7. Depression is the common emotional coloring of a woman who is about to abandon a recently born or soon expected baby. Nearly always it can be shown that when it came to signing the paper, the woman was tearful, agitated, self-deprecatory, and depressed. The psychiatrist has to determine whether this is a psychotic depression (and, if so, whether it is part of long-range manic-depressive psy-

chosis), a psychoneurotic depression, or what might be called a "simple situational" depression.[9] Did she give away the baby because she was depressed, or was she depressed because she was obliged to surrender the baby? In the latter situation, her competency to sign would not be affected. Whether a psychotic depression would invalidate a signature is a question to be determined from the special facts of the case, but in general the reasoning of paragraph 1 above would apply: that is, even though she was psychotically motivated in deciding to surrender the baby, the fact would remain that she knew what she was doing. And that is the basic test.

8. Pressure on more or less normal women is the most commonly cited reason for seeking to invalidate a surrender. Women come to court—sometimes months, sometimes years afterwards—and try to regain custody of the child. They admit that they signed a surrender, but argue that they were "talked into it" or subjected to pressure or to unfair persuasion. For instance, this would be a typical story:

An intelligent, unmarried woman becomes pregnant. The man quietly fades out of the picture. Her first impulse is to have the baby delivered in her own community, keep the child at home with her parents, and return proudly to work as soon as she can. She says she does not feel ashamed, has no desire to conceal her motherhood, and looks forward eagerly to the adventure of rearing a child. However, her parents are horrified and suggest that she take a four or five months' leave-of-absence from her job, visit a cousin in a distant city, have the baby there and arrange for its immediate adoption. Then she can return home and resume life as if nothing had happened. When she demurs, the pressure begins. She is told that if she proceeds with her quixotic plan she will be branded at home as a "tramp"; that no man will ever marry her; that her employer will never let her return to work; that her friends will desert her; that she will sink into the gutter; and that the baby will never have a chance to develop into a happy, normal child. Finally she yields to this pressure, departs, has her baby at a hospital in a distant city. She shares a room with three other new mothers. Their husbands visit every evening. She has no visitors but the distant and none-too-sympathetic cousin. The whole experience is frightening and guilt-laden. She signs the surrender paper, knowing that it is not what she wants to do, and returns home thoroughly disgusted with herself. A few months later she is wooed by a young man. She tells him the whole story, but he still wants to marry her. They are married and now she wants her baby

---

[9] Called in various nomenclatures: adult situational reaction, simple adult maladjustment, gross stress reaction, or simple situational depression.

back. So does the husband, who agrees to cherish it as if it were his own. She asks a court to revoke the surrender, contending that she signed it under pressure so great as to be tantamount to undue influence.

With numerous minor variations, this is a surprisingly common story. It occurs with married women too, when for financial reasons, or because of already having many children, or by reason of poor health, the couple relinquish a new baby to an eager adopting family. The situation changes; some of the other children die or move away, the financial and medical conditions improve. Now the couple want their baby back and assert that they were subjected to extreme pressure and gave their original consent practically under duress.

This is judged like any other contract. Somebody signs an ill-advised and foolish agreement every day. Often they were "talked into it" by a salesman, or pressured into it by the importunities of friends or relatives. A man who agrees to buy his wife a mink coat cannot later cancel the agreement on the theory that she "nagged him into it." Unless the psychiatrist can find evidence of a mental disorder of sufficient intensity to destroy competence, the surrender document would be held valid.

Placement of Child of Psychotic Mother

When a baby is born to a psychotic mother, the family ordinarily make their own provisions for rearing the child. Sometimes, however, the courts step in, either because the family refuse to or are unable to make arrangements, or because in the opinion of a social agency (or a faction within the family) the arrangements are completely unsatisfactory. In that situation, the psychiatrist will be asked two questions: (a) Is the mother's mental illness of such severity and probable duration that she will not be able to rear the baby? (b) If so, what arrangement would be best for the welfare of the child? The possibilities to be considered here include: placement with relatives, temporary (foster-home) placement with a strange family until more permanent plans can be made, placement in an orphanage, or permanent adoption. Other things being equal, the child will probably be best off if he can be placed with his grandparents or other close relatives; adoption is the second best plan; and placement in an orphanage the least desirable. If it is a matter of making a temporary disposition, a foster home is better for the welfare of the child than an orphanage. The emotional security that comes from even a foster home more than counterbalances the physical, educational, and hygienic benefits of an orphanage. A question that calls for nice psychiatric judgment is whether, even with a psychotic background, the natural mother cannot, in the long run, provide the best care for her child.

Placement of Delinquent Child

If a child appears before the Juvenile Court, and the decision is that he must no longer remain in his own (presumably delinquency-breeding) home, the judge must make some affirmative disposition. The easiest step would be to send him to a state home. However, several noninstitutional possibilities may be considered. They are (a) to send him to live with relatives in a different community, (b) to place him in a foster home until the situation in his own home improves, (c) to declare that the parents have forfeited their parental rights, extinguish those rights, and arrange for a permanent adoption, or (d) to place the child briefly in an orphanage or "protectory" until plans, (a), (b), or (c) can be consummated. These possible dispositions are reviewed in Chapter 10, pages 152 to 155.

Conflicting Interests of Child and Parent

One basic legal question is raised by many of these situations. Which is the prime determinant, the welfare of the child, or the rights of the parent? Consider the following situation:

An unmarried woman gives birth to a child and, in a purely informal and private arrangement, allows him to be adopted by a couple who have no children of their own. No papers are signed. The child is simply delivered to his new home when he is ten days old, and from that point on he takes the last name of his new "parents." The birth certificate is correctly filed, though the address given on it is that of the adopting parents. For six years this situation remains unchallenged. The child assumes that this couple are his own parents. His mother visits fairly often, and is introduced simply as an aunt. One day the mother marries the father of the baby. Then she visits her child with his "uncle." They get along well. Within a year, it appears that the mother is never going to be pregnant again. They now decide they want their own baby back, and since there was never any legal adoption, they foresee no difficulties. However, the adopting parents refuse to surrender the child and the case reaches a court. The attorney for the natural parents takes this position: A mother's right to her own child is paramount unless it can be shown that the mother is unfit. In this case there is no such contention. This never was an adoption anyway; it was only a temporary foster-home placement. The attorney for the adopting parents, however, argues that the prime determinant is not the mother's right but the child's welfare. I testified in this case that it would be emotionally harmful to rip a child out of a secure environment at the age of six. On cross examination, the attorney for the natural parents stumped me with this: "I have just one question, doctor; is it or is it not true that blood is thicker than water?" (I told him that it was true only in the chemical sense, but that emotionally a child might well be more secure with non-relatives than with his own flesh and blood, depending on circumstances).

In this case the issue was squarely focused on the one question: was the child's welfare or the parents' unrelinquished right the paramount criterion? The court decided that its function was to protect the rights of children first and that everything else was secondary to that, and refused to return the child in spite of the informal nature of the adoption. I am told that in some states the child would have been returned, because the courts would hold that there never was an adoption and that therefore the foster-parents were holding the child illegally. Even if it jeopardized the welfare of the child, the courts would send him back to his natural parents. Before going further with situations like this, the doctor should ascertain from the attorney which legal standard applies in his state.

Chapter 7

LAST WILL AND TESTAMENT*

A person's mental ability to make a will is known as testamentary capacity. A psychiatrist is frequently called—usually after the subject has died—to tell the court whether the testator [1] did or did not have the mental capacity to make a valid will.

Criteria of Testamentary Capacity

A person making a will must (1) know that he is making a will, (2) know the nature and extent of his property, and (3) know the natural objects of his bounty. These are the three "tests" which, in a sense, the patient must "pass" before he is considered mentally competent to make a will. The psychiatrist must measure the subject by these three tests. What do they mean?

1. The testator must know what he is doing when he signs the will. If the doctor is told that when the will was signed, the patient was toxic, dehydrated, feverish, confused, and unable to talk; that his hand had to be guided in signing the will; that he showed no recognition of the people around him; and that he died a few hours later, he would probably feel that the testator did not know that he was making and signing a will. And if this is so, the testator fails to pass the first test. He did not know he was making a will; hence the document is invalid.

2. The testator must know the nature and extent of his property—not that he must know to the square inch the exact acreage of his land nor that he must remember the serial numbers on his government bonds. But he must have a substantially accurate idea of what he owns. If the will reads, "I bequeath to my loving sister Jane my gold cuff links, to my loving nephew Claude the contents of my safe deposit box, and to my loving brother Kilroy the Brooklyn Bridge," it may be assumed that the testator thought that he owned the Brooklyn Bridge. It would appear that he did not know the extent of his

---

* This chapter is an expansion of a section of the author's "Orientation to Forensic Psychiatry," *Archives of Neurology and Psychiatry,* June, 1947.
[1] The testator is the person making the will.

property (obviously not, if he thought the Brooklyn Bridge was part of his own property). Thus he fails to pass test number two, and the will is invalid.

3. The natural objects of one's bounty are the people for whom he would naturally want to do favors. If a man has any bounty to distribute, he would normally pass it out to his closest relatives, warmest friends, and most loyal servants. The law does not require him to bequeath anything to these "natural objects of his bounty." He may cut them off without a penny and the law will not thereby presume that he lacks testamentary capacity. But it insists that he know who they are. If the doctor is told that the testator thought that his sister Fanny was alive when actually Fanny died thirty years ago, he is justified in assuming that the patient did not have a clear idea of the natural objects of his bounty. If he insists that the man who represents himself as his nephew Elmer is actually an impostor, when all the evidence indicates that Elmer is only Elmer, it would appear that the testator does not know one of the objects of his bounty. Thus he fails to pass the third test, and the will is invalid.

An important corollary to these criteria is this: the defects in question must arise because of disease of the mind. If he does not recognize Elmer because Elmer had been away from home for ten years, this would not invalidate the will, since the non-recognition would arise from a simple extraneous circumstance and not from disorder of the mind.

Effect of a Psychosis

The fact that the testator was psychotic when he made the will does not necessarily invalidate the document. The claimant must prove that the psychosis impaired one of the three essential elements of the testamentary capacity. It has been held that an inmate of a mental hospital may make a perfectly valid will. "It is not the medical soundness of mind that governs," explained the court in a typical case,[2] "but rather testamentary capacity as defined by law. The fact that the testator was committed to an institution for the insane does not justify the assumption that he lacked legal mental capacity."

Even a formal adjudication of psychosis will not by itself invalidate a will. The law recognizes that a patient (in a severe depression, for example) might be sick enough to require treatment, institutionalization, even the appointment of a guardian; yet might still know the nature and extent of his property and the natural objects

[2] *In re* Whitemarsh's Estate, 234 New York S. 505; also see Livandais v. Bynum, 116 Southern 223.

of his bounty. As one court puts it, "The distinction between an adjudication of insanity and an adjudication that he is incompetent to dispose of his property is a substantial one." [3]

On the other hand, a psychosis does invalidate a will if it touches on one of the three elements of testamentary capacity. If, for example, the testator has paranoid delusions (not simple prejudices, but delusions of paranoid intensity) against one of his relatives, the psychosis must affect his understanding of the natural objects of his bounty. Similarly, delusions of great wealth or poverty might cause failure under test number two. Under such circumstances the will would be invalidated.

The Effect of Senility

The frontier between simple senility and senile dementia is a vague one, yet it is the psychiatrist's responsibility to draw the line. "Extreme age, mental sluggishness, and defective memory do not render a testator incapable of making a will if he is able to recall to mind his property and the natural objects of his bounty," said one court. [4] The witnesses will describe the testator's mental capacity by giving anecdotes of his odd behavior. The psychiatrist has to pierce the verbal fog and determine whether the described behavior is that of a psychotic or simply that of a man in his dotage with no psychotic delusion formation or psychotic dementia. In one case [5] a will was held lawful although the court said, ". . . he was peevish, childish and made himself obnoxious by continually repeating the stories of his early life. But all these go with advancing years . . . there was nothing in the record to show that he was so lacking in capacity as to be unable to remember and identify his property or unable to remember and identify the natural objects of his bounty." The psychiatrist must always return to the three basic criteria and use them as his yardstick. No matter how psychotic the patient, if he passes these tests and if his delusions do not impinge on these specific qualities, the will is valid.

Belief in Spiritualism

As a man (or woman) grows old, he sometimes seeks solace by trying to communicate with friends who have long since died. A belief in spiritualism itself will not invalidate a will since obviously such a belief does not necessarily affect the testator's knowledge of

---

[3] Waters v. Waters, 207 Northwestern 598 (Iowa).
[4] Forberg v. Maurer, 168 Northeastern 308 (Illinois).
[5] *In re* Cooper's Estate, 206 Northwestern Reporter 95.

his relatives or of his property.[6] On the other hand, where "the testator was laboring under a delusion that the spirits of the dead were directing him in all his business," [7] the will would be invalid, since the delusion goes beyond belief in spiritualism and affirmatively affects the actual process of making the will. (In this case, the testator obtained advice from the spirits as to how he should dispose of his property.)

Alcoholism and Addictions

Proof that a testator was a chronic alcoholic or a drug addict will not, by itself, invalidate a will. The authoritative Alexander puts it this way:

A person through excessive use of drugs or drink may become so obscured that he is, for the time being, comparable to a mad man. In such a condition he cannot make a valid will. But the effects of alcohol and drugs wear off, and though they may leave the user weakened in mind and body, yet so long as there has not been a destruction of the mentality which the law requires for making a will, it cannot be said that the fact that the testator is addicted to drinking or drugs incapacitates him from making a will.[8]

As a matter of fact, a will made while the testator was drunk was admitted to probate in a case [9] where it appeared "that his drunkenness did not prevent him from knowing what he was about." The evidence indicated that while the man was drunk, he knew he was making a will, knew who his relatives were, and how much property he had. On the other hand, courts will be suspicious of any will signed while the testator was drunk, especially if an heir was present at the time. Generally speaking, if a testator was under the influence of drugs while making his will,[10] the document will be considered invalid unless the defense can show affirmatively that the testator met the criteria for legal capacity.

Ideas of Infidelity

Senile psychotics often have delusions of marital infidelity. Sometimes ideas of infidelity are the only outspoken manifestations of the

[6] Franzman v. Nalty, 271 Southwestern 1034 (Kentucky); Whipple v. Eddy, 161 Illinois 114; *In re* Chaffin, 32 Wisconsin 564; Scott v. Scott, 212 Illinois 603; Gass v. Gass, 22 Tennessee 277; Brown v. Ward, 53 Maryland 376. There are similar decisions in almost every state.

[7] Middleditch v. Williams, 45 New Jersey Equity 726.

[8] J. E. Alexander, *Commentaries on the Law of Wills* (San Francisco: Bender-Moss Co., I (1918), 475, cited in many cases, as for instance in Payne v. Chance, 4 Southwestern (2d Ser.) 328 (Texas). This work is an authoritative legal text on the subject of testamentary capacity.

[9] Pierce v. Pierce, 38 Michigan 412.

[10] Thomas v. Young, 22 Federal (2d Ser.), 588.

mental disturbance. The courts draw a line between a belief in the wife's unfaithfulness based on misinterpretation of external circumstances and a belief based on a psychotic delusion. The latter invalidates the will because it comes under test number three. In one such case,[11] the court said, ". . . to justify the rejection of the will, it must be established that the false belief is the figment of a deranged mind and not the result of an impression produced by extraneous circumstances. The burden is on the petitioner to prove the non-existence of the extrinsic evidence on which the belief rested."

Whims and Prejudices

A person is entitled to enjoy a wide range of unreasonable prejudices, crack-pot ideas, and bizarre notions, without sacrificing his testamentary capacity. Nephew August may attack the will which disinherited him on the grounds that Aunt Agatha cherished an unreasonable belief that August was the very devil because he had a nose shaped just like her uncle's. If the psychiatrist finds that Aunt Agatha literally thought that August was a devil, this would be a psychotic delusion touching on test three, and it might invalidate the will. But if, as is more likely, Aunt Agatha was using "devil" in a figurative sense, then her unreasonable prejudice does not upset the testament. So, an unreasonable prejudice against the wife in the McDowell case, cited above, did not invalidate the will. As a matter of fact, one court accepted a psychotic explanation as a last resort, only if the testator's conduct "did not admit of explanation on any other ground." [12]

Undue Influence

It is not the psychiatrist's responsibility to evaluate undue influence. Only an influence which destroys the testator's free agency is an undue influence. It must be, in effect, a substitution of one person's will or intention for another's. The psychiatrist may be able to help the court by indicating whether a person of the temperament described would be unusually gullible or unusually stubborn. For example, if the evidence indicated that one testator had a conversion hysteria and another had a paranoid delusion, the psychiatrist could point out that the former person was far more likely to be responsive to a friend's influence than the latter.

[11] *In re* McDowell, 140 Atlantic 281 (New Jersey).
[12] Snell v. Weldon, 243 Illinois 496.

Participation of the Psychiatrist

In most medico-legal cases, the doctor examines the patient and testifies as to his findings. In will litigation, the psychiatrist rarely has the chance to examine the testator who is necessarily quite dead when the case comes to court. The practitioner usually has to depend on a hypothetical question [13] describing the testator's behavior and conclude from the hypothesis whether the subject could have passed the three tests on the day he signed the will. The psychiatrist confers with the attorneys prior to the trial and tells them what facts he will need for an honest opinion. The doctor studies each of the three tests against the background of the case, and asks that the lawyer include in his hypothesis not only general information about the testator's conduct, but also a battery of facts focussed on these three criteria. It is the lawyer's job to find witnesses who had enough knowledge of the testator's behavior to present an adequate description to the court and to the doctor. These facts are then assembled into the hypothesis which is given to the psychiatrist on the witness stand. On these facts (that is, on the hypothesis) the doctor bases his conclusion as to the mental capacity of the testator.

In the rare cases where the lawyer has the client examined before the will is prepared, the psychiatrist's job is naturally much easier. In addition to the routine mental examination, the doctor will analyze the patient's thinking processes from the point of view of the three tests. For example, he will ask the patient to name the members of his family and indicate their relationships to him, and he will later verify these statements. He will ask the patient for a brief description of each relative to see if any undue emotional response is produced when the patient talks about any of them. The examiner will take careful and accurate notes and preserve them. He will prepare a report for the attorney, quote freely and verbatim from the patient's own remarks, and be certain that the report contains enough facts to support the conclusion about the patient's mental capacity. He will carefully preserve a carbon copy of this report and use it later (when called as a witness) to refresh his memory. (See Chapters 19 and 22 for the mechanics of testimony.)

In some cases, a psychiatrist who had examined the patient in life, for some other purpose, is called as a witness after the testator has died. If the examination had revealed no mental derangement, and if the will had been made at about the same time, the doctor's opinion is naturally of prime value to the court. If the examination

[13] See page 272 for explanation of the hypothetical question.

had revealed some mental disorder, chances are that the focus of the examination was not on testamentary capacity, so that conclusions as to mental capacity to make a will have to be made more or less inferentially. Still, this is more direct evidence than reliance on a wholly hypothetical question. Even though he had not specifically examined for testamentary capacity, the doctor should be in a position to give honest and accurate answers to such questions as "Did he have sense enough to know what he was doing when he signed a document?" or "Did his delusions extend to members of his family?"

Chapter 8

APPRAISAL OF THE SEX OFFENDER

There is a vast literature on the psychodynamics of sex pathology. Little of this, however, tells the psychiatrist how to examine a sex offender within the framework of the criminal law, how to appraise his responsibility, and how to prepare a report which will be comprehensible to lay officials. The examiner is usually expected to make recommendations too, and here he often must be reminded of the conflicting needs of the patient and of the community.

Medico-Legal Classification of Sex Offenders

When a specific psychiatric disorder is found, this is reported as the primary diagnosis. If, for example, the defendant is a mental defective who has engaged in coitus with animals, the psychiatric report would list the mental deficiency as the Number 1 diagnosis. This is desirable because it is the extent of the mental deficiency, not the nature of the sex behavior, which determines the patient's criminal responsibility. It also serves to remind the court (and ultimately the public) that a sex offense is not an isolated category of behavior, but is part of a general psychosomatic entity. If a defendant has been arrested for exposing his genitals to unwilling female observers, the examiner might find this to be a manifestation of a compulsive neurosis. In that case, the psychoneurosis, not the exhibitionism, would be set up as the primary diagnosis. His criminal responsibility will be appraised in terms of the resistibility of the impulse, which in turn requires an assay of the nature and extent of the underlying psychoneurosis.

Five psychiatric syndromes embrace the great majority of sex offenders. These are: (1) mental defectives, (2) psychotics, (3) psychoneurotics, (4) alcoholics, and (5) psychopaths. If the psychiatrist finds the existence of any one of these, the report first highlights this basic psychiatric category.

If the offense was committed while the defendant was drunk, and if the examiner believes that he would not, when sober, engage in such behavior, the diagnosis should be set up as acute alcoholism.

Responsibility is evaluated according to the formulation suggested in Chapter 1. Of course it is known that alcoholism will not cause abnormal sex behavior unless some other psychopathology underlies the alcoholism. This may be reviewed in the report, but for forensic purposes emphasis should be placed on the acute alcoholism. It is this (not the underlying psychopathology) which will determine the defendant's technical responsibility and the immediate disposition of the case.

The word "psychopath" is now known to the more sophisticated judges and prosecutors, who think of the "psychopath" as an anti-social rebel with an inadequate conscience. It is impossible to effect any short-term change in this point of view. The examiner, there-fore, should reserve the unqualified term "psychopath" for the "asocial and amoral" type. If the defendant does not fit into this or any other group, he may be described as a "sexual psychopath."

Some sex offenders will be, for all practical purposes, normal individuals. For example, a man with no access to feminine com-pany may play the male role in an act of fellatio or buggery. While by definition this might be "abnormal," the man is not by this act substantially altering the basic nature and direction of his sex drive. If the examiner is satisfied that this homosexual act was *not* the pre-ferred channel of gratification, but was practiced only *faute de mieux,* then he should list the patient as a normal male. Some psychiatrists never report a subject as normal on the theory that everyone has some kind of personality oddity. However, in the criminal court the psychiatrist's job is to draw the line between the essentially nor-mal and the essentially abnormal. A large proportion of defendants will be reported as without any substantial mental disorder.[1] Again, a man may frequently engage in cunnilingus. The question here is whether this is (*a*) a technique of wooing, (*b*) a prelude to coitus, (*c*) a substitute for coitus, or (*d*) an occasional variant. If the man consistently *prefers* cunnilingus to the more usual type of inter-course, then it seems fair to consider this an abnormality, since it does consistently vary from the norm. But if the cunnilingus is only

---

[1] Unless the psychiatrist believes that sexual misconduct, *per se,* is automatic evidence of a mental disorder. For instance, in David Abrahamsen's *Report on the Study of 102 Sex Offenders* (Utica, N. Y.: State Hospitals Press, March, 1950), it is reported: "Of the 102 men studied, every one suffered from some type of mental or emotional disorder." Of course, the group here sampled was atypical in that it included only those whose offenses were serious enough or repeated enough to have justified a sentence to Sing Sing. However, some psychiatrists believe that *all* sex offenders have mental disease of some sort. This seems to be stretching the concept of "mental disorder" to the point where it becomes so nonspecific as to be meaningless.

a prelude to or a casual variant from ordinary coitus, then, other things being equal, the subject should be reported as normal.

In official government nomenclature (Army, Navy, Veterans Administration) all nonpsychotic sex deviates are classed as psychopaths. Government psychiatrists are, of course, fully aware of the fact that many of these patients are psychoneurotic. The term "psychoneurosis" (or its equivalent) is avoided in these cases for purely administrative reasons. A psychoneurosis is a disease and carries with it certain potential rights to compensation, pension, line-of-duty status, and disability claims. The public is not ready to accept the idea that sexual perversion can be acquired in line of duty or that any pension should derive from it. It therefore becomes administratively necessary to exclude nonpsychotic sexual deviations from listing as psychoneurosis, even when this classification is medically sound. However, in the civilian criminal courts there is no administrative need for this subterfuge. If the examiner believes that the sexual aberration is part of a psychoneurosis, it should be so reported.

The differentiation between a psychopath and a psychoneurotic in this area turns largely on the presence or absence of anxiety. There is, for example, the psychopath who is constantly seeking sensual pleasure and who will try anything. One year he smokes marihuana, the next year he tries a sexual variation. The examiner will find no anxiety here, except perhaps some anxiety to escape conviction. The defendant will show none of the real criteria of psychoneurosis. On the other hand, there are persons with overt anxiety and ill-concealed guilt feelings who seem driven to sexual aberration and whose clinical picture is clearly that of the neurotic.

The neurotic sexual deviate, when apprehended, usually goes into a depression, sometimes into a panic. The psychopath is more likely to deny everything, offer evasive explanations, boast of his abnormality, or plunge into that curious "psychotic-like" episode which so frequently characterizes the cornered psychopath.

After the neurotics, psychotics, defectives, alcoholics, and unqualified psychopaths have been accounted for, there still remains a small residue of unclassifiable sex offenders. Some of these are simply normal persons with isolated or casual sexual idiosyncracies—of great interest to the psychopathologist, but of little importance to criminal law. Most of the dangerous sex offenders will fall into the psychotic, psychoneurotic, or mentally defective groups and should be so classified. The law's chief concern is with sex deviates who inflict trauma —emotional or physical—on their victims, and most of the aggressive offenders suffer from compulsive drives (usually psychasthenic or psychotic) or from defective inhibitions (usually in psychopaths).

Whether it is proper to set up a special category of "sex psychopaths" is a moot question. The classification has little medical justification but it is forensically convenient, since it permits special legislation towards a group which would otherwise be subjected to a monotonous series of repetitive jail or prison sentences.

Psychiatry is a social science and the psychiatrist cannot ignore the intense emotional charge which surrounds sex offenses. The doctor, of course, will not be swept along in a stream of public panic when a particularly outrageous sex crime hits the headlines. At the same time he cannot take the position that the offender is simply a sick man who needs only outpatient treatment.[2] Much of the public disgust at sex crimes arises from guilt feelings. "Exhibitionists and peeping Toms," writes Bowman [3] "are looked upon as terrible sex criminals. Yet many of those upset at such types of behavior will go to night clubs to see nude women dancing in suggestive fashion. These same persons become indignant, however, if some individual is caught peeping through a window while a girl is undressing."

There is some evidence that the public clamor itself may precipitate aggressive sex behavior in unstable offenders. Sane persons with perverted and aggressive sexual drives know that they "ought not" yield to such urges. They know it is "wrong" to assault, kill, or torture victims as part of a sexual act. They are, indeed, fearful of being forced to yield to such impulses. Such persons are in a state of precarious balance. Dwelling on details of a crime described in the newspaper, having access to victims in a private place, and having the opportunity of fondly studying gruesome and sadistic pictures are factors that may be sufficient to overturn the unstable balance in which these people constantly live.

A disproportionate number of male sex offenders are senile. This is particularly true when the victims are children. Presumably a child represents the only available market for the shoddy, libidinous wares of the worn-out old man. He thinks he would be scorned by more sophisticated partners. Seldom, however, does the senility amount to a frank psychosis, and even less often may it be said that the assailant did not know the nature of his act or did not know that

[2] *Ibid.* Dr. Abrahamsen, one of the most optimistic of the psychiatrists studying this problem, found that only eight of the 102 sex offenders in his study were suitable for outpatient treatment. This accords with general experience and indicates why a recommendation for outpatient treatment may have to be ignored by the law-enforcing authorities.

[3] Karl Bowman, *Mental Hygiene,* XXII (January, 1938), 10.

it was wrong. If the psychiatrist finds that the offender actually was incapable of realizing that his act was wrong, and if this was because of a senile dementia, then the defendant would probably be irresponsible under the McNaghten rule. (See Chapter 1.) Such a person is, however, a continued danger to children; in fact, his irresponsibility makes him doubly hazardous, and the psychiatrist who helps free the patient from a criminal charge has a duty to see to it that the defendant is confined to an institution thereafter.

Some psychiatrists take the position that a sex offender must not be diagnosed or adjudged solely as a sex offender. They point out that an unlawful sex act may be only a superficial manifestation of a deep-seated psychiatric disturbance. From the medical viewpoint, it seems absurd to set up a single symptom and legislate about it as if it were an isolated trait. An inexperienced psychiatrist, indeed, might argue that if sexual offenses are to be classed as crimes by themselves, then hallucinations or ideas of reference ought to be separately categorized. This is, however, a naïve point of view.

Aggressive sex offenses are numerous, conspicuous, and in a high proportion of cases, dangerous to the safety of the community. The public sees them as criminal acts. The psychiatrist may insist that sex offenses are only symptoms, to be judged in terms of the offender's total personality and treated as forms of illness. The doctor who adheres to this simply forfeits his own usefulness to the courts. If the sex offense is provably a part of a psychosis, the examiner is on firm ground in taking this position. But in other cases such a point of view (i.e., viewing sex offenses as symptoms of sickness) is currently so much at variance with public thinking that the psychiatrist will be of no use in the administration of justice if he insists on it.

Reporting the Sex Offender to the Court

Sent to examine a sex offender, the psychiatrist often becomes so interested in the psychopathology of the patient that he forgets to report on responsibility, the one fact in which the court is most interested. It is poor policy to present to the court, prosecutor, or jury a dynamic explanation of the offense. Learned as he may otherwise be, the average judge simply will not believe the doctor who tells him that a voyeur has an unconscious wish to be struck blind or that the mouth is an erogenous zone. Interpretations like these belong in the classroom and in the conference room, but never in the courtroom. They clutter up the record with legally irrelevant testimony, they confuse the court and jury, and they tend either to discredit the psychiatrist or to make him sound like someone living in a dream world who has no contact with social reality. Actually there are only seven questions which the courts want answered about the defendant, and the experienced psychiatrist answers all these questions in his report and in his testimony. With respect to the offender, these are the questions that must be answered:

1. Is he—or was he—insane?
2. If not, what is the psychiatric diagnosis?
3. What is his intelligence level?
4. Did he know the nature and quality of his act?
5. Did he know that the act was wrong?
6. Was he in the grip of a powerful or irresistible impulse at the time of the offense?
7. What are the chances that this condition will respond to treatment—and to what treatment?

If the offender was drunk [4] at the time of his act, these questions should be answered with respect to his mental condition at the time, plus a report as to whether he was likely to commit such acts when sober; and in question 7 the term "this condition" should include both the alcoholism and the abnormal sex drive.

If the examiner limits his report and his testimony to a consideration of these seven questions, he will of course be omitting parts of the story of great importance to the psychiatrist. However, he will spare himself the embarrassment of ill-informed cross-examination before a frankly incredulous jury, he will save a good deal of his own and the court's time, and he will focus his report on the exact questions at issue. The dynamic material should be retained in the doctor's record and used in connection with subsequent therapy, if any.

Sociologic Classification

The psychiatrist divides sex offenders into clinical categories (alcoholics, psychopaths, mental defectives, etc.). Law enforcement officials need a behavior classification, dividing offenders into two major groups: (1) those who are a menace, and (2) those who, at worst, are only nuisances.

To the psychiatrist this seems to be a naïve classification. A man with an urge to commit rape might be much less "sick" (psychody-

---

[4] There is a high correlation between alcoholism and overt sexual offensiveness. In his study of 102 sex offenders at Sing Sing Prison, Abrahamsen found that "alcoholism is associated with or a precipitating factor in over one half (56) of the 102 cases. The tendencies which get these men into trouble can seemingly be held in check when they are sober; but when they have too much to drink, impulsive antisocial behavior occurs." *Op. cit.*, p. 21.

namically) than a "peeping Tom." Yet, sociologically, the rapist is a menace, the "peeping Tom" a nuisance. Since we are using legal concepts as our frame of reference, the psychiatrist too must use this "behavior" classification in reporting on and in appraising sex offenders. In this field, therefore, the psychiatrist, like the sociologist, divides sex offenders into two categories: the traumatizing and the nontraumatizing.

1. The *traumatizing* (or "menace") group includes offenders who (*a*) inflict physical harm, (*b*) inflict emotional trauma, or (*c*) recruit sex inverts from the ranks of the previously normal. In general, the acts which constitute "traumatizing" offenses would be: forcible rape, sexual assaults, and murders, corrupting the morals of a minor, carnal abuse, seduction of little girls, incest against children, and initiating children or previously heterosexual adults into homosexual practices.

2. The *nontraumatizing* (or "nuisance") category would include indecent exposure of the genitals, statutory rape with a nonvirgin, voyeurism ("peeping Tom" activities), hoarding of obscene pictures, open lewdness, homosexual acts between mature, cooperative adults (if practiced in private), prostitution, and exhibitionism.

The frontier between these two groups is, of course, hazy. For example, a man may have a compulsive urge to ring doorbells and to expose his genitals to the first female who opens the door. If the door were opened by a nine-year-old girl, this exposure might be very disturbing to the child; the offense would have to be classed as "traumatizing" and the offender as a "menace." On the other hand, a mature and sophisticated woman might open the door and react by no more than a giggle. Then the act would have to be classed as nontraumatizing.

This sociologic differentiation into traumatizing and nontraumatizing acts is of considerable practical importance. Since our mental hygiene resources are so limited, it seems best to use them for the major offenders, rather than to divert our meager psychiatric manpower into the treatment of the vast number of "nuisance" offenders. Furthermore, when harsh laws are enacted for the disposition of sex offenders, the nuisance-type is caught more often than the "menace" type. After a few years, the courts and public become tired of disposing of minor offenders in this fashion; the state hospitals become filled with a host of nontraumatizing offenders, and sooner or later this kind of situation is reached: A man who stopped his car on a rural road, and who got out in order to urinate, is arrested for open lewdness. No psychiatrist is willing to swear that he is *not* a sex psychopath, because that kind of negative diagnosis cannot be proved. The "offender" is then placed in a state hospital, not to be released until he is certified as cured. However, no hospital official can risk issuing a certificate that he will never commit a sex offense for the rest of his life. The net result is life imprisonment (in a hospital, but in confinement none the less) for a man whose only offense was having a full bladder at an inopportune time. Eventually this kind of situation leads to nullification of the law—a contingency that does not arise when the special legislation is limited in the first place to major offenders.

The way in which special legislation tends to pick up minor offenders is illustrated by New Jersey's experience with its law. Tappan [5] reports that of the first 83 cases only 26 could be classed as major traumatizing offenses. The remaining 57 were cases of open lewdness, statutory rape, private voluntary adult homosexuality, indecent exposure, and other "minor" acts. Similar experiences are reported in other states.

Extent of the Problem

Opinion as to the magnitude of the problem tends to veer to the two extremes. On the one hand, there are numerous and dire announcements which would suggest that armies of "sex fiends" are patrolling the streets; and at the opposite pole are certain sociologists and psychologists who, in an anxiety to neutralize this hysteria, insist that the entire problem has been vastly overemphasized. Those who paint a picture of a community menaced by a hundred thousand aggressive sex offenders are, of course, inaccurate. Those who point out that the overwhelming majority of sex offenses are "minor" in nature are technically accurate, but they are none the less somewhat distorting the truth. The point is this: if on any day the total number of technically illegal sex acts were to be counted, some 95 per cent of them would be nontraumatizing acts. This is because most of those "illegal" acts would consist of fornication between unmarried partners or homosexual acts between mature adults. As against this large number, the incidence of rape or carnal abuse would naturally be small. Hence, in a strictly statistical sense, it is correct to say that most sexual "crimes" are minor, nontraumatizing acts. But this gives a misleading picture. In New York City, in a ten-year-period

[5] Paul Tappan, *The Habitual Sex Offender* (Trenton, N. J.: Report of the Commission on the Habitual Sex Offender, 1950), p. 29.

(1930 to 1940) there were 333 convictions for carnal abuse and 418 for forcible (not statutory) rape.[6]

This aggregates 751 cases of major traumatizing sex offenses in one decade in a single city in those two classifications alone: an average of 75 per year. Add to this the cases in which offenders are not apprehended, plus the number in other categories of major sex crimes, and the actual incidence in this one city would surely exceed a hundred a year. The national total must be at least ten times (probably nearer twenty times) the New York City figure: certainly not fewer than 1500 cases a year. This constitutes a sizeable problem (1500 major aggressive sex crimes a year would come to five per day) and it cannot be disposed of by simply stating that most sex offenses are in the "minor" category. Take another example: Records of the New Jersey state police show that 45 per cent of the subjects in their "sex file" had been convicted of rape. Rape, of course, is a major or "traumatizing" (menace) type of offense. In citing this figure, Tappan [7] adds that "most of these offenses are of a minor character rather than a menace." Tappan is technically correct, since only 45 per cent were cases of rape, and 55 per cent were not cases of rape; and 55 per cent is, of course, "most" of a hundred per cent. But if 45 per cent of the cases were traumatizing, it seems like a play on words to use this figure to prove that "most of these offenses are of a minor character."

Some students of the subject keep insisting that the sex offender is seldom a repeater. The inference is that many more of these offenders should be placed on probation, and that this could be done without danger to the community because "so few" are repeaters. For example, Tappan [8] writes: "Sex offenders have one of the lowest rates as repeaters of all types of crime." However, both the dynamics of sex psychopathy and the actual statistics seem to contradict that optimism. Obviously the sex offender has an urge to keep repeating acts from which he derives major gratification. Furthermore, about 50 per cent of forcible rape and carnal abuse convictions occur in persons who already have accumulated a sex offense record.[9] The figures can actually be read either way. Thus, the New York Court of General Sessions convicted 333 persons of carnal abuse during one decade (1930 to 1940). Of these 333 there were 158 who had

[6] *Report of the Mayor's Committee for the Study of Sex Offense* (City of New York, 1940).

[7] *Op. cit.*, p. 20.

[8] *Ibid.*, p. 14.

[9] *Report of the Mayor's Committee for the Study of Sex Offenses* (City of New York, 1940).

previous records. This amounts to 47 per cent. A congenital optimist might look at that figure and state: "Observe that most of these offenders had no previous record." Yet "most of the offenders" amounted to 53 per cent. In other words, 47 per cent did have previous records; and when one considers that many second offenders are never apprehended, it becomes obvious that recidivism in traumatizing sex behavior cannot be dismissed lightly.

Homosexuality

The commonest of the sexual aberrations appears to be homosexuality. Statistics on the subject are, of course, incomplete. The term "homosexual" should be reserved for men whose *preferred* method of sexual gratification is through contact with other males. To be sure, the word "homosexual" could apply equally well to corresponding contacts between women, but unless otherwise specified a homosexual is presumed to be a male. Homosexuality between women is known as *lesbianism*. Only an insignificant proportion of lesbians become involved with the law. For some reason, the law and the public seem more tolerant of female than of male homosexuality. This extends to all personal contacts. Thus two women may dance together or kiss each other in public, without arousing comment. If a pair of men danced together or greeted each other with kisses on the mouth, it would certainly cause many raised eyebrows.

A man who prefers sexual contact with women, but who occasionally plays the male role in sodomy, is not considered a homosexual. The touchstone of homosexuality is that it is the preferred (often the exclusive) method of sexual contact. While the occasional or casual homosexual is legally guilty of sodomy, he is not, from the psychiatrist's viewpoint, a true homosexual. He may be branded as a "sex psychopath" according to the definitions in some of the special legislation on the subject, but the psychiatrist will report him as normal, if his homosexual activities are infrequent, if he plays only the male role, and if in general he prefers heterosexual relations. The offense itself can then be listed as "casual homosexuality." Embraced in the category of "casual homosexuals" are (a) first offenders, (b) men who play only the male role in casual homosexual contacts, (c) those who engage in homosexual activity only when drunk but who, when sober, seem sexually normal, (d) men impelled by curiosity, desire for novelty, or extraordinary persuasion to engage in homosexual experiments, and (e) psychopaths with a picaresque urge to try anything once.

The word *sodomy* implies any kind of sexual experience which a court may consider "unnatural." Most psychiatrists use it as synonymous with homosexuality, though it sometimes is extended to cover relations with animals. In some vocabularies, on the other hand, sodomy means buggery. *Fellatio* is the form of homosexuality in which the penis is received in the mouth; when the penis is placed in the anal area, it is known as *buggery*. Whoever furnishes the penis plays the male role: whoever receives the penis, plays the female role. Playing the male role in fellatio is also known as *irrumation*. Simultaneous and reciprocal fellatio is known as *sixty-nine*.

The true homosexual consistently plays the female role (or engages in sixty-nine). He is likely to be an old offender. His motivation will not be curiosity, adventure, or whimsy, but simply a wish to enjoy sexual pleasure in the manner most gratifying to him. His homosexual desires may be enhanced by alcohol; they do not depend on it. In appearance, true homosexuals vary from thoroughly masculine-looking to obviously effeminate men. The diagnostic features of the extreme homosexual are listed below. Few will show all these characteristics; a true homosexual will show many of them.

Appearance. While sometimes he is short and lean, the homosexual is more likely to be plump, well-rounded, smooth-skinned, pallid, and "pudgy."

Speech. The confirmed practitioner of fellatio tends to develop a characteristic speech. Words are carefully lipped or mouthed, syllables sharply articulated, vowels drawled or drawn out. Sentences often show rising inflection. There may be a lisp. This speech is heard more commonly among practitioners of fellatio than among those who prefer buggery, and is probably related to a localization of pleasure sensations in tongue and lips with consequent tendency to play with, linger over, and fondle those organs while talking.

Language. A confirmed homosexual who has lived near a large city will probably have acquired the special "language" which has grown up among them. The doctor is suspicious of the man who says he is a homosexual but who is unfamiliar with their jargon. In the lexicon of the sodomist, a normal (heterosexual) man is a *square;* to wear women's clothes is to *go on the drag;* another homosexual is a *gay;* an elderly sodomist is an *auntie* or a *grandma;* an accomplished practitioner of fellatio is a *blow-queen,* while a mature devotee of buggery is a *brown-queen.* A confirmed homosexual who stubbornly denies his perversion, insisting that he is normal, is said to be *keeping his hair up,* while breaking down and confessing is termed *letting his hair down.* When excited, the homosexual may use the female pronoun, not only with reference to other "gays" but even when referring to normal men. Homosexuals sometimes call each other *queens, belles,* or *queers.*

Heterosexual Life. To the complete homosexual, contact with women is as unattractive as sodomy would be to a normal man. Many homosexuals have experimented with heterosexual activity, and those who "keep their hair up" may insist that they enjoy such contacts; but they can usually count on their fingers the number of heterosexual experiences they have ever had. A moderate proportion of confirmed homosexuals are married—either as an experiment, or as a sort of camouflage, or because of family pressures and misguided medical advice.

Early Personal History. In some cases, early history discloses beginning sexual inversion as young as age 8 or 9. The boy may cling to dolls, long after the normal youth has discarded them. (He may develop an 'artistic talent' justifying the interest in dolls on the basis of wanting to make clothes for them.) He shuns rough street sports. He may experiment with his mother's rouge, powder, or lipstick. He does not mind playing with girls in the street or schoolyard during the 9-to-12 age period when normal boys are bored with feminine companionship. Conversely, at the age when the average boy begins to slick down his hair and carry home the girls' books, the budding homosexual finds male companionship more exciting. Histories of this type would be revealed more often if the examiners would carefully comb through the early development of the subject.

Social Life. Intelligent homosexuals tend to drift into work which brings them into contact with males. Thus, without quite realizing why, they may find themselves in church work, the stage, club leadership, the sea, social work, teaching, and the like. Let it be said at once that there is no implication that club leaders, actors, sailors, teachers, or welfare workers are inherently effeminate, but simply that many intelligent homosexuals drift into those activities. Most workers in these fields are, of course, entirely normal. Homosexuals are generally somewhat above average in intelligence. They often display neatness, orderliness, passion for detail, and meticulous personal cleanliness. The emotional relationship between the homosexual and his affinity is important and should be thoroughly explored by the examiner. These relationships have a range parallel to that of the variety of heterosexual relationships. Some establish a mimicry of marriage. Often when the "man" consorts with others, the "female" suffers the pangs of jealousy. They speak, indeed, of being "in love" with each other—at least the homosexual partner uses that term—and they engage in lovers' quarrels. Well established, domesticated homosexuals look with sour disapproval on the promiscuous "gays" who pick up consorts in streets or taverns. At the lower end of the scale is the homosexual equivalent of the prostitute, who will offer or ask for money in exchange for homosexual accommodation. The typical homosexual becomes sexually excited when he sees other men partly undressed in bathrooms. The examiner should always inquire about the subject's relationship with his partner. Is he "in love" with him? Jealous when he goes out with others? What kind of men does he prefer? Does he painfully miss his consort when the latter goes away? Are his relationships with other men faithful or promiscuous?

Self-Evaluation. The subject's own attitude toward his inversion is worth recording. Some are ashamed, some are brazen. Some live in dread of exposure, others exhibit their homosexuality for all to see. The commonest attitude is one of quiet acceptance of the homosexual status. He has come to, accept his inversion without defiant self-advertisement on the one hand or abject self-pity on the other. Some of them say that "sodomy" is "sinful" or "wrong" but that they can't help themselves. Most of them answer that society condemns them because "people don't understand." The confirmed homosexual is not interested in any treatment leading to possible "cure." He says he prefers not to give up a known pleasure for an unknown one. Occasionally one sees a neurotic homosexual who envies the normal man and expresses a wistful desire to be like him. But he is reconciled to his own status and does not seriously expect any reconversion. The subject's own evaluation has a place in the report.

Localization of Homosexual Pleasure. If you ask a homosexual to localize the source of his pleasure, he is likely to say that it "feels good all over." But, if the possible loci of the sense of gratification are reviewed, he can sometimes localize it more accurately. As some index of the intrenchment of the drive, it is important to ascertain whether the seat of the gratification is in the genitals or in the receiving organ. Young homosexuals usually get an erection and ejaculation while playing the female role; thus some of the pleasure is genitally centered. As they become more mature, their locus of gratification shifts. An older practitioner of buggery will report that what he is seeking is a pleasant rhythmic sensation in the rectum. The fellationist has more difficulty in reporting localization, but we know that the mouth is an erogenous zone, that kissing, smoking, tasting, even talking can be an emotionally rich experience to a normal man, and it is in the mouth rather than the penis that the pleasure-sensation is localized in the more sophisticated practitioner of fellatio. The interviewer should inquire whether the homosexual gets an erection and whether maximum pleasure seems centered in the receiving organ or in the genitalia.

Mannerisms. The gestures, gait, and mannerisms of the homosexual have been portrayed often in ribald mimicry. And the confirmed homosexual does exhibit many of these features. One or more of these may be found in the well-intrenched homosexual, though seldom all in one person: a hip-swinging gait, a tendency to keep elbows flexed when carrying a package, flexion movements of the wrist in raising the fore-arm (as, e.g., in lighting a cigaret), fluttering movements of the eyelids, with grimacing of the mouth and upwards turning of the eyeballs during animated conversation.

Responsibility of the Homosexual.—Unless he is a deteriorated psychotic, the defendant will almost certainly be technically responsible for the act of sodomy. The homosexual knows, better than anyone else, that his inversion is condemned by society as "wrong" and therefore he does meet the major requirement of the McNaghten rule (see Chapter 1). Enlightened juridical opinion frowns on making a criminal case out of an ordinary act of voluntary homosexual contact between adults. The general attitude is the same as that toward heterosexual intercourse. While fornication is a crime in most states, little effort is made to prosecute people for privately practiced, voluntary, adult relationships. With homosexuals as with heterosexuals, cases reach the court chiefly when elements of force, conspicuous disorder, corruption of children, impairment of public morals, or incidental criminal acts are involved. The defense of irresistible impulse is sometimes set up. But here, as with heterosexual acts, society expects the defendant to restrain his impulse until he finds a cooperative adult partner in a private situation.

A particularly difficult problem is presented by the homosexual who recruits previously heterosexual males and initiates them into homosexual activities. There is no sound scientific evidence that homosexuality is "inborn." On the contrary, most cases seem to have developed out of adolescent associations, apart from the small but conspicuous group of men who showed feminine identification in childhood. Probably at least fifty per cent of male homosexuals were introduced to the inversion by friendly, affectionate adolescent partners. From one point of view, this type of recruitment is not the busi-

ness of law enforcement offiicals, since the project was voluntary.
Yet the psychiatrist must recognize that, in our society, homosexuality
is not a desirable goal; that the man who recruits others into homosexual activities is doing a good deal of emotional harm to the new
recruit and bringing tragedy to the family. Thus, in a very practical
sense, the identification of recruiting homosexuals is a legitimate
function of law enforcement agencies, and the psychiatrist can be
asked, in good conscience, to cooperate in any such project.

The defense of irresistible impulse is sometimes advanced in arrests and trials for sodomy or kindred offenses. If, as is very rarely
true, the defendant would have proceeded with his act even in the
presence of a police officer, then irresistible impulse may be reasonably
argued. However, this defense would not immunize the offender from
conviction except in the few states (see page 12) in which "irresistible impulse" is acceptable; and, even then, only if the impulse was
rooted in psychotic or, at best, neurotic drives. It would not be
applicable to such impulses in a psychopath.

In most cases, it is obvious that the presence of a policeman or,
indeed, the presence of any third party would have stopped the offender from proceeding with the act. Under these circumstances
there can be no legal validity to a plea of "irresistible impulse," since
the impulse could have been, and would have been, resisted in the
presence of an observer. This fact may not diminish the neurotically
compulsive character of the impulse, but it does legally extinguish
the defense of irresistible impulse.

Other Sex Offenses

For forensic purposes, all sex offenses are measured by the same
responsibility yardstick. It is necessary first to make a clinical psychiatric diagnosis; then to determine whether that condition (whatever was clinically diagnosed) robbed the defendant of knowledge
of the "nature" of his act. If he knew what he was doing, the next
question is: Did he know it was wrong? (Here, the word "wrong"
means: Did he know it was something generally condemned by
society?) If he did not know this, was his ignorance the result of
his mental disorder? It is conceivable, for instance, that an imbecile
might not know that it was "wrong" to have sexual contact with
animals. If this is the case, his failure to understand the "wrongfulness" of the act is due to a psychiatric disorder, namely mental deficiency. Under those circumstances, he would not be criminally
responsible. Many sex offenders set up the defense of irresistible
impulse. For an analysis of this, see page 11.

Sexual Factors in Other Offenses.—Not infrequently an indictment charges a crime which appears at first to have no sexual component. Psychiatric study indicates, however, a definite sexual tincture to the act. This occurs in two situations: (*a*) symbolic acts, such as arson due to pyromania, and (*b*) acts with obvious sexual motives which take the form of general crimes (for example, a murder committed in the course of an attempted rape). The prosecutor, judge, and jury can understand that the second type of crime has a sexual motivation. They cannot see the sexual factor in pyromania, kleptomania, poison-pen letters, etc. It is almost impossible for the psychiatrist to persuade the lay observer that these acts are sexual symbols. While a dynamic explanation may be included somewhere in the psychiatric report, it is necessary to evaluate the defendant's responsibility in terms of the arson, theft, or libel itself. The judge or juror senses a difference between an arson perpetrated to collect insurance money, and an arson resulting from pyromania. He understands the first and he is nonplussed by the second. However, it must be noted that the pyromaniac is actually more dangerous to the community than the commercial arsonist. A psychiatrist who pleads for the release and *outpatient* treatment of a compulsive pyromaniac may be helping to turn a firebug loose on a sleeping city. Many of these represent genuine irresistible impulses, but they are technically "guilty" because their impulses (to set fires) could have been resisted had an observer been present at the time. This legally takes them out of the "irresistible" category.

When a crime of violence is secondary to a sexual drive, a curious situation is produced. Let a man kill a business rival, and few psychiatrists will come to his defense. Let a man attempt to rape a child and kill her in the process, and numerous experts will, in all good faith, seek to exculpate him because the crime resulted from an unhealthy mind. This comes close to the ironical situation where the more repulsive and outrageous the crime, the more likely it is the offender will escape "punishment." A man with a neurotic drive to attack little children is more dangerous to the community than one who wanted to wipe out a single business competitor. Yet the more dangerous offender has less chance of getting a death sentence than the other.

The psychiatrist must not talk himself into the untenable position that a defendant is less responsible for a crime with a sexual component than he is for one without it. The offender is entitled to exculpation if, by reason of a psychosis or mental deficiency, he really did not know what he was doing or did not know that he was doing

something generally considered wrong. Most sexual crimes do *not*
fit into this classification. The offenders generally know quite well
what they are doing; and, by efforts to avoid identification and apprehension, they indicate that they know they are doing something generally considered wrong. Under these circumstances the law imposes
full accountability.

Disposition of Sex Offenders

Since sex offenses seem inexplicable to many laymen, the general
public demand is for "psychiatric treatment" for these defendants.
The usual thesis is that these offenders should be compelled to enter
state hospitals, the idea being that this is exactly analogous to the
involuntary commitment of psychotics. It is pointed out that there
is no "sentence" to a state hospital, no law which says that the schizophrenic must "serve" ten years or the manic five, but that it is left
to the staff to determine when the patient has recovered enough to
be safely returned home. The analogy, however, is faulty. Schizophrenics and manic-depressives can be *treated* at state hospitals. Considering the mass methods of treatment made necessary by their
fantastic case loads, the hospitals, in fact, achieve a most creditable
recovery rate. But successful treatment of a sex offender is an ex-
quisitely rare phenomenon and the overcrowded, understaffed wards
of a state hospital scarcely provide the proper vehicle for such treatment. Very intensive psychotherapy offers hope in some cases, but
the proportion who can be "cured" of their aggressive sex drive is
very small. Few statistical studies have been made available, but it
is a matter of common psychiatric observation that cured sexual
psychopaths are rare. Probably the best study is that reported by
Abrahamsen [10] who, with a highly skilled team, analyzed 102 sex
offenders and reached the following prognostic conclusions:

18 per cent "were likely to commit new attacks if released and are
not treatable by present methods."

31 per cent "because of personality make-up, age or alcoholism were
not suitable for treatment and were likely, after release to continue as a danger to public morals, to women, or to children."

43 per cent were found to be "offenders who could be placed in a
treatment center with good prospect of improvement."

8 per cent "could be released on parole and treated on an outpatient
basis."

[10] *Op. cit.*

From this it would appear that under the most favorable conditions with a staff of psychiatrists, psychologists, and social workers devoting full time to the project, it would be possible to return some 8 per cent of the offenders to the community and to rehabilitate another 43 per cent in special in-patient institutions. Under ordinary conditions, where it is not possible to detail a full staff to the treatment of these offenders, the recovery rate would obviously be even lower than this 8 per cent.

Legislative Status of Sex Offenders

Nine jurisdictions in 1951 had special statutes dealing with sex offenders. It is probable that during the next few decades, one state after another will enact such legislation; and in most such states psychiatrists will be consulted in the framing of these laws. It is therefore appropriate that existing legislation be reviewed here.

Most of the jurisdictions have written into the law a definition of sexual psychopathy. In Michigan (PA 1939; No. 165) and in Illinois (c.38, L.1938), the definition in substance is:

Any person suffering from a mental disorder who is not insane, nor feeble-minded, whose mental disorder has existed for more than one year, and whose mental disorder is coupled with propensities to the commission of sex offenses, is hereby declared to be a criminal sexual psychopath.

In Minnesota (section 526.09, Statutes of 1945) and in Wisconsin (c.459, Laws of 1947), the following definition is used:

. . . emotional instability, impulsiveness, lack of good judgment, failure to appreciate the consequences of his act, or a combination of such conditions as to render such a person irresponsible for his conduct with regard to sexual matters, and thereby dangerous to others.

The California statute (c.447, Laws of 1939) speaks of

. . . marked departures from normal mentality in a form predisposing to the commission of sexual offenses to a degree constituting a menace to the safety of others.

In the District of Columbia, Public Law 615 (80th Congress) defines a sexual psychopath

. . . as a person not insane who, by a course of repeated misconduct in sexual matters has evidenced such a lack of power to control his sexual impulses as to be dangerous to others . . .

In Ohio there is a general definition of "psychopath offenders" which includes these elements, any one of which is sufficient: emotional immaturity, emotional instability, deficient powers of self-discipline and marked deficiency of moral control.

Chapter 20 of the 1949 laws of New Jersey recites the sexual offenses—sodomy, indecent exposure, etc.—and requires commitment to a hospital if the defendant, in such a case, is found to be "suffering from any form of abnormal mental illness which resulted in the commission of the offense."

A review of these definitions indicates that, with the exception of the New Jersey statute, they must have been worded by lawyers rather than by psychiatrists. They cast a net which is wide· but full of large holes. They contain terms which themselves need definitions ("propensities to the commission of sex offenses," for instance, "such conditions as to render a person irresponsible," or "departures from normal mentality"). They ignore sexually motivated crimes that superficially show no sexual component—such as certain forms of pyromania. And they exhibit the basic defect of all legal definitions: they become frozen into the law with such firmness that, when scientific progress makes them obsolete, they are almost impossible to change.

The New Jersey definition reflects acceptable psychiatric doctrine. The sweeping statement, "suffering from any form of mental illness which resulted in the commission of the (sexual) offense," gives the psychiatrist the latitude he needs. He does not have to split hairs between psychopathy and a compulsive neurosis. It is sufficient if the patient's mental disorder caused him to commit the act.

The New York Law [11] makes no effort to define sexual psychopathy. It provides a "one day to life" sentence for certain sex offenses, and gives the State Board of Parole authority to terminate the sentence, absolutely or conditionally, whenever, after examination of psychiatric reports, they think it safe to do so. It applies to a list of specified offenses such as sodomy, rape, carnal abuse, etc.

The law requires the State Department of Mental Hygiene to furnish the State Department of Correction with psychiatric and psychologic services and provides for automatic psychiatric examination of persons sentenced to this "one day to life" term and also of persons convicted of any crime for which such a sentence might be imposed. Persons serving such sentences must be re-evaluated every two years. A person convicted of one of the named sex offenses may not be placed on probation nor given a suspended sentence until after the

[11] This is in part an amendment to the Mental Hygiene Law (effective April 1, 1950) and in part an amendment to certain sections (690, 1940, 1944, 2010, 2184, 2186, 2188, and 2189) of the Penal Law.

judge has read the psychiatric report. There is, however, no provision for committing nonpsychotic offenders to hospitals.

Since most sexual psychopaths are sane, special legislation is needed to provide for the defendant's involuntary admission to a mental hospital. All the laws, except the one in New York, provide this. In New Jersey and Ohio, conviction of sex crime is essential before the rest of the statute can operate. In Illinois, Michigan, and California, a criminal charge—but not necessarily a conviction—is required before the court can classify and dispose of the defendant as a sex psychopath. In Wisconsin, Minnesota, Massachusetts and the District of Columbia, no formal criminal charge is necessary. The court may act on information received even in the absence of any criminal charge. This seems like a wise provision, since the whole theory of the law is that sexual psychopathy is sickness, and there would seem to be no more logic in insisting on a criminal charge than in requiring it before imposing a quarantine for small pox. All jurisdictions require examination by two physicians, and most of the laws make some provision for a hearing before a jury, usually optionally. The statutes require admission of the offender to a state hospital. Usually the patient cannot be released until the hospital authorities certify that he is no longer a menace to the community. Since few hospital officials will make any such statement about a psychopath, it is necessary to provide an appeal mechanism. In New Jersey the patient cannot be kept in the hospital longer than the maximum sentence period provided by law for his crime. In some jurisdictions, the finding of sexual psychopathy stays criminal action, a doubtful provision since it will allow an offender to get away with murder by accompanying that crime with a sexual act.

It is not the place of this book to suggest reforms in the law. However, since some readers of this volume will be consulted when new legislation is under study, it seems relevant to point out some desirable features of such statutes.

A workable law on the subject must take cognizance of two facts: the public insists that such crimes must not go "unpunished," and sexual psychopaths are seldom cured. Thus a statute which forbids criminal prosecution of a psychopath violates the first principle; and one which requires a sex offender to stay in the hospital until cured violates the second.

1. There should be no attempt to define sexual psychopathy. Such a definition is both impossible and undesirable. It is impossible because the concept of psychopathy has no sharp frontiers; it grades

imperceptibly into the neurotic at one edge, the psychotic at another, the normal at a third. It is undesirable because, once laid down in law, it must be strictly followed, and a case can be squeezed out of the formal definition by ingenious legal reasoning; and because, if it is limited to aggressive acts, you start an endless chain of arguing about the definition of "aggressive"; if you limit it to repeated acts, you have to redefine the adjective "repeated"; if you exclude the insane, you open the door to further dispute; and, finally, it is undesirable because once crystallized in law it becomes burdensome to change. Newer psychiatric knowledge may require changes or point up the inadequacy of a definition; yet it would require the concurrence of two committees, two houses of the legislature and one governor to change even a single word in a legally established definition.

It would seem better to permit the court to order a psychiatric examination on any person charged with any offense in which there may be a sexual component. No harm is done in accomplishing an unnecessary examination. Then each case could stand on its own merits.

2. Sometimes the complaining witness will not file formal charges. Where the victim is a juvenile, provision should be made allowing children's aid and welfare societies to initiate complaints, at least to the extent of getting the offender examined.

3. The psychiatric examination should be done in an institution, not in a clinic or doctor's office. A period of observation is necessary in all but the most obvious cases. The indispensable social history takes time to assemble, so that it is important that there be no sense of urgency in getting the examination done and opinion written immediately. Furthermore, total diagnosis may require a variety of tests (psychological and medical) which are most expeditiously accomplished when the subject is in an institution. The law should specify both a minimum and a maximum observation period. Five and thirty days respectively are good figures. A minimum period is necessary, since otherwise the superintendent of an overcrowded hospital may have one of his doctors race through an examination one morning and send the patient out. A five-day hospital stay guarantees at least a minimum of daily observation by the ward physician. A ceiling on the observation period is desirable to protect the full rights of the accused.

Many good psychiatrists are, of course, found outside the staffs of state institutions. Their talents should also be made available. Since institutional observation is a desideratum, the law should permit the chief executive of an institution to call in as a consultant a qualified psychiatrist not on his staff.   To assure that only qualified consultants are selected, the statute should lay down some basic requirements.

4. The law should specifically indicate what questions must be answered in the psychiatric report.   If the statute merely calls for a "report," the judges will be getting, in too many cases, paragraphs of jargon which avoid the real issues.   Thus the law should state that the report on each case must, in addition to any other relevant material, specifically answer the following nine questions with respect to the defendant.

   a) Is he insane?

   b) What is the clinical-psychiatric diagnosis?

   c) What is his intelligence level?

   d) Does he know the nature and quality of the act charged?

   e) Does he know that the act charged is generally considered wrong?

   f) Was he in the grip of an irresistible impulse at the time of the offense?

   g) Was the offense committed while he was drunk?   If so, is it likely that such offenses would be committed while he is sober?

   h) What is the prognosis of the condition listed in answer (b)?   In this case, specifically, what are the chances of the condition responding to treatment?

   i) What sort of treatment program is practical in this type of case?

These answers will be more useful to the court than speculations on the superego, the libido, and anal eroticism.

5. If the accused is charged with a major crime, the normal processes of criminal law should be allowed to take their course.   *After* sentence (or after dismissal if a not-guilty verdict is rendered), consideration may be given to applying the recommendations.   If a death sentence is pronounced, it should be executed unless the defendant is criminally irresponsible under the existing precedents and interpretations of the McNaghten rule.   The phrase "major crime" will have to be defined to make this operative.

6. If the accused is not charged with a major crime, the psychiatric disposition may well take precedence over the legal disposition. This would likewise be true where the accused is acquitted, and where the courts take cognizance of a case where no crime is charged.

7. The psychiatric report should be forwarded to the court, the prosecutor and to the defense counsel, and the signers of it should be available for direct and cross-examination.   If the court does not elect to impose a penitentiary, reformatory, or prison sentence, the psychiatric disposition should be ordered.   Short jail sentences should

not be imposed at all. If a penitentiary, reformatory, or prison sentence is pronounced, the psychiatric report should become part of the prisoner's case-record and called to the attention of the warden. Services of the mental hygiene clinics of the state hospitals should be available to the prisons, reformatories and penitentiaries, in these cases.

8. Where the court does not or cannot impose confinement in a penal institution, the judge should, after study of the psychiatric report, make one of these dispositions:

    a) dismissal without supervision.

    b) commitment to a mental hospital.

    c) probationary supervision.

9. To implement this, a new type of commitment may be needed. This will be a commitment by direction of the court and will require no applicant, no medical certificates, and no affidavit of insanity. The psychiatric report should become part of this new type of commitment paper. Also bound into the paper should be a detainer so that the patient will not be turned loose without the court's knowledge. Eventually it is hoped to have a new kind of state hospital for this sort of nonpsychotic patient. Until that day arrives, special wards or wings of existing institutions should be set aside for this group.

A patient committed under this act should be allowed to request his own parole after he has been in the institution some specified minimum period, and at intervals thereafter. Each such request should be given serious consideration by the staff and their recommendation transmitted to the sentencing judge or his successor. Some appeal mechanism should be provided here. When paroled, the patient should be placed under probationary supervision.

10. A defendant placed under supervision, or placed on parole from an institution, should be assigned to the care of a probation officer. The latter will be authorized to obtain psychiatric guidance, to require regular attendance at a mental hygiene clinic as a condition of remaining on parole, to supervise the nature and conditions of work, to call on the assistance of social agencies, and to follow all the other activities of sound probation practice. The law should not require *private* psychiatric care as a condition of remaining on parole or probation. (While such care should not be discouraged, it would lead to favoritism, and financial embarrassment if attendance at any doctor's private office on a fee basis were an absolute essential.)

11. For protection of the constitutional rights of patients, several safeguards should be written into the statute. Thus, the accused

should have the right to call psychiatrists and other experts on his own behalf. Many of the hearings and trials ought to be held privately but a public hearing should be granted if the accused insists on it. While records of the trial, hearing, and commitment are, perhaps, public documents, some clause should be written into the law protecting the accused from the unnecessary disclosure of such records. A ticklish problem is presented by the question of the unprivileged status of doctor-patient communications in some states. Obviously the interview between the accused and the doctors cannot be considered privileged or confidential with reference to the subsequent reports, trial, or hearing. Doctors should be immune from being compelled to testify about those interviews on matters not relevant to new issues. For instance, if years later one of these patients is involved in an auto accident, and there is a damage suit, the plaintiff might want to discredit the defendant by showing that he had once been labelled a sexual psychopath. The doctor should not be compelled to testify about this in the tort action. There should be specific protection against compulsory self-incrimination. Thus, the doctors who prepare the report should be required, before interviewing the patient, to tell him that they are taking notes, that a report will be sent to the court, and that the results of the interview will be made available to the judge and both attorneys. The fact that such an explanation was given should be incorporated in the report.

12. A good social history is necessary in making an appraisal of this kind of patient. Trained social workers (not detectives) are needed to obtain the background data. Probation officers, hospital social workers, and the professional employees of established social agencies should be used. They can be depended on not to jeopardize the defendant by asking employers, friends, neighbors, etc., questions which might expose him.

13. It may be necessary to cut corners off certain legal formalities in order to do an effective job. For instance, in ordinary criminal actions, it might be improper (before adjudication of guilt) to hear about other criminal acts by the defendant. In this kind of case, the rule should be waived, and the record of previous sexual offenses made available to the psychiatrists, the attorneys, and the court. The present commitment law will have to be modified to allow commitment to a mental hospital without a medical affidavit of insanity. The habeas corpus provisions may remain unchanged. The lunacy jury likewise should be waived; and, unless it is intended to proceed with a criminal trial on indictment, there need be no guarantee of hearing by a jury.

However, where it is intended to proceed with criminal trial, there should certainly be some provision for a jury, even though the defendant is a psychiatric problem. If there is no arrangement for a jury, disposition becomes in effect, the responsibility of the psychiatrist. Doctors however are, by training, temperament, and experience, inclined to think first and last of the welfare of the individual patient. This is a noble attitude which ought not be destroyed. But in cases of this sort, it has to be neutralized. Perhaps the psychiatrist really believes that a particular defendant will not be a menace if allowed to roam in the community and take outpatient treatment. Let him, then, convince a jury of laymen. If he is not able to do so, his case is not strong. Provision for a jury is also necessary at the other end of the scale. Under some of the existing laws, a sex psychopath can be released from a hospital only if the superintendent certifies that he is cured. Naturally few doctors will sign an affidavit like that. The result is virtual life imprisonment. Provision for some kind of hearing before a nonmedical tribunal is the defendant's only chance to avoid life imprisonment for an offense that may have been no more serious than emptying his bladder behind a tree in a public park.

14. Provision should be made for administrative (rather than judicial) hearing and disposition of sexual psychopaths whose acts have *not* led to criminal charges. Sometimes these will be self-referred; that is, by men and women, troubled over their own sexual aberrations, seeking help. Sometimes the subject's own family will ask that the community step in and help. Sometimes the victim refuses to file formal charges, yet there is general community or police familiarity with the identity of the offender.

For these cases there should be some mechanism like this: any interested person should be able to notify the Commissioner of Health of the existence of the problem. The Health Commissioner, rather than a prosecutor, police official or court, should be the first official contact point. The reason is simple: the health department has benign, protective, and face-saving implications. All the other agencies (police, judges, prosecutors, mental hospitals, prison executives) are psychologically identified with coercive and stigma-carrying implications. The public and the families of patients and victims should see this as a health problem. The Commissioner of Health can then be empowered to initiate a preliminary inquiry and then to order the patient to a hospital for study and report. This will require enabling legislation, since normally such an order would be beyond his authority. The order to the hospital should be returnable before the

Domestic Relations Court. We have to use the judicial power at this point, but the Domestic Relations Court is vested with more administrative and less pure judicial authority than any other. When the report is submitted, the patient appears before the court which may now take full jurisdiction over him. However, this court holds a hearing, not a trial; it is a tribunal accustomed to receiving and evaluating psychiatric and social agency testimony, anyway. The court should then be empowered to order one of the dispositions in 8 with the implementation detailed in 9 and 10.

Noncriminal Sexual Psychopathy

The psychiatrist sometimes is asked to appraise sexual behavior in medico-legal cases outside the realm of the criminal law. For example, he may be asked whether the existence of a perversion in an old man is sufficient to indicate that he does not have capacity to make a will. For a discussion of this, see Chapter 7. Also, divorce proceedings are sometimes based on a complaint of cruelty, with evidence that the cruelty consisted in making "unnatural" sexual demands. Actually the psychiatrist has little to contribute here, since a judgment as to whether such demands are or are not cruel is entirely up to the courts. He may, however, be helpful in expressing expert opinion as to whether such acts are "normal," and as to whether they indicate "degeneracy" or character defects, and as to whether they are "willful."

Chapter 9

MEDICO-LEGAL ASPECTS
OF ALCOHOLISM

The gulf between the thinking of physicians and lawyers is most vividly illustrated by their different concepts of alcoholism. To the physician, alcoholism is a disease: an alcoholic is a sick person. To the jurist (or at least to the law, as written and practiced) alcoholism is a bad habit and the alcoholic has a character defect. To be sure, many individual judges and attorneys accept the thesis that alcoholism is a disease; but this only complicates the problem because the word "disease" means one thing to the doctor and something quite different to the lawyer. Since psychiatrists frequently report to judges, probation officers and lawyers on problems of alcoholism, it is worth taking time to review this semantic confusion.

The Social and Legal Concept of Alcoholism

To the doctor, disease is a deviation from health. Alcoholism is unhealthy, and therefore by this broad definition it is a disease. Since the alcoholic deviates from the norm of good health, he is in that sense a sick man.

However, the word "disease" presents quite a different picture to the layman. In nonmedical eyes, a disease is an affliction; something which "falls upon" a person; something he does not seek; it requires treatment by a doctor, and the treatment consists in the doctor doing something to the patient. When the doctor tells the court that this defendant has a sickness, namely alcoholism, he does not mean to put the alcoholism in the same semantic category as pneumonia or pernicious anemia. But that is precisely the way the judge will read the report. He will reason—and this fallacy is understandable—something like this: "In pneumonia a patient might have a delirium during which he might assault his attendant. This assault is obviously the result of an unfortunate illness which the patient did not seek, and which the doctor will cure with sulfa drugs. But the psychiatrist says that alchoholism too is an illness. I must believe him because he is an expert. So when an alcoholic assaults someone, this is the result of a disease, and we should "forgive" the patient and wait until the doctor does something to him to cure him."

If the lawyer or judge reasons this way, he runs into two difficulties. First, he has misread the doctor's report. (Or, more accurately, the doctor has unintentionally misled him by using the word "illness" in a specialized sense.) Second, the law as written will not allow the court to dispose of the problem as if it were a disease. The law says, for instance, that drunkenness is no defense to a crime committed in that condition. However, febrile delirium *is* a good defense for an assault committed while delirious. In some states, alcoholism is grounds for divorce; disease never is.[1] An automobile driver is excused (criminally, not civilly) if he has an accident because of an attack of allergic migraine while driving, but not if his accident is due to a paroxysm of acute alcoholism.

The law does not treat alcoholism as a disease, and this the psychiatrist must face. The concept of alcoholism as an illness is thus completely out of place in the forensic framework. It is out of place for two reasons: First, because the law says that alcoholism is *not* a disease; second, because in accepting the statement that it *is* a disease, the jurist does not understand what the doctor means.

A third—and perhaps somewhat theoretical—factor also operates with respect to the criminal law. Consider the thesis that the alcoholic is not responsible for his acts because he is in the grip of a disease. This implies a dogma of universal irresponsibility: that is, a doctrine that no one is ever responsible for his acts because everyone is the product of his environment plus his heredity (neither of which he chooses), and his "character" is simply the mechanical result of a battery of conditioned reflexes. This may be correct, but—

Such a doctrine is unworkable. It happens to be a fact that some people are kindly, others are selfish; some behave *as if* they were controlled by a conscience, some act *as if* they had no conscience. Regardless of the psychologic origin of these drives, they do exist. In the aggregate they constitute something we have agreed to call "character." There is a group of disorders which, *as an operational concept,* seem to be disorders of character. Included in this group would be alcoholics.[2]

The point is that the community is not yet ready to give up the idea that people should be held accountable for doing what they know

[1] Except in those very few states where insanity is "grounds" for divorce.
[2] Henry A. Davidson, "Role of the Psychiatrist in the Administration of Criminal Justice," *Rutgers Law Review,* IV (June, 1950), 578.

is wrong. Perhaps this idea is obsolete. However, society shows no intention of abandoning it, and the psychiatrist who will not function within this concept is of no use to the courts. Perhaps the doctrine of universal irresponsibility is sound; but until the courts adopt it, the doctor must conform to the forensic dictum that if the alcoholic suffers from a "disease," it is a self-induced one.

The medico-legal status of alcoholism has already been considered in parts of several previous chapters. This material will now be reassembled and reviewed.

Alcoholism and Criminal Responsibility

Alcoholism has an astonishingly high rate of association with criminal behavior. Catton,[3] for example, makes the blunt statement: "Alcohol has been among the causes of over half the murder cases which I have studied." And in alcoholism, the incidence of assault also is high. It is associated with desertion, wife-beating, and sexual offenses [4] of all sorts. Alcoholics have a high suicide rate and a high accident rate. And, of course, it is a factor in many automobile deaths.

The law on this is fairly simple. Self-induced alcoholism is not a defense to a crime committed while drunk. The only loopholes are: a plea for mercy or mitigation based on the theory (a) that the man became an alcoholic because of an underprivileged or overprotected childhood; or (b) that the drunkenness so befuddled the defendant that he was unable to form a clear intent. For a more detailed discussion of the latter point, see page 10 in Chapter 1.

Alcoholism and Annulment of Marriage

If either member of the wedding party is so drunk that he (or she) did not understand what he (or she) was doing at the ceremony, the marriage is voidable at the petition of the then intoxicated spouse. Since courts are reluctant to annul marriages, they will require some affirmative evidence that the degree of intoxication was serious enough to rob the participant of knowledge of the implications of marriage. Whether the sober spouse can come into court to annul

---

[3] Joseph Catton, *Behind the Scenes of Murder* (New York: W. W. Norton & Co., Inc., 1940), p. 63.

[4] David Abrahamsen, *Report on Study of 102 Sex Offenders* (Utica, N. Y.: State Hospitals Press, 1950), p. 21. In this report, Abrahamsen found that there was a high correlation between alcoholism and overt sexual offensiveness. "Alcoholism is associated with or a precipitating factor in over one half of the 102 cases. The tendencies which get these men into trouble can seemingly be held in check when they are sober. But when they have had too much to drink, impulsive antisocial behavior occurs."

marriage based on his mate's drunkenness is an unsettled legal point. If, after the drunken spouse regains his (her) sobriety, the couple continue to live together as man and wife, this will be construed as a "ratification" and the courts will not later annul the marriage on the grounds of intoxication at the time of the ceremony.   For further discussion of this, see page 78, Chapter 5.

Alcoholism and Testamentary Capacity

It seldom happens that a man tries to make a will while drunk. Acute alcoholism is thus rarely a factor in the probating of a will. Chronic alcoholism, however, presents a common problem.   The mere fact that the testator was a chronic alcoholic will certainly not invalidate the will.   To make a will, the law requires that the testator know (a) that he is making a will, (b) who the natural objects of his bounty are, and (c) the nature and extent of his property.   As Alexander [5] puts it: "So long as there has not been a destruction of the mentality which the law requires for making a will, it cannot be said that the fact that the testator is addicted to drinking incapacitates him from making a will."

Even if the testator was acutely drunk when he signed the will, it might be valid.   In one such case,[6] the will was upheld because the court found that "his drunkenness did not prevent him from knowing what he was about."   In general, the tendency is to view with suspicion a will signed when the testator was drunk, placing on the heirs the burden of proving that, in spite of his drunkenness, he still had testamentary capacity.   (See Chapter 7 for analysis of the elements of testamentary capacity.)   With chronic alcoholism, on the other hand, the courts are more likely to assume the testator's capacity and place on the challengers the burden of showing that he lacked the mental ability to make a will.

Alcoholism and Competency

The question of competency is reviewed in some detail in Chapter 13, and the reader is referred to that section for an analysis of the components of competency.   The general principles apply to alcoholism as to other disorders.   It will first be assumed that the subject is competent.   Whoever contends that a patient is unable to manage his affairs because of alcoholism must prove that the subject's judgment has been seriously affected by a disorder of the thinking proc-

[5] J. E. Alexander, *Commentaries on the Law of Wills* (San Francisco: Bender-Moss Co., 1918), Vol. I, p. 475.
[6] Pierce v. Pierce, 38 Michigan 412.

esses. In the absence of a special inebriety statute, alcoholism without psychosis will not justify a finding of incompetency. In a few states the law does recognize the chronic inebriate as incompetent and provides (by special legislation) for the appointment of a guardian for the chronic alcoholic. In most jurisdictions, however, non-psychotic alcoholism does not impair competency. If the alcoholic chooses to squander his pay check in a saloon every Saturday afternoon while his children starve, the courts take the position that the proper remedy is the criminal prosecution of the defendant for non-support, rather than the appointment of a guardian to conserve his assets.

Drunken Driving

The medical examination of the drunken driver is an emergency procedure. Since psychiatrists are not generally geared to emergency calls, they seldom come to a police station to examine a driver. There are, however, several situations which might bring the psychiatrist into contact with a drunken driver. Sometimes a driver appeals his conviction by a police court, and asks for a psychiatrist to testify that he had some other condition which produced the findings that the police surgeon interpreted as acute alcoholism. A patient already under psychiatric care might insist on having his own psychiatrist at the station before submitting to examination by the police doctor. And, in emergencies, even a psychiatrist might be called to help the local police determine whether a driver was drunk.

Criteria.—Courts are a little vague as to what they mean by "drunken" driving. Some judges hold that if the alcohol has, in any way, and to any degree, affected the driver's coordination or speed of reflex action, then the driver is under the influence of alcohol. Since, in theory at least, even very minute amounts of alcohol would produce some—albeit a negligible—alteration in reflex speed, anyone who drives before he has eliminated *all* the alcohol is, by that definition, a drunken driver. In Pennsylvania [7] the standard appears to be that the driver is drunk "if he does not possess that clearness of intellect which he would otherwise possess"—a reasonable-sounding criterion, though difficult to interpret. In Ohio, [8] on the other hand, it appears that a man is not "intoxicated within the meaning of the law . . . unless it is shown that he has lost the control of either of his faculties . . . or of the muscles of locomotion." The essence of this formula is the meaning of the phrase "lost control." In one sense, a

[7] Elkins v. Bushner, 16 Atlantic 102.
[8] Gard v. State, 33 Ohio Circuit Court Reports 632.

person does not lose control of his muscles unless and until he is paralyzed. In another sense, if he is less coordinate than normally, then he has lost at least some of the control which he previously could exercise over those muscles. Most courts solve the problem by shunning any general formula and seeking to determine in each case whether in fact the drinking made the driver unsafe.

It is considered amateurish to measure the extent of intoxication by determining the quantity of alcohol consumed. Many experiments have been made in an effort to correlate the quantitative alcohol intake with the effect on the subject's coordination. Using speed of reaction to traffic signals as a criterion, Heise [9] found that as little as five ounces of alcohol taken by mouth will substantially reduce the speed of reaction. However, in clinical practice, this kind of criterion means little. The effect of the alcohol depends on the subject's habituation, on the form of the beverage, and on whether it was taken on an empty or full stomach. In extreme cases, where the ingestion of large quantities of alcohol is shown or admitted, the fact of drinking may be adequate to prove that the driver was drunk. Ordinarily, however, recourse must be had to clinical or chemical tests, or, better, to a combination of both.

Clinical Tests.—The clinical evidences of acute alcoholism are a matter of common knowledge. For convenience they may be summarized as follows:

Clothes: Untidy, stained with vomitus, smelling of alcohol.

General Appearance: Bloodshot eyes, incoordinate, loud, hiccoughing, red-faced.

Breath: Varying degrees of alcoholic odor.

Coordination: Tested by straight-line walking, turning, finger-nose testing, and balance.

Speech:

    Content: Incoherent, sarcastic, over-amiable, or over-hostile.

    Articulation: Thick, stammering, slurred, or whispering.

Eyes: Dilated pupils, reddened conjunctivae, or glassy appearance.

Mentality: Orientation, clarity of thought, euphoria, excitement, depression.

Part of the examination—and sometimes a much neglected part—consists in obtaining from the defendant, and from those with him, an adequate history. Certainly the patient has to be asked whether, where and how much he was drinking. But it is also necessary to

[9] H. Heise, *Journal of the American Medical Association,* CIII (September 8, 1934), 739.

anticipate certain defenses by asking questions pointed at possible defenses. This is not done to trap the defendant. It protects him, in fact, since the courts will be much more reluctant to accept a defense which seems to have been introduced as an afterthought than to credit one which came out naturally during the medical examination. The common defenses are:

1. The odor on my breath is due to antifreeze which spilled on me when I was filling the radiator.
2. I use a mouthwash and perhaps that contained alcohol, thus causing the odor on my breath.
3. I am a diabetic and this swaying is due to acidosis or to insulin.
4. I had a blow on the head recently and that is why I stagger.
5. I didn't sleep last night and that is why I am "groggy."
6. These findings are the effect of the medicine a doctor is giving me.
7. I have been unable to walk straight ever since I hurt my back.
8. Dust blew into my eye which accounts for the redness.

An adequate "drunken driving" examination therefore includes inquiry into all these possibilities. Any doctor will see at once the logical line of questioning—such as the date of the head injury, the period of unconsciousness, the name of the treating doctor, the dentist or physician who prescribed the mouth wash, the brand name of the mouth wash or the pharmacy which furnished it, if it was a prescription, the nature of the back injury, etc.

Chemical Tests.—Several schedules for measuring intoxication against urine-alcohol content are available. The usual formula is that 2.6 parts of alcohol per thousand parts of urine (that is, 2.6 milligrams per cubic centimeter [10]) is the upper limit of safe driving. Anything in excess of that points to intoxication. Stuporously alcoholic subjects will show urine alcohol in excess of 4 milligrams per cubic centimeter.

A blood-alcohol level [11] in excess of 160 milligrams per hundred cubic centimeters (also expressed as 0.16 per cent) is enough to make a driver unsafe according to the report of the National Safety Council.[12] More elaborate scales are also available. For example, using milligrams per hundred cubic centimeters as the yardstick, a figure under 50 suggests that the defendant has been drinking but is

[10] Bogan says that even with only 2 milligrams per cubic centimeter of urine, the defendant is unfit to drive. E. Bogan, *The American Journal of the Medical Sciences,* CLXXVI (August, 1928), 153.

[11] At least five cubic centimeters of whole blood will be needed. An anticoagulant should be used.

[12] *Journal of the American Medical Association,* CXIV (February 3, 1940), 415.

not much affected by the alcohol; between 50 and 150 points to his being definitely under the influence of alcohol. When the blood alcohol reaches 250, the defendant is certainly drunk.

Admissibility of Tests.—Attorneys sometimes resist the taking of blood and urine samples, or appeal the admissibility of chemical findings, alleging that this is compulsory self-incrimination. Their theory seems to be that this, in effect, compels a witness to testify against himself, which is unconstitutional. However, most courts analogize this to the requirement that a defendant allow his fingerprints to be taken, whether he wants to or not. In many courts, this matter has already been disposed of [13] by a ruling that "compelling" the suspected driver to submit to blood or urine tests is *not* a breach of his constitutional rights. In some states there are specific statutes permitting such chemical tests.

[13] State v. Morkrid, 286 Northwestern 412 (Iowa), for example.

Chapter 10

THE PSYCHIATRIST AND THE
JUVENILE COURT

No psychiatrist should offer his services to a juvenile court unless
he has a fair idea of the anatomy of the court's structure. Basically,
a juvenile court is an administrative rather than a judicial tribunal.[1]
The child is not on trial. In theory, at least, the court is an instrument to determine whether the child has been neglected to the point
where his parents have forfeited their guardianship to the state.
That, indeed, is what the word "delinquent" means. Delinquent
taxes, for instance, are abandoned or neglected taxes. A delinquent
child is an abandoned or neglected child. If the court administratively
decides that the child has been neglected, the parents surrender
guardianship to the state, and the state can place the child in an
institution simply as a technique of asserting its guardianship.

Anatomy of the Juvenile Court

The difference between the criminal court and the juvenile court
is of more than academic interest. If the juvenile court were thought
of as a tribunal where the child was "on trial," it would need a jury,
since this is guaranteed by most state constitutions. Yet a jury
would be absurd in a juvenile court. The only way a juryless juvenile
court can enjoy constitutional sanction is either—

    a) To consider it an administrative agency for determining the
    child's status rather than his guilt; or

---

[1] This is the present concept. It is the result of considerable evolution in judicial
thinking. For example, between 1932 and 1948 the high court of New Jersey showed
a change in the reasons for denying the juvenile court exclusive jurisdiction over
murder cases. In 1932 (177 Atlantic Reporter 91) the New Jersey Court of Errors
and Appeals denied the juvenile court's jurisdiction over a child charged with murder,
on the grounds that in establishing that court the legislature surely did not intend
"to create a refuge for juvenile felons." In 1948, the high court again sustained the
right of the regular county court to try a juvenile for murder. But this time (58
Atlantic Reporter 2d, 780) the reason was that the juvenile court was depriving the
child of the right to a trial by a jury. Thus the concept in less than two decades had
shifted from one which held that the juvenile court was too lenient, to one which held
that it deprived the child of certain rights.

b) To set up the fiction that the child has been offered but has waived jury trial.

The juvenile court may waive jurisdiction and refer the child for actual trial by a regular court in Alaska, Arkansas, Illinois, Kentucky, New Hampshire, Oklahoma, Oregon, South Carolina, South Dakota, Utah, and Washington, regardless of the child's age. Such practice would, of course, be followed only in "major" crimes. In appropriate cases the Minnesota Juvenile Court can refer for trial for crime a child over age 12; in Mississippi over age 13; in Alabama, Hawaii, Massachusetts, North Carolina, North Dakota, Pennsylvania, and Virginia over age 14; in Michigan over age 15; and in California, Delaware, District of Columbia, Indiana, Maryland, Nevada, New Jersey, Rhode Island, and West Virginia over age 16.[2]

In an ordinary criminal court, witnesses are sworn, testimony is transcribed and trials are open to the press and public. All this clashes with our concepts of how to handle disturbed children. The psychiatrist who assumes that the juvenile court is just another court runs into several errors. He becomes formal and stuffy. He calls the judge "Your Honor." He straitjackets his statements within the frame of formal testimony. A juvenile court should be thought of as an informal conference of people puzzled about a child's behavior, anxious for help, willing to hear the views of the psychiatrist in whatever form he can give them.

Usually every county or group of counties has a juvenile court, but in many jurisdictions the judge is not assigned exclusively to juvenile court work. A common arrangement is for a criminal court judge to sit one day a week or one day a month in the juvenile tribunal. Naturally a separate juvenile court has a more plastic attitude toward child offenders than a court where the magistrate spends 90 per cent of his time hearing adult criminals. The psychiatrist should know this if he is servicing a juvenile court. And he should also know the judge. Some judges are suspicious of psychiatrists; some are dependent on them. Some judges deliver homilies on bad boys and good homes. Some have a thoroughly modern approach to the problem. There are judges who believe that all bad boys are feeble-minded, others who are convinced that television-viewing causes all delinquency, and still others who are sure that compulsory church attendance will cure juvenile misconduct. All these types exist. The psychiatrist impairs his usefulness if his first report to such a judge is filled with mentions of the oedipus complex and the

[2] F. B. Sussman, *Law of Juvenile Delinquency* (New York: Oceana Publications, Inc., 1950).

superego. These judges are sophisticated and intelligent men and can be indoctrinated with psychiatric concepts. But not all at once. The experienced psychiatrist working with a new judge (new to him, that is) introduces only a small dose of psychodynamics in each report, until slowly the judge and probation office have been inoculated with something of a psychiatric point of view. At the opposite extreme are the judges who think that psychotherapy is the cure for everything.

The psychiatrist must also know the probation office. The probation officer has a dual function. He investigates the child's background before the judge makes his decision. And, if the decision is to place the juvenile "on probation," the child is then assigned to a probation officer who functions as a case worker. The probation office always aims at being a topnotch social agency. Of course, here and there will be found an occasional officer who is a political hack or who believes that badness can be whipped out of boys, but for the most part probation officers are serious and effective students of child guidance. The psychiatrist will work closely with the probation officer and he should, therefore, early in his contacts, find out something of the professional background and orientation of his fellow-worker.

Probation offices are sometimes part of a *state* court system, sometimes attached to specific courts, occasionally are *city* agencies, but most often are *county* units. There is also a federal probation office, which necessarily devotes most of its time to adult offenders. However, some children do become involved with the federal law (stealing automobiles and taking them across state lines, buying or selling marihuana, or pilfering from mail boxes, for instance); and these children would be investigated by probation officers attached to the United States District Court.

In many states, there are two juvenile court age "ceilings." One is the age range of "exclusive" jurisdiction; the other of "concurrent" jurisdiction. For example, in Connecticut the "exclusive" age limit is 16 and the "concurrent" age ceiling is 18. This means that a child under age 16 must be disposed of in the juvenile court and nowhere else; but if he is between the ages of 16 and 18, both the juvenile and the criminal courts have jurisdiction at the same time (hence "concurrent"), and the public authorities select one tribunal or the other depending on the seriousness of the offense or the general public policy. From summaries prepared by Sussman,[3] it appears that the exclusive age ceilings are:

³ *Ibid.*

Age 13—Mississippi.

Age 16—Alabama (boys only), Connecticut, Georgia, Kansas, Maryland, New York, North Carolina, Oklahoma (boys only), Pennsylvania, South Carolina, Vermont, and Wisconsin.

Age 17—Illinois (boys only), Kentucky (boys only), Louisiana, Maine, Massachusetts, Michigan, Missouri, Tennessee, and Texas (boys).

Age 18—Alabama (girls), Alaska, Arizona, California, Colorado, District of Columbia, Idaho, Indiana, Minnesota, Nebraska, New Hampshire, New Mexico, Delaware, Hawaii, Illinois (girls), Kentucky (girls), Montana, Nevada, New Jersey, North Dakota, Ohio, Oklahoma (girls), Rhode Island, South Dakota, Texas (girls), and Utah.

Age 19—Wyoming (boys).

Age 21—Wyoming (girls).

The range of concurrent jurisdiction ages is 16 to 18 in Connecticut, Pennsylvania, and South Carolina; in Michigan 17 to 19; in Louisiana 17 to 21; and in California and Colorado the range of ages is from 18 to 21.

Jurisdiction is "concurrent" at all ages up to 18 in Florida, Iowa, Oregon, Virginia, and Washington. This means that, depending on circumstances, a child under 18 can be tried in the criminal court or disposed of before a juvenile court.

Special rules prevail in murder cases in Colorado, Delaware, District of Columbia, Idaho, Indiana, Iowa, Louisiana, Maine, Maryland, Massachusetts, Mississippi, Montana, Nevada, New Hampshire, New Jersey, New York, Pennsylvania, South Carolina, Tennessee, Vermont, Virginia, and West Virginia. In these states the juvenile court has no jurisdiction over murder. See below on page 155 for more details on juvenile murders.

A juvenile court rarely hears formal evidence, though it does have authority to swear in witnesses. However, the judge's concern is not with whether the child committed the crime, but with what kind of person the child is. Instead of a parade of witnesses testifying that the child was seen near the scene of the crime, for instance, the judge hears the opinions of parents, teachers, social workers, family doctors, etc. Technically most of this is sheer hearsay and would therefore be excluded from a criminal court; but the juvenile court is an administrative tribunal and therefore the whole picture is considered regardless of the technicalities of evidence.

The Place of the Examination

In most enlightened states, a child cannot lawfully be detained with adult criminals; he is not supposed to be held in a jail while awaiting hearing. This imposes certain problems when the court is dealing with a runaway lad or with a viciously misbehaving youngster. In many places there are "parental homes," child shelters, and welfare institutions where such children may be temporarily housed. In most counties, there are no such institutions and all sorts of makeshifts are used. Sometimes the child is placed in the infirmary of the jail, for instance, or the warden's wife or the jail matron may have a small suite of rooms in which children can be detained.

All this is of interest to the psychiatrist because the physical environment in which he conducts his examination is a factor in the validity and interpretation of his findings. Where the doctor has any choice, he will prefer having the child brought to his office or to a hospital clinic. A conference room in the court house or adjacent to the probation office is less desirable but is better than a jail. Generally speaking, the aim should be to examine the child in surroundings which do not symbolize coercive authority. If a juvenile court has its own full-time clinic, for instance, this should not be located in the court house, but in some outside building not associated with the majesty of the law.

Examination of the Juvenile Offender

Preliminary Briefing.—Asked to examine a juvenile, the psychiatrist will first request a complete case summary. In any well equipped county, the probation officer will have already prepared an investigation which will include the usual items of a psychiatric history. For instance, most children have received intelligence tests in school, and the probation officer should have the scores listed in his investigation. Where the probation office is negligent about assembling the data, or where the facts are not available, the psychiatrist may have to do the testing. For that reason, he should come to the examination with some kind of simple psychometric testing equipment. He should also come prepared to do a physical examination.

The Physical Examination.—There are three reasons for doing a physical examination. First, every once in a while the doctor will find an endocrine defect, or some infirmity which limits the child's school or play activities. Second, children old enough to get into trouble usually have had pleasant relations with doctors and unpleasant relations with truant officers and social workers; by emphasizing his doctor-role, the psychiatrist gets off to a head start on the matter of rapport. A third reason is that some judges absolutely insist on a thorough physical examination and ask if it has been given. It is good to be able to answer "Yes" with a clear conscience.

The Psychiatric Interview.—Before he sees the child, the examiner thoroughly reviews the history. He then sees the child alone, later the parent alone. In certain cases he will also want to see the child and parent together.

The actual psychiatric interview need not be detailed here since it is familiar to any psychiatrist. The examination is oriented to answering the query: What values was the child seeking from his delinquency? If, for instance, we are dealing with truancy, we want to know what there was about school that was so distasteful to the child, and what he found to do during the hours he should have been in school. If we are dealing with theft, we will want to know what he sought to buy with the money or other objects which he stole. The examiner must know the culture pattern of his neighborhood. For instance, in a neighborhood where all normal boys steal from pushcarts or store-fronts, theft becomes a way of winning community acceptance. This, in turn, points up something about the recommended disposition: if the court returns the child to that environment, stealing may be repeated because the motivation is still present. A suggested examination form will be found on page 365.

The Psychiatrist's Own Orientation.—The psychiatrist will want to keep in mind the kaleidoscope of delinquency-breeding factors so that he may weigh each one as he examines the child. There are two orientations to this problem: one school of thought emphasizes factors *within* the child (sense of rejection, for instance); another emphasizes factors *outside* the child (slum living, for instance). Proponents of the first thesis argue that most slum children do *not* become delinquents, therefore slum environment cannot be the cause, and that there must be something within the child's psyche which turns him to delinquency. Proponents of the environmental thesis point out that only an infinitesimal proportion of juvenile offenders comes from well-favored homes, and that it is the neighborhood culture which sets the pattern that the child follows. Plant [4] has successfully combined both theses, by pointing out that congested living

[4] James S. Plant, *Journal of The Medical Society of New Jersey,* XXXIII (February, 1936), 83.

causes certain changes in the child's personality which, in turn, favor the development of delinquency. Thus, he writes:

Extroverts may be individually healthy, but they are too sudden-about-the-house, too bouncy, for group living. Experiments in asking school teachers as to their greatest problems have invariably led to their naming the extroverted children in their rooms.

While academic schooling is a rural as well as an urban phenomenon, its word-centered activities are not counterbalanced in city living with periods of wide-flung play and responsible work. The construction of playgrounds and the development of the progressive education movement which recognizes the importance of *doing* things quite as much as *thinking* things, are valiant efforts at partially meeting this situation in the city.

Introversion is marked by a split between emotional content and emotional expression. On this basis the development of various forms of vicarious play-life in the city is of outstanding importance. The best example, of course, appears in the movies where the individual experiences intense emotions of every sort with no opportunity to express these feelings in any adequate way. The city similarly presents huge stadia at which thousands of people congregate to watch eighteen or twenty-two individuals physically express what everyone feels.

Tied into this last point is the more general one that the complexity of city life does not allow at any point an adequate expression of the emotions involved in the situation. The best example is that of reactions to a fire. The devastating tragedy of a fire in the country is in marked contrast to the efficient orderliness with which this sort of crisis is met in the city. But in the country each person may *do* something about a fire; what country person has not given full vent to his terror and awe as he has frantically saved furniture or animals until someone shouted that the roof or the chimney is to fall? Here again is the squeezing out of the activity or expressive elements of mental life where one lives in the city.

One notes that in this matter of the presentation of stark tragedy, for instance, to the individual when there is complete absence of any possibility of his reacting adequately to it, the radio has very much intensified the whole problem. For city and country person alike, the radio is rapidly forcing the development of that type of individual who can have intense emotional content without the necessity of expressing it or "draining it off" through appropriate physical activity.

For any who doubt the traumatic introverting factors of city life, I recommend that you watch city children for the first two days of their life in summer camp,—during which time they simply race wildly about as though in hunger for mere motor expression.

While occasional juvenile delinquents do come from comfortable homes, the proportion is so low that for all practical purposes delinquency may be considered a problem of the slums. In the slums delinquent behavior is almost a norm.

Broken homes play a huge role, and so do disciplinary defects in the home: either excessively lax or excessively harsh discipline. The doctor will want to evaluate these possibilities. He will appraise the factor of "bad companions"—which is the mother's favorite explanation. (The mothers of the bad companions, however, say that this little patient is the bad companion to *their* children.)

The examiner must consider, but not too pompously, the role of television, moving pictures, comic books, and the radio. He weighs the influence of neighborhood saloons, brothels, gambling houses, and other socially disorganizing forces. He determines whether the child was rejected, unwanted, overprotected, or insecure. He matches the child's mental age with his school grade. He computes the extent, if any, of his scholastic retardation.[5] He finds whether his patient is essentially a word-minded, hand-minded, or idea-minded child. He wonders whether the school furnishes adequate gratifications to a child with that kind of aptitude. For instance, a twelve-year-old might be in the seventh grade and have a mental age of twelve: all of this sounds normal. Suppose he is manually and mechanically apt but disinclined to be bookish. If the school program is made up largely of abstract material, that child is likely to revolt against school—if he is normal.[6]

The emotional, sociological and intellectual climate of the home would seem to be a major factor in the development of delinquency. However, it is an oversimplification to say that slum-living leads to delinquency, for instance. It is the reaction to the slum of a particular kind of child that results in antisocial behavior. Somewhat surprisingly, the Gluecks in their monumental study [7] found that the following factors were, in their phrase, "of little or no significance in causal dynamics":

> *Background of parents:* Their health, schooling, nativity, and age; and whether the parents had been reared in homes characterized by poverty, drunkenness, or retardation.

[5] A suggested formulation for this will be found on page 160.

[6] One of the most practical books on this subject is: Harry Baker and Virginia Traphagen, *The Diagnosis and Treatment of Behavior Problem Children* (New York: The Macmillan Co., 1935). Neither author is a psychiatrist but, if the examiner is, the suggestions, tests, diagnostic formulations, and suggestions in this book will neatly complement the psychiatrist's own findings.

[7] Sheldon Glueck and Eleanor Glueck. *Unravelling Juvenile Delinquency* (New York: Commonwealth Fund, and Cambridge: Harvard University Press, 1950), p. 272.

Home background: Living in underprivileged areas, housing, size of household, or culture conflicts between the parents or between parents and children.

School: Age at school entrance; dislike of certain school subjects. (Major scholastic maladjustment, however, did correlate high with delinquency.)

Emotional stress: Delinquents in general did not show more manifest emotional stress than did nondelinquents. As a matter of fact, the nondelinquents had a higher incidence of "general neuroticism," and a higher incidence of feelings of insecurity or anxiety. But the delinquents did show a higher proportion "of boys who had a feeling of not being recognized or appreciated."

Intelligence: Between matched pairs of delinquents and nondelinquents there was little to choose in terms of total intelligence. However, the delinquents did show lower *verbal* intelligence.

The point seems to be that both groups of children have emotional problems. The delinquent is likely to try to resolve his problems by aggressive behavior while the nondelinquent is more likely to meet the problem by getting sick or developing other "neurotic" symptoms. In their final summary, the Gluecks offer the following excellent formulation:

The delinquents as a group are distinguishable from the nondelinquents: (1) in being essentially mesomorphic in constitution; (2) in being restless, energetic, impulsive, extraverted, and aggressive; (3) by being hostile, defiant, resentful, suspicious, adventurous, and nonsubmissive; (4) in tending to direct and concrete, rather than symbolic, intellectual expression; (5) in having, to a far greater extent, been reared in homes of little understanding, affection, stability, or moral fibre by parents usually unfit to be effective guides and protectors.

In general, the high probability of delinquency is dependent upon the interplay of the conditions and forces from all these areas.

In the exciting, stimulating, but little-controlled and culturally inconsistent environment of the underprivileged area, such boys readily give expression to their untamed impulses and their self-centered desires by means of various forms of delinquent behavior. Their tendencies towards uninhibited energy expression are deeply anchored in soma and psyche and in the malformations of character during the first few years of life.[8]

The psychiatrist will frequently be asked to give talks on the general subject of juvenile delinquency. Some doctors become so concerned with the question of the internal psychic conflicts of the child that they underemphasize the social forces. It must be remem-

[8] *Ibid.,* p. 281.

bered that the same extroverted, pushing, aggressive tendencies which, in the slum, lead to delinquency will prove to be a channel towards socially acceptable leadership in better favored environments.

Writing the Report.—The way in which the psychiatrist writes his report depends somewhat on the kind of person who is sitting on the judge's bench. While the diagnosis and recommendations will be the same regardless of the court personnel, the wording of the report is fashioned according to the understanding, prejudices, and sensitiveness of the judge and probation officers.

The report is generally addressed to the judge even though the examination had been arranged through the probation office. It is good practice to have it typed in quadruplicate: one copy for the judge, two for the probation office, and a copy retained for the doctor's own file. If there is a subsequent placement with an institution or agency, the probation office can send one of its carbon copies and will appreciate being spared the need for retyping the report. It is well to be on cordial terms with the probation office.

The report contains the usual identifying data and indicates where the examination was made and at whose request. This is mentioned because an examination in a hospital clinic has different connotations from one conducted in a jail, and these in turn have a different meaning from an examination at the doctor's office. In a short paragraph the examiner reviews the details of the offense committed by the child. It is true that the judge already knows them, but the summary is useful for the doctor's own files and to any agency to whom the report might be forwarded. After that comes a brief account of the family and personal history (or at least of the significant details), with focus on broken home, if present, neighborhood living conditions, previous offenses, school record, and the like. It is not necessary to rewrite the entire probation office investigation. The doctor merely pulls out the significant items and weaves them together.

He then describes the physical findings, mentioning height and weight, whether overweight or undersized for age, noting such items as poor vision or hearing, deformities, blemishes, etc.

This is followed by a summary of the mental examination. The intelligence should be given. If an I.Q. is mentioned it should be interpreted, using some such term as "intellectually retarded but not feeble-minded," or "intelligence substantially normal," or "intelligence normal in the field of manual and mechanical aptitude but with defects in ability to handle abstract concepts," and so forth. The child's attitude toward his offense is recorded, with an appraisal of his insight into that attitude. The usual headings of a formal psychiatric report are not set up, though in appropriate cases there is no objection to the standard listings of stream of talk, emotional stability, judgment, orientation, insight, etc. Usually, however, a formal "state hospital" kind of psychiatric report is a waste of space.

The next item should be diagnosis. Under physical diagnosis there might be such findings as acne vulgaris, hypertrophied tonsils, myopia (giving figures), dental caries, malnutrition, and the like. Under psychiatric diagnosis there should be some estimate of intelligence and some formal psychiatric label (if indicated). Thus, the psychiatric diagnosis might be: "Primary conduct disorder; normal intelligence; I.Q.—95"; or, perhaps "Mental deficiency, Binet I.Q. 64 (moron); with secondary anxiety symptoms." The formal psychiatric label does not tell the judge very much. Certainly "primary conduct disorder" or even "conversion hysteria" are not helpful. It therefore seems advisable to follow this with an account of the mechanism of the delinquency.

By setting up a paragraph captioned "Mechanism of the Delinquency" the examiner is compelled to assemble his ideas as to what caused the child to deviate from "normal" behavior. This is good discipline for the psychiatrist and it also has another value—it gives the judge something to quote. For instance, the doctor might write: "Here is a girl who in competition with others is ill-favored indeed. She has neither beauty nor wealth nor brains. She has been endowed with no charm of personality nor grace of manner. In the struggle to compete with other girls for the attention of the boys, she has had but one weapon, and that is her own body. Under the circumstances, small wonder that she bargained for popularity with this only asset." The judge might well cite this in a talk to a civic organization or Young Women's Club the following week, and thus acquire a reputation for rare psychologic discernment.

Some judges do not want the examiner to make recommendations. This, they feel, would be a usurpation of a judicial function. Most of them, however, do welcome suggestions. If he knows his recommendations are wanted, the psychiatrist concludes his report with a suggested disposition. These possibilities are discussed on page 152.

Evolution of a Juvenile Court Judge

Typically when a judge is appointed to the juvenile court, he starts to read books on child guidance and delinquency and comes to the conclusion that boys are not really bad, and that what they need is kindness, understanding, and a second chance. His predecessor, toward the end of his term, has become "hard boiled." The record might show that during the past year, for instance, the retiring judge had disposed of 80 per cent of the defendants by sending them to reformatories. The new judge is shocked and says that when he mounts the bench he is going to find a more constructive solution than the reformatory.

The new judge is sworn in. The bench is decked with flowers, and the new magistrate makes a speech in which he says (1) that he will administer the court humanely, (2) that he knows children, (3) that there really is no such thing as a bad boy, and (4) that he is a great believer in the gospel of the second chance. After the flowers are cleared away, the docket is brought out. Here is a sixteen-year-old girl who was arrested for consorting with two married men. Since the age of thirteen, she has been running away from home, usually with men. The parents have kept this out of the courts, but now a social agency has stepped in. The girl is untrained and has never done gainful work. The new judge listens and says that in his opinion society is at fault. Everyone has treated the girl as a criminal. Now for the first time she is going to be treated with understanding. He places her on probation and says that the probation officer will be a big sister to her. The next day the girl runs off with a truck driver.

During the first year the judge keeps making this kind of error. In an effort to give every juvenile another chance, he returns to the community a host of boys and girls who engage in vandalism and malicious mischief or who roam the streets with no exposure to teaching or training. Each time, the boy looks solemnly at the judge and says he has learned his lesson and now he will be good. The judge is touched and, in spite of the record, returns him to his family. After about a year of this the judge becomes indignant. He feels personally affronted. The boy promised him faithfully that he would never steal again, and now he has let the judge down.

Over the years the judge learns that many of the defendants simply cannot be handled outside of an institution. By the time he has reached his last year, he has become as "tough" as his predecessor.

The psychiatrist's position and usefulness are affected by this. If the judge is new, recommendations for commitment to a reformatory must be explicit, with a clear prediction of further delinquencies should the child be put on probation. The new judge may disregard the recommendation, only to find later (by a continuing record of delinquencies) that the examiner was sound in his judgment. On the other hand, if the psychiatrist enters the picture after the judge has been in office several years, his difficulty will be to get the court to accept a noninstitutional disposition in favorable cases. In a situation where the doctor recommends commitment to a reformatory or correctional home, he need not be too strong or too explicit because the veteran-judge will not need convincing. Thus, in a very real way, the phrasing of the report (though never the actual recommendation) depends on the judge's age-in-office plus his general orientation.

Disposition of the Juvenile Offender

There are only nine possible dispositions and the examiner considers all nine of them, one by one, before he makes a final recommendation. The possible dispositions are:

1. Dismiss the matter and take no further action.
2. Reprimand and dismiss.
3. Make restitution.
4. Send to a mental hygiene clinic, private doctor, or social agency.
5. Transfer to a different school or different kind of school.
6. Place in a foster home, or with relatives.
7. Place the child on probation.
8. Commit (if appropriate) to a colony for mental defectives, a state mental hospital, child treatment center, or state special school.
9. Send the child to a state home, reformatory, or other correctional institution.

Dismissal with a reprimand after eliciting a promise of good conduct is somewhat amateurish. If the child has no guilt feelings, the reprimand is useless. If he does have guilt feelings, it is unnecessary. *Restitution* is possible in cases of vandalism, petty theft, or malicious mischief. The theory is that if the boy has to work after school to earn the money to pay for the broken window, he will be more careful next time. It is unsuited to any but the mildest problems.

The psychiatrist recommends attendance at a *mental hygiene clinic* if, in clear conscience, he thinks that psychotherapy will help. But he is careful not to oversell psychiatry. A good touchstone is this: Do not recommend sending a problem child to a fellow-psychiatrist or clinic if, in all honesty, you know you could not get results with the child yourself. Some cities have guidance bureaus or juvenile clinics which combine case work and psychiatric functions. For his own community, the doctor should know where these clinics are; and he should know something of the skills of their personnel before he makes this recommendation.

If the problem centers around school maladjustment, he considers sending the child to a *different school*—one where he does not already have a bad name—or to a vocational instead of an academic type of public school. In rare cases he recommends a boarding school.

Where the home is broken and emotional, social, and economic conditions are wretched, the doctor considers *foster-home placement* if the child is young; or sending him to *live with relatives* in a different kind of milieu if the child is older. It may be desirable to seek a rural rather than an urban environment or *vice versa*. The experienced examiner does not make this recommendation until he has inventoried the family possibilities.

Probation is a common recommendation. This is not to be confused with parole. Parole is conditional release from an institution; probation is a supervised suspended sentence.

When a child is on probation, he is assigned to a particular probation officer. Small units may have only one or two officers in the agency, while larger offices may have twenty or thirty. A plan is drawn up which usually requires the child to report to the office at certain intervals, and which includes periodic visits by the probation officer to the home and to the school. The value of this procedure depends on the skills of the officer as well as on the personality of the child. One probation officer may discharge his duty by saying perfunctorily at each visit: "How are you doing, Johnnie? Fine, glad to hear of it. Keep up the good work." Needless to say, this is not probation, though with some officers this is about all probation amounts to. The skilled probation officer, however, engages in a genuine case work process, builds up a rapport with the juvenile, seeks to effect an identification, perhaps even a transference, and manipulates the environment to the benefit of the child. Manipulating the environment may include such procedures as getting him into the Boy Scouts or into a social club,[9] helping him find a job or a hobby, getting a summer camp placement for him, and giving general counsel and guidance.

[9] Usually, juvenile delinquents have not been participating in playground programs, Boy Scouts, social clubs, or other supervised recreational activities. These provide a wholesome outlet for a restless, energetic, extraverted temperament and therefore such a recommendation seems obvious in almost all cases. However, only the amateur expects much from this. In practice, the juvenile delinquent will almost always reject supervised recreational outlets. He considers them as "sissy" activities. He may perfunctorily attend the playground or boys' club, but nine times out of ten he finds inadequate outlets in these socially approved programs. Occasionally the playground or club has an inspired leader who by some kind of interpersonal magic can hook the interest and win the affection of the delinquent. And in such a situation the recommendation will be practical and effective. The psychiatrist will recognize, even if the worker does not, that this success was not due to the organized activity of the club or playground but to the transference relationship to the leader.

To do a really polished job, the psychiatrist who recommends probation should also recommend the program, giving concrete suggestions as to the patient's social and vocational life, possible school transfers or grade adjustment, and the like.

Commitment to a colony for epileptics or mental defectives or admission to a state hospital is recommended in appropriate cases. Usually the doctor is expected to make out the commitment papers at the same time. Since the probation office has a notary public attached and a supply of commitment papers, it facilitates matters to do it right there. Usually the county physician, police surgeon, or jail doctor will sign the other half of the commitment paper.

The final recommendation, when nothing else seems suitable, is *commitment to a correctional institution*. These sentences are usually indeterminate. Some schools have a system of determining parole by setting as a goal a certain number of "merit points" and releasing the boy when he has earned a certain amount of credit scored on a sort of efficiency-rating basis. Other institutions present cases periodically to staff or parole boards which determine when the inmate is suitable for conditional release.

A recommendation of commitment to a correctional institution is not to be viewed by the psychiatrist as a sign of defeat. If he takes that attitude, he will desperately try all sorts of halfway measures even in cases where a correctional institution is the only workable answer. There are certain positive values in such placement. The institution provides regular hours, well-balanced meals, specialized training, and a routine which some delinquents find more security-giving than the amorphousness of free life. In my own study,[10] it appeared that two thirds of the graduates of correctional institutions at the "state home" level remain law-abiding citizens. Many of them earn their livelihood from trades taught at the school. The alumni record for institutions at the "reformatory" level, however, is not so good. In their parole study of the Concord (Massachusetts) Reformatory, for instance, the Gluecks[11] found that most of the graduates became criminals. Let it be remembered, however, that the "reformatory" type of institution receives, essentially, those young persons who failed on parole from "state homes." Thus, the statistical dice are loaded against the reformatory.

When environmental conditions are permanently bad, when the juvenile already has a bad name in the community, when the home

[10] Henry A. Davidson, *Alumni of Delinquency* (Verona, N. J.: Mimeographed publication of the Newark City Home, 1935).

[11] Sheldon Glueck and Eleanor T. Glueck: *Five Hundred Criminal Careers* (New York: Alfred A. Knopf, Inc., 1930).

is sordid, broken or vicious, when rebellious ways of behavior are deeply entrenched in the personality of the juvenile, then commitment to a correctional institution may be necessary. The psychiatrist who naïvely recommends keeping all such children home, and treating them with kindness and appeals to reason, soon makes himself a joke in the community, forfeits the confidence of the court, and terminates his own usefulness. It is well for the psychiatrist to show softness of the heart; but this quality is not to be confused with softness of the head.

Murder by Juveniles

Psychiatrists and social workers are sometimes astonished to find that, in many states, children's courts try all offenses except murder. The reasons for exempting homicide from juvenile court jurisdiction seem rather technical and, to many non-lawyers, inadequate. Actually, there are four practices with reference to this jurisdiction:

1. The juvenile court may have exclusive jurisdiction over *all* offenses committed by children under the specified ceiling age. This is the practice in about one half of the states.

2. The juvenile court may have initial and primary jurisdiction over homicides by children but also has the right, at its own option, to transfer such cases to the docket of the ordinary adult court. This is the rule in California, Connecticut, and Ohio; and, presumably, in Michigan.

3. The prosecutor can elect to try murder committed by juveniles in the ordinary adult court, or he can allow the juvenile court to take jurisdiction. Or—what in practice amounts to the same thing—the grand jury, by indicting or refusing to indict, can determine in which tribunal the case will be disposed of. Illinois and New York are examples of states where this is the rule.

4. By statute or interpretation, the juvenile court has no authority at all to try murder cases. Pennsylvania, Maine, Massachusetts, New Jersey, and Wisconsin are examples of this practice.

New York's original children's court law excluded cases in which death or life imprisonment could be imposed. In 1948 this was amended and, under the revised statute, the juvenile court has exclusive jurisdiction where the child is under the age of fourteen. Older children are presented to the grand jury, and that body, by bringing out or impounding the indictment, determines the course of the case. In practice, grand juries in New York nearly always recommend transfer of such cases to the children's courts.

In New Jersey the legislature tried to bring murder by juveniles into the docket of the juvenile court, but the upper courts consistently ruled that this was unconstitutional. The theory was that murder was an offense *sui generis,* and under common law a person charged with first degree murder cannot waive jury trial. The right to an open jury trial in murder cases, the New Jersey court ruled,[12] is inalienable. As a correlative of this, then, the adult county court could not, by legislation, be shorn of its exclusive jurisdiction in murder cases. As recently as 1948, this line of reasoning was confirmed, and the juvenile court was again told [13] that it had no right to try murder cases if the defendant was over the age of seven.

Even from the psychologic viewpoint, and apart from any purely "legal" line of reasoning, murder by juveniles is not quite in the same category as the "ordinary" delinquencies. An Ohio study,[14] for example, showed that compared with the juvenile who "ordinarily" appears on the docket of the children's court, the youthful murderer is likely to have (*a*) a superior family background, (*b*) no record of previous delinquencies, and (*c*) more intelligence than the truant or thief who usually appears before the juvenile court judge. Furthermore, the young murderer is more likely to be exceedingly dangerous to society, because (1) he is less restrained and more impulsive than the usual adult murderer, (2) he is much sicker (in terms of psychopathy) than the usual juvenile delinquent, and (3) he is less responsive to psychotherapeutic and "correctional" measures than the truant or thief. Probably a high proportion of juvenile murderers are psychotic or pre-psychotic. However, every psychiatrist is aware of the special difficulties of making such diagnoses in young adolescents. A pre-psychotic child may well give a clinical picture indistinguishable from that of the "psychopath."

Murder is, of course, exceedingly rare in the annals of juvenile crime. The Gluecks,[15] in their definitive study of a thousand consecutive juvenile delinquents, were unable to find a single child who had committed a homicide. Nor were any homicides found in the group studied by Slawson.[16] My own analysis of alumni of a juvenile correctional institution [17] failed to turn up a single homicide among

[12] Commonwealth v. Safis *et al.,* 186 Atlantic Reporter 177.

[13] State v. Smigelski, 58 Atlantic Reporter (2d Ser.) 780.

[14] *Group Study of Juvenile Homicide* (Columbus, Ohio: Ohio Bureau of Juvenile Research, 1949).

[15] Sheldon Glueck and Eleanor T. Glueck. *One Thousand Juvenile Delinquents* (Cambridge: Harvard University Press, 1934).

[16] John Slawson. *The Delinquent Boy* (Boston: the Gorham Press, 1926).

[17] See footnote 10, this chapter.

the offenses of 1700 boys. The Ohio study [18] revealed 54 juveniles charged with homicide in that state over a period of a quarter of a century. The Gluecks' earlier study [19] did show thirteen homicides among 500 criminal careers, but since the average age was twenty, this is scarcely a "juvenile" group.

Although juvenile murderers "tend" to be somewhat more intelligent than other delinquent boys,[20] some of the former do turn out to be mental defectives. One reason, of course, is that mental defectives are more easily apprehended than offenders of normal intelligence. They are over-represented among the statistics simply because an offender does not become a statistic until he is caught. Mental defectives lack more subtle methods of reacting to frustration, hence are more prone to react with violence. Unfortunately the mechanism in a mental defective is likely to be permanent, so that a mentally deficient juvenile murderer is always a potential menace to the community. This is mentioned because sometimes psychiatrists participate in protecting the defective murderer from a life or death sentence, on the theory that special consideration is required because of the offender's youth and low intelligence. This is a humane viewpoint, but the fact remains that there is very little chance of altering the violently explosive reaction pattern of the defective delinquent, and the court should be made aware of that.

Most juvenile murderers, however, are not mentally defective. They are emotionally very sick adolescents, either pre-psychotic or "psychopathic." The mechanism of the impulse to murder in these children has been analyzed by Bromberg [21] and by Alexander and Healy.[22] The psychodynamic explanations are interesting and well expounded in the psychiatric literature. However, these explanations are of little practical value to the court which has the responsibility for "disposing of" these young offenders. From a practical viewpoint, the significant factor is that juvenile murderers, whether psychopaths, defectives, or pre-psychotics are serious threats to the community because the dynamic mechanism which led to one murder is not likely to be changed by treatment or imprisonment. Making a recommendation to the court thus imposes on the psychiatrist a peculiar responsibility, one which highlights the tragic dilemma of

[18] See footnote 14, this chapter.
[19] See footnote 11, this chapter.
[20] See footnote 14, this chapter.
[21] Walter Bromberg, *Crime and the Mind* (Philadelphia: J. B. Lippincott Co., 1948).
[22] Franz Alexander and William Healy, *Roots of Crime* (New York: Alfred A. Knopf, Inc., 1935).

the immediate interests of his patient compared with the interest of society as a whole. No psychiatrist wants to be responsible for a death sentence or for a sentence of life imprisonment, particularly when the defendant is a sick child. Yet he cannot, in clear conscience, be the instrument for allowing such a dangerous child to be returned to the community.

Sussman [23] has made an analysis of juvenile court statutes and practices with reference to jurisdiction over murder cases. In many states the law specifically exempts "crimes punishable by death or life imprisonment" (the law in Colorado, Indiana, Iowa, Maryland, Massachusetts, and Mississippi) or "capital crimes" (the way it is worded in Delaware, Maine, Louisiana, Nevada, Vermont, Virginia, and West Virginia), or it may exclude murder by name (the rule in Montana, Pennsylvania, South Carolina, and Tennessee). The last two states also exclude rape from the jurisdiction of the juvenile court. In New Jersey, as described above, the juvenile court has lost jurisdiction over murder cases not by statute but by judicial interpretation of the Constitution. In many states, even where the law places murder outside the coverage of the juvenile court, child-murderers can be disposed of in that tribunal by setting up the offense as "delinquency" rather than as a "murder." To what extent this subterfuge is used depends on the attitudes of prosecutors, the strictness of courts, and the state of public opinion.

[23] Op. cit.

Chapter 11

MALINGERING

The psychiatrist will consider the possibility of malingering in three situations:

1. In criminal cases, when psychosis or mental deficiency is advanced as a defense.
2. In personal injury actions, when psychosis or psychoneurosis is alleged to be the result of the injury.
3. In certain special situations where nervous or mental disease might be a basis for excuse from hazardous or arduous duty.

Of the various psychiatric disorders, the only ones likely to be malingered are amnesias, psychoses, psychoneuroses, and mental deficiency. With modern methods of electro-encephalography, the malingering of epilepsy poses only minimal difficulties. Other psychiatric disorders, such as psychopathic personality, alcoholism, etc., are hardly likely to be malingered.

Malingering does not, by itself, prove a mental disorder. A defendant faced with the near certainty of being hanged would be very sane and sensible in trying to escape with commitment to a hospital. On the other hand, in criminal cases a defendant is not likely to malinger a psychosis unless the charge is a capital one. There would be little point in pretending insanity to escape a short prison sentence.

Malingered Mental Deficiency

Unless the medical examiner is peculiarly inept, it is difficult to malinger mental deficiency with any success. The Stanford Binet test or, indeed, any psychometric test using an age-grade scale will usually expose malingered deficiency. If a subject can do all the nine-year-old tests but consistently fails at the six-year level, for instance, he is probably a malingerer. Sometimes a schizophrenic will show a bizarre distribution of age scores, but a psychotic who is that badly fragmented should be diagnosable as such in the course of a routine psychiatric examination.[1] Of course, a certain amount

[1] This is one reason for insisting that a psychiatrist, not a psychologist, make the definitive diagnosis. As a matter of fact, a well trained clinical psychologist will

of age overlap will occur in genuine mental defectives. If a subject passes one or two nine-year tests and fails one or two seven-year tests, this does not, by itself, suggest malingering; but a wild and wide scatter of passed and failed tests, with no approach to the pattern of normal age-grade development, is highly suspicious.

The defendant's life history also bears on the genuineness of the alleged mental defect. For instance, if the defendant is a high school graduate it is altogether unlikely that he could be a mental defective. The American school system is paced at one school year per mental-age year, first grade being scaled for a mental age of six. Thus, if the defendant successfully completed the first year of high school (the ninth grade) and dropped out of school in the second year (tenth grade) one would expect to find a mental age of about fourteen. The formula is: add five to the last successful school grade. This cannot be used too rigidly because some schools push poor students ahead regardless of achievement or mental age, and because some schools have much lower standards than others. Nevertheless, the formula is seldom more than two or three years out of line. In the example cited, the man who had completed first-year high school (ninth grade) ought to have a mental age of fourteen; with a three-year margin of error, he would have a mental age of at least eleven. This in itself would indicate no serious mental deficiency, since for purposes of criminal responsibility an adult with a mental age of eleven would be considered accountable for his crimes. Similarly the vocational history can be studied to support or contradict the test findings. It is obvious that certain vocations could never be successfully pursued by mental defectives.

In evaluating the genuineness of a pleaded mental deficiency, the examiner (or the probation office on his behalf) should check the psychometric tests done in the schools, in the army, and in connection with pre-employment examinations in many large industries. Where these tests, made long before the crime, show normal intelligence, a low score in a test done *after* the crime is naturally suspect.

Malingered Amnesia

What does the examiner do when the defendant says, "Everything went black," or "I awoke from a daze and saw the body in

---

recognize a psychotic either from the general pattern of his remarks and attitudes or from projective tests. However, too often the testing is left to psychometrists or to psychologic technicians rather than to clinical psychologists. In any event, the possibility of physical factors in these cases is so great that the correlation of the laboratory findings—including the psychological tests—must be made by a doctor of medicine.

front of me"? In these, and in many similar situations, amnesia is
alleged. By itself, amnesia does not necessarily exculpate the defendant. If within the amnesic framework he acted as if he knew his
behavior was wrong, he would probably be accountable. However,
it is the psychiatrist's job to determine the nature of the amnesia.
There are six possible explanations:

1. Hysteria	4. Head injury
2. Psychosis	5. Epilepsy
3. Alcoholism	6. Malingering

The differential diagnosis among these conditions was reviewed
on page 16. The diagnosis of malingering should not be made until
the other five possibilities have been reviewed and discarded. Thus,
before labelling the amnesia as spurious, the doctor should have
reports showing a negative skull X-ray, an electro-encephalogram
which does not reflect either an epileptic nor a traumatic pattern, a
negative neurologic examination, a life history which does not suggest hysteria, a picture inconsistent with alcoholic amnesia, and a
clinical examination negative for psychosis. Hypnotism or interview
under narco-analysis will not identify malingered amnesia (though
it may be otherwise useful) because in both hysterical and malingered amnesias, some recapture of memories will take place under
narcosis or hypnosis. Generally, a malingered amnesia is both
patchy and self-serving, whereas a genuine amnesia usually extends
to all areas of memory and is not limited to facts which might hurt
the defendant's case legally. For instance, a patient with hysterical
amnesia is likely to forget his name as well as the circumstances of
the crime. A defendant who is pretending amnesia rarely alleges
loss of his own identity. Because it has little effect on the defendant's responsibility, the appraisal of the genuineness of an amnesia
is forensically less important than it might seem. The emotional
trauma of committing a crime might induce a hysterical amnesia;
but this would not absolve the defendant. This would be equally true
of the amnesia of pathologic intoxication. Even if he is personally
convinced that the amnesia is spurious, it is seldom necessary for
the medical witness to put it that bluntly. It is sufficient if he testifies
that from the defendant's behavior it is clear that he knew he was
doing something wrong, and that no psychosis was found. If asked
directly whether he thinks the amnesia is assumed, he might answer
that he wouldn't say so, since it is not uncommon for the emotional
effect of committing a crime to induce a period of amnesia.

The situation is somewhat different where the amnesia began an appreciable period *prior* to the crime, and continued unabated. However, in such a case, it is up to the defense to prove affirmatively that the amnesia antedated the criminal act.

Malingered Psychoses

Malingered insanity sets a two-way trap for the psychiatrist. If he labels the patient a malingerer when he turns out to be genuinely psychotic, he is failing in a primary duty of a psychiatrist: to recognize a psychosis when he meets it. If he places the stamp of genuineness on a defendant who, it turns out later, was malingering, he damages his own reputation for acumen and impairs his subsequent usefulness to the courts.

The sophisticated psychiatrist considers the possibility of malingering at every examination of a defendant in a criminal case. Even the most expert examiner will be in error now and then; criticism will come not from his making an occasional wrong diagnosis, but from his failing to consider all the diagnostic possibilities. Hence the first step in recognizing a malingered psychosis is to consider seriously its possible existence.

The next step is to study the patient's life history. The public, and even sometimes the courts, assume that there is some sort of "sanity test" in the psychiatrist's brief bag, which can be pulled out and applied to the defendant. For that reason attorneys and judges sometimes expect the doctor to function like a machine, and simply talk to the patient and come up with a diagnosis. Only an inexperienced psychiatrist allows himself to give an opinion without having an opportunity to review the defendant's history. If a vagrant is arrested for a crime and furnishes no historical material, the doctor should (except in the most obvious cases) withhold judgment until the prisoner has been identified and his past history made available. Thus, following an acute catatonic episode, a patient may, in cross-section, present the picture of sanity, so that the casual examiner would incorrectly assume that the alleged "brainstorm" was spurious.

The third step is to make a clinical diagnosis of the apparent psychosis. This seems too obvious to justify listing here. However, when an effort is made to fit the clinical symptoms into a recognizable diagnostic category, it sometimes cannot be done; and that fact alone may point the way to an ultimate determination of malingering. For example, a defendant may keep talking to the doctor about his own wealth and power, so that the examiner concludes that here we have a man with obvious delusions of grandeur—delusions of such absurdity as to indicate a psychosis. If now he tries to attach a formal diagnostic label, he may—for the first time—notice that the overall clinical picture is not that of a schizophrenic nor that of a manic; and that the history and laboratory findings do not support a diagnosis of paresis. This nonconformity of the symptoms to any recognizable psychosis might thus be the first item to arouse suspicion of malingering.[2]

It next becomes necessary to turn attention to the specific symptoms offered by the defendant.

Delusions.—The frequency order of delusions (persecution, grandeur, unworthiness) is about the same among malingerers as among genuine psychotics. In both groups, delusions of persecution are the most common. The psychotic has learned that his delusions are not readily accepted and ordinarily does not gratuitously volunteer information about them unless very distressed. A malingerer, on the other hand, finds it necessary to keep reminding the examiner of his delusions. Well-organized delusional systems take time to develop. Since a malingerer had no delusions prior to the crime, it is necessary for him to develop them rapidly. If the past history shows no delusional material prior to the crime, and the examiner soon thereafter uncovers an elaborately organized delusional network, there is a suspicion of malingering. Of course if no past history is furnished, this criterion has no value. In psychotics, a delusion is not an isolated symptom. The patient's general behavior conforms to it. A malingerer may simply announce his delusion and feel that that is enough. This is not to say that a psychotic with a grandiose delusion always acts as if he is self-important. Many schizophrenics will uncomplainingly mop the ward floor while embracing delusions that they are kings or millionaires. But the schizophrenic's total behavior will be consistent—if not consistent with grandeur, at least consistent with schizophrenia.

Persecutory Delusions.—In nondeteriorated patients the life pattern does conform to the delusion. A person who believes he is being persecuted usually acts as if he were worried about it. One exception is the old paranoid schizophrenic who may seem quite indifferent considering the seriousness of the threats he describes. A malingered persecutory delusion has no historical roots. The defendant's actions prior to the crime (or even prior to his apprehension)

---

[2] Henry A. Davidson: *Bulletin of the Menninger Clinic,* XIV (September, 1950), 157.

are not consistent with those of a person worried about being the victim of persecution.

Grandiose Delusions.—Intrinsically, there is nothing to distinguish the spurious grandiose delusion from the genuine one. However, when an effort is made to fit the delusion into a clinical picture, the discrepancy usually becomes manifest. Generally speaking, there are only three psychoses in which a grandiose delusion might be a common symptom: manic states, certain forms of schizophrenia, and general paresis.[3] Each of these in turn produces a fairly well defined clinical pattern. The malingered grandiose delusion seems to be either (*a*) an isolated symptom; or (*b*) part of a bizarre, overdramatized constellation of behavior which does not fit any psychosis.

Delusions of Unworthiness.—These are seldom malingered. This type of delusion carries with it a strong sense of guilt; and defendants who set out to malinger generally avoid any kind of reaction associated with guilt feelings. Of course one occasionally runs across an exceptionally shrewd person who feels that his best defense is a clamorous insistence of his own unworthiness. It is difficult for the genuinely guilty defendant to go through with such a plan because of the lurking fear that he might be believed. Genuine delusions of unworthiness are found chiefly in depressions, and here the physical and general life picture (see next paragraph) should be clear enough to establish the diagnosis.

Depression.—A patient in a genuine depression will, after a time, begin to show distinct physical signs of his lowered metabolism. Temperature may become subnormal. The hair and skin are often dry. Even the red blood count tends to fall below normal. He becomes constipated. The facies eventually freeze into an aspect of worry or concern. After a short time, the patient is walking with his head and trunk bent. The malingerer seldom knows these things; and if he does, he finds it hard to sustain the picture hour after hour, day after day. (Also see negativism and mutism, below.)

Mutism.—Consistent mutism is at once the most difficult form of malingering to expose and likewise the most difficult to maintain. If a defendant, from the moment of his apprehension, all through his indictment, arraignment, pretrial confinement, and trial, remains

[3] Occasionally delusions of grandeur are found in some of the organic psychoses, such as those associated with drug addiction, senility, toxic states, and cerebral arteriosclerosis. However, these organic psychoses are not readily malingered since there are numerous objective evidences of their existence.

absolutely mute, no psychiatrist can insist that this is malingered.
Fortunately for the cause of justice, this monolithic silence is almost
unbearable to the sane man. To maintain it would require that the
defendant sit in his cell or walk in the yard day after day, hearing
himself discussed, hearing statements made that ought to be contra-
dicted, charges that can be denied, hearing all this, and saying nothing. It would require him to deny himself the solace of companionship in his most trying period, to spurn all offers of friendliness, to
eat only what is put before him, to do without tobacco or any other
little luxury to which he may have become accustomed, and in which
he can indulge by uttering only a brief request. Few sane persons
are cast in so heroic a mould that they can do this sixty minutes an
hour, twenty-four hours a day. Even so, there are ways of testing
the genuineness of this mutism. Whether these methods are ethical
or legal is to be determined individually in each case. But an attendant *can* awaken a patient out of a sound sleep and harass him with
questions. Intravenous injections of barbiturates *may* interrupt the
mutism. Electrical transcribing devices hidden in a cell *may* pick up
conversation. Catton [4] tells how, in one case, he added whiskey to
the food (and placed it in the gavage) of a patient arrested for committing a murder while drunk—a defendant who had remained per-
sistently mute. "The insanity defense," said Catton, "was dissolved
in five ounces of the same liquid that precipitated the killing."

Excitement and Mania.—It is practically impossible for a sane
person to keep up the unrelenting overactivity of the patient with an
acute mania. The premature ending of the excited period (by reason
of obvious fatigue) is suggestive of malingering. In true mania,
the patient generally becomes toxic, often feverish. The tongue becomes coated, the pulse fast. These findings are difficult to malinger. The flight of ideas of the manic has an idiomatic quality
which is easy to recognize but hard to imitate. Catatonic excitement
is easier to simulate, since it does not require the consistent overactivity or peculiar word usage characteristic of the manic. However, in a catatonic, the pre-arrest history would reflect a schizophrenic background, whereas in a manic it might well be negative.
The examiner would be suspicious of an apparently catatonic excitement in a defendant whose previous personality had shown no schizoid traits.

[4] Joseph Catton, *Behind the Scenes of Murder* (New York: W. W. Norton &
Co., 1940), p. 178.

Negativism.—Since the jailors will not let a prisoner starve, it is not too difficult for a malingerer to refuse food. It is much less likely, however, that a defendant will deliberately be incontinent and lie in his own feces. Yet this would occur in true negativism. Much of what passes for negativism is readily seen to be spurious when practiced by inept malingerers. There is, for instance, a behavior equivalent of the "Ganser" type of reaction. Thus, asked to put out his tongue, the defendant might point to his ear; asked to lift his right hand, he might lift his left foot. These are "approximate answers" cognate to the verbal responses in the Ganser syndrome. There is no psychosis in which this kind of response is typical. A negativistic catatonic might shut his mouth firmly when told to open it; he would hardly, however, rub his ear or scratch his nose in response to such a request. This kind of reaction always suggests (though by itself does not prove) malingering. Catatonic negativism is occasionally malingered, though the waxy flexibility is difficult to maintain for any long period. Insensitivity to pain is appraised by noting whether the patient reacts (by pupillary changes or muscle reflexes) when pricked unexpectedly in the back. To be sure, a catatonic will exhibit reflex responses to pain, but in catatonic negativism the reflex response is the same whether the patient sees the painful stimulus or not. In malingered anesthesia, on the other hand, the patient will react one way to a pain which he expects and another to a pain which is inflicted suddenly. Specifically, if the examiner approaches with a pin, allows the patient time to alert himself, then pricks the subject's hand, there may be no reaction at all, or there may be some preliminary boarding of muscles, and no pupillary response. If the examiner, without warning (and without giving the patient a chance to see what is going on) suddenly pricks the subject on his back, there is likely to be a reflex muscle contraction plus pupillary dilatation.

Stereotypy.—Occasionally a defendant gets the idea that simple repetition of the same phase or same gesture over and over again is a touchstone of insanity. Verbal stereotypy does occur in true depressions and in genuine schizophrenia. But it is never the only symptom. Where the constant repetition of a phrase or movement is alone alleged to be evidence of a psychosis, the doctor will justly be suspicious of it.

Bizarre Behavior.—The experienced examiner will recognize when the very bizarreness of behavior reflects malingering. His difficulty will not be in recognizing the sham, but rather in explaining it to a jury. Here, for example, is a transcript of a story (initials substituted for names) which appeared in an eastern newspaper during the 1940's:

> X and Y who acted like mad dogs in a murderous payroll robbery and like apes when brought to trial yesterday, were locked up out of the public gaze today to await their next appearance in court . . . The defense lawyer contended that they were insane and they gave no outward indications to the contrary. They walked into the court room with an ape-like gait, arms hanging loosely, heads wobbling from side to side with their chins held against their chests for pivots . . . Attendants had to prod them along like animals. X poked the fingers of his hand into his mouth and gnawed them. Y ate pieces of paper from the table. X then rolled up a paper napkin and ate it. Y lowered his brow to the edge of the table and rubbed it like a horse scratching his head on a post. X took a pair of soiled underpants from his pocket and wrapped it around his neck. Then he licked it and wrapped it around his head. At recess, both prisoners had to be lifted from their chairs like sacks. They sloughed out of the room like apes . . .

Obviously these are dramatic, easily practiced, outlandishly bizarre acts which represent the lay concept of madness. They do not conform to any particular psychosis. Most laymen believe that the essence of insanity is a delusion of misidentification; the traditional psychotic, in lay lore, is the patient who thinks he is Napoleon, or a poached egg on toast, or—as in this case—an animal.

When bizarre behavior is malingered, it is generally childish and exhibitionistic. Collie [5] tells of a defendant who, on being arraigned, suddenly stood on his head. It is the kind of thing a child might do to illustrate his concept of queer behavior. Again, a delusion of being an animal is incredibly rare in true psychoses. To play at being a horse or a tiger is a common juvenile game, and when an adult pretends he is an animal, it is more likely to be malingering than psychosis. When bizarre behavior is being feigned, it is thrust upon the examiner; in a true psychotic, it is but a casual by-product of the total psychosis. Exhibitionism is not characteristic of psychotics, and it is this exhibitionistic clownishness which gives malingered insanity the air of being a "show." Contrary to lay opinion, the psychotic is not a buffoon. Buffoonery suggests feigned insanity.

The Ganser Syndrome.—Sometimes a prisoner appears stupid or stupefied. He gives answers which are, in general, relevant to the question; but which may be either absurd in content (such as giving

[5] John Collie, *Fraud in Medico-Legal Practice* (London: Edward Arnold & Co., 1932).

the date as January 35) or only approximately correct (such as giving 75 as the product of eight times nine). If, in answer to a query a patient says he has thirteen fingers, the reply can be classed as "approximate" (the error being only 3/13) or as absurd. There is no agreement as to whether this syndrome is a psychoneurosis, a psychosis, or a manifestation of malingering. Support can be found for any of these theses. Wertham [6] classifies it as a form of malingering, disposing of the reaction in these words: "A Ganser reaction is a hysterical pseudo-stupidity which occurs almost exclusively in jails and in old-fashioned German textbooks. It is now known to be almost always due more to conscious malingering than to unconscious stupefaction." On the other hand, Stedman's medical dictionary [7] defines the syndrome as "acute hallucinatory mania" which would place it in the class of psychoses. Singer and Krohn [8] bracket the Ganser reaction in the general category of hysterical symptoms, classing it as a psychoneurosis.

It is unwise and unnecessary for the examiner to cite a Ganser reaction as evidence of malingering. It is unwise, because some authorities do list it as a genuine psychosis. And it is unnecessary because, even if it be conceded that the defendant now has a genuine psychotic reaction, the fact remains that it did not begin until *after* apprehension and thus has no bearing on the defendant's responsibility at the time of the alleged criminal act. Certainly the defense attorney cannot successfully argue that because his client had a psychotic (or psychotic-like) reaction *after* arrest, therefore he must have had a psychosis *prior* to his arrest. It is necessary for the expert witness to point out that this syndrome is an acute reaction to an external situation—either to the confinement in jail or to the defendant's fear of his own future. It is the result of the defendant's behavior, not the cause of it.

Malingered Psychoses in Personal Injury Cases.—The foregoing paragraphs apply principally to psychoses malingered by defendants in criminal cases. A psychosis or mental deficiency is also sometimes feigned by a plaintiff in a personal injury action. Some of the differential points listed above are equally applicable to this type of case. For example, the suggestions on the detection of malingered mental deficiency are appropriate in personal injury actions too,

[6] Frederic Wertham, *The Show of Violence* (Garden City, N. Y.: Doubleday & Co., Inc., 1949), p. 191.
[7] Norman B. Taylor, *Stedman's Medical Dictionary* (Baltimore: The Williams & Wilkins Co., 1949), p. 473.
[8] H. D. Singer and W. O. Krohn, *Insanity and the Law* (Philadelphia: P. Blakiston's Son & Co., Inc., 1924), pp. 180, 187.

except for one detail. It will be contended by the claimant's family that the injury caused the mental deficiency; therefore a normal past history and normal school and work record will not have the same probative value in these that it has in criminal cases. However, the suggestions about internal inconsistency of psychometric tests apply to both personal injury claims and to criminal cases. Only a substantial degree of structural brain damage could provoke a post-traumatic mental enfeeblement. The neurologic, electro-encephalographic, roentgenologic, pneumo-encephalographic, and projective test responses will, in the aggregate, confirm or disprove the extensive brain damage.

Psychoses malingered in personal injury claims differ from those feigned in criminal actions in two particulars: first, in motivation; second, in opportunities for observation. While any capital-case defendant in his right mind would prefer a mental hospital to the scaffold or to the electric chair, the motivation is much weaker in injury claimants. The fraudulent plaintiff is willing to go to a great deal of trouble and discomfort to get a substantial award, but he is rarely willing to have himself committed to a mental hospital. He shares with most laymen the idea that such confinement will "make him crazy." It therefore becomes necessary for him to malinger only to the extent that he seems disabled and unemployable. To pretend to be committable would be, he feels, to carry it too far for his own good. This limitation does not apply to the defendant in a capital case, for whom the mental hospital is, in truth, an asylum. Because of this restriction, personal injury claimants generally confine their psychotic symptoms to feigned dementia, "harmless" delusions and depression. Unless carefully coached, the uneducated fraudulent claimant usually tries to present a picture which, to the doctor, looks like a mixture of mental deficiency and simple schizophrenia. A "Ganser" type of reaction ("the syndrome of approximate answers") is not uncommon in this kind of malingering. The fraudulent injury claimant, while he is afraid to go as far as the malingerer in a criminal case, enjoys one great advantage: he is not under 24 hour observation. In criminal cases, malingered insanity occurs chiefly in very serious offenses in which bail is not permitted so that generally the defendant is in confinement for months between apprehension and trial. This affords the psychiatrists unlimited opportunity for personal observation and for the study of behavior reports prepared by guards or attendants. In personal injury actions, on the other hand, the doctor can see the claimant only at intervals and for short periods of time.

Malingering of psychosis in personal injury claims is relatively rare. Much more frequent is a feigning of a psychoneurosis; or the mimicry of a disability which looks "organic" to the patient but "hysterical" to the doctor. See below.

Malingered Psychoneurosis

Since it does not impair responsibility, psychoneurosis is rarely malingered in criminal cases. In a personal injury action, however, there may well be a temptation to feign psychoneurosis. How common this is, no one knows. Obviously no statistical compilation is possible. Most authorities believe that "pure" malingering (i.e., malingering uncomplicated by any psychoneurotic factors) is rare, though Baro [9] writes that "malingering is the most common picture seen after industrial injuries." The general opinion, however, is that the common pattern is one of hysterical overlay superimposed on the organic effects of injury, complicated by a conscious exaggeration of some of the functional or organic symptoms. Theoretically that fragment of the symptoms which accounts for this conscious exaggeration would be malingered. In practice it is impossible to make any such neat partition, and the matter is usually compromised by discounting part of the patient's complaints—the extent of the discount depending on the examiner's orientation.

There are some claimants who choose to manufacture a neurosis out of whole cloth. As a yardstick for the practical differentiation of a true psychoneurosis from a malingered one, the following criteria [10] are suggested:

Criterion 1: If the patient asserts inability to work but retains capacity for play (as evidenced by enjoyment of theater, television, card games, etc.), he is probably a malingerer; or at least there is a strong conscious overlay to his psychoneurosis. In general, a psychoneurosis (except for conversion hysteria) cuts into the entire personal life of the patient, bleaching the color out of his recreational pleasures as much as it robs him of his zest for work.

Criterion 2: Faithfulness in swallowing the medicines, submitting to the prescribed injections or other treatments, and attending the required offices or clinics is common in neurotics, rare in malingerers.

Criterion 3: If all evidence indicates that the claimant, prior to the accident, has always been a responsible, honest and adequate

---

[9] Walter Baro, *Industrial Medicine*, XIX (February, 1950), 69.
[10] Adapted from a paper by Henry A. Davidson in *American Journal of Medical Jurisprudence*, II (February, 1939), 94.

member of society, he is probably not now a malingerer. Malingerers are not drawn from the ranks of people sobered by responsibility, nor do they spring from those who have known the satisfactions of competence and adequacy. Unfortunately, the reverse is not true. Irresponsible persons, inadequate, unsuccessful, and incompetent ones, do not necessarily become malingerers either. Indeed, they provide fertile soil for psychoneuroses. This criterion then is a negative one. If the patient fits into the responsible-honest-adequate class he is probably no malingerer. More, we cannot say.

Criterion 4: If the accident was a frightening one (even though not a serious one), and if the content of much of the patient's thinking, dreaming, and talking revolves about the details of the accident, he is probably a neurotic. The patient's assertion that he dreams or worries about these details must be verified by others who have heard him talk about the subject in situations having no relationship to the litigation.

Criterion 5: Evidence (as by moving pictures, testimony of detectives, etc.) that the claimant uses allegedly paralyzed limbs or carries on allegedly lost functions when he considers himself free of observation is *prima facie* proof of malingering if the patient has asserted that he is never able to use the limb or perform the function. When functional loss is noted during examination but when—on questioning—the petitioner admits that the condition is inconstant, this evidence has much less meaning. Genuine neurotics frequently can carry on certain functions when composed, but are unable to do so during the emotional stress of examination or litigation. Under such circumstances this reduces evaluation of disability; but it does not invalidate the diagnosis of hysteria.

Criterion 6: If, between accident and trial, the patient had long been hospitalized (especially if in a ward with many neurotics or seriously sick patients) and if aggravation of posttraumatic symptoms began during hospitalization, he is probably a neurotic. Malingerers, disturbed by what they witness in such wards, are not likely consciously to copy symptoms they see there.

Criterion 7: Rorschach and other projection tests show a characteristic pattern in the psychoneurotic. The malingerer is more likely to give the responses of the psychopath or of the normal adult than that of the neurotic. Sometimes the malingerer purposely tries to give responses which—he thinks—would be appropriate for a neurotic. Unless the claimant happens to be intimately familiar with the test, such efforts result in suspiciously bizarre response patterns. Reactions under hypnosis or narcosynthesis are not reliable indicators of malingering. The general assumption is that under the influence of an intravenous barbiturate the malingerer will tell the truth, while the neurotic will abreact and possibly show even more acute symptoms. This may be true. On the other hand, Baro [11] tells us that "malingerers exaggerate their complaints under sodium amytal [12] while neurotic patients lose their complaints." If so, an intravenous barbiturate would not only be unhelpful; it might be misleading.

Criterion 8: Willingness to submit to surgical operation is fairly good evidence that the claimant is not a malingerer. Willingness to go to a psychopathic ward or mental hospital for observation or treatment is also evidential of the claimant's good faith. The healthy malingerer has a dread of psychopathic hospitals, and is usually convinced that simulation of psychosis in such surroundings will actually "drive him crazy."

Criterion 9: If (unless so advised by counsel) he refuses a bona fide offer of employment which would call on abilities or skills in which he claims no disorder, he is probably a malingerer. Or if not a malingerer, he has a neurosis not properly chargeable to the defendant. If he actually goes to work, such procedure may indicate that the disability is not great; but it likewise establishes the fact that the claimant is no malingerer. Such activity is quite consistent with psychoneurosis. Refusal to accept work calling on use of an allegedly disabled area, however, does not necessarily stamp the patient as a malingerer.

Criterion 10: Eagerness for re-examination, with manifestations of satisfaction at being examined and re-examined by groups of doctors, is more consistent with psychoneurosis than with malingering.

Libel, Slander, and Reports of Malingering

If a physician, in a report or in testimony, states that a claimant is a malingerer, he is, of course, calling him a cheat. Whether this is actionable as libel is a question to be determined by the courts of each state. In general, a report sent in good faith, to a person lawfully entitled to receive it, would not be libellous, and testimony in court, under oath, enjoys even greater protection. In practice, however, it is seldom necessary for the examiner to make himself vulnerable, since he can indicate his disbelief of the claimant without baldly branding him as a malingerer. For example, a statement in a written report or in testimony might run something like this: "I

[11] *Op. cit.*
[12] Amytal is a trade name registered by Eli Lilly and Company for their brand of amyl ethyl barbituric acid.

am unable to find anything to account for his pain (or other symptom) nor can I find any medical evidence to confirm the patient's allegation that he is in great pain (or has some other disability)." This is, of course, somewhat evasive, but it has the desired effect and it does cloak the doctor against libel suit. Collie,[13] I think, is unnecessarily glib and positive when he writes:

> When a medical man is asked to report, he is at liberty to express freely his honest opinion. I may have to say and write that a litigant is a cheat, but I am careful that my report is not malicious, for I am merely stating what I believe under privileged conditions. I may be mistaken: even so, my opinion is not libellous if it is my honest opinion given to the person who is entitled to it. Under these circumstances, it is absolutely privileged.

There are two defects in this dogmatic assurance. If an examiner mails a report to an insurance company attorney or adjuster, he has no assurance that the letter will not be opened and read by a clerk or secretary; and in some jurisdictions, this would constitute "publication," since the clerk is not the person for whom the report was intended. Again, the question of "malice" is one of proof. Though the doctor may have no malice in his heart, the claimant could start suit (particularly if he wins a judgment on his injury action) and might cite some evidence indicating that the doctor was careless in his examination and hasty in his conclusion of malingering. A sympathetic jury might bring in a libel verdict against the physician. Since it is not necessary to make a flat accusation of cheating, the doctor who does so renders himself unnecessarily vulnerable. The examiner is somewhat safer when testifying in court, under oath, in response to a proper question. Thus, Collie writes:[14]

> Absolute privilege covers cases where the administration of justice necessitates complete immunity: anything said by a witness in the box, for example. In such cases, the privilege afforded by the occasion is an absolute bar to action.

Though generally true, this is a bit too sweeping. Certainly before the doctor plans to announce publicly that the claimant is a fraud, he would do well to confer with the attorney as to his (the physician's) liability to a slander action. It is not really necessary, in the interest of justice, for the medical witness to say any more than that an examination failed to disclose any findings which would support the patient's complaints or explain his behavior.

[13] *Op. cit.,* pp. 55, 56.
[14] *Op. cit.,* p. 57.

Chapter 12

COMMITMENT PROCEDURES

Commitment procedures [1] vary so much from state to state [2] that no one description is universally applicable. The psychiatrist is often impatient with the legal details necessary to effect an involuntary commitment. He reasons that a psychosis is a disease, and should no more need formal legal adjudication than pneumonia or appendicitis. However, it is not that simple. Since a commitment deprives a patient of his freedom, it seems proper that at some point an agency of society should step in and agree to this deprivation of liberty. Even a patient who is detained for contagious disease has the right to a legal determination of the propriety of his detention. Without the sanction of law there would be no way of forcing the patient to remain in a locked ward.

Commitment is a process whereby at the request of the relatives, one or two doctors explain to a court why it is necessary to deprive the patient of his freedom. In many cases, the court's approval is only a *pro forma* endorsement of the medical decision. But doctors, families, and patients are best protected when the proceedings are ratified by a judicial agency. A physician who cannot demonstrate to a judge that the patient is psychotic has a weak case.

Preliminary Procedures

The Petition.—First step in a commitment procedure is a petition. Usually the petitioner is a member of the family, but in some states any "reputable citizen" may initiate the application. And generally police officers, overseers of the poor, a sheriff and the executives of institutions also have the right of petition.

[1] Certain other medico-legal aspects of commitment are reviewed in Chapter 13. In particular, see the material beginning on page 196 with reference to the effect of commitment on civil rights and effect of release (from a hospital) on restoration of such rights.

[2] There are three readily available, compact, state-by-state, analyses of commitment procedures: *Press Release,* of the Federal Security Agency (September 5, 1950); *Commitment Procedures* (Topeka, Kansas: Group for the Advancement of Psychiatry, Report No. 4) 1948; and Franklin N. Flaschner's article in the *Yale Law Journal,* LVI (August, 1947), 1178. This excellent paper is a goldmine of information about commitment laws.

The Examination and the Certificate.—Nearly all states require that two physicians examine the patient, though in some (Connecticut, for instance) a patient may be committed in an emergency and for a short period, on a certificate signed by a single physician.[3] Eligibility requirements for physicians vary. Some states require that the doctor have been in practice a certain number of years; or that he have specified qualifications. Physicians who are close relatives of the patient or who are on the payroll of the receiving institution are generally ineligible to sign commitment papers. Only one doctor is needed in Alabama, Arkansas, Idaho, Kansas, Missouri, New Mexico, Ohio, and Oregon. The other forty states require two medical signatures except for the occasional statute allowing a single medical examination in emergencies.

The time between the examination and the judicial determination is necessarily short, since the patient's mental condition may change, and an old examination would thus be outmoded. For this reason, physicians signing commitment papers are scrupulous about dating the document, so that the date of the actual examination of the patient is clearly indicated.

The Problem of Notice.—To psychiatrists, perhaps the most infuriating of the legal features of commitment is the requirement that "notice" be given to the patient. Certainly a paranoic given formal notice that he is about to be committed will either seek to flee or will be prompted to violence. A person in a depression may commit suicide on receiving this notice. If the patient is already in a hospital on a temporary, voluntary, or emergency paper, the ward physician has the unenviable task—in many states—of facing the patient and telling him that steps have been initiated to declare him "insane." In fact, in four states—Idaho,[4] Kansas,[5] Mississippi,[6] and New Mexico [7]—a warrant is actually served by the sheriff. The procedure is generally defended as the only way to preserve the civil rights of the patient and to prevent "railroading." In this connection the following remarks of Bowman [8] are appropriate:

Following the regular procedure, the wife swore out a warrant, the sheriff arrested the patient and he was taken to the jail to await a hearing. He hanged himself in the jail. To those sticklers for the defense of the legal rights of the patient, I would point out that his legal rights were well pre-

---

[3] Flaschner, *op. cit.*
[4] Idaho Code (1932), Section 64/201.
[5] General Statutes of the State of Kansas (Supplement of 1945), Section 59/2003.
[6] State Code of Mississippi (1942), Section 6909.
[7] Statutes of New Mexico (1941), Section 37/202.
[8] Karl Bowman, *American Journal of Psychiatry*, CIII (July, 1946), 5.

served . . . he was not sent to a hospital without due process and a chance to appear before the judge. Perhaps if he had, he might be alive today . . . The public is so obsessed with the alleged infallibility of legal procedure that they insist on protecting . . . the legal rights of the patient without thinking of what his medical rights are . . .

In more and more states, there is growing the conviction (expressed either by statute or by court ruling) that if, in the opinion of disinterested psychiatrists, it would be harmful to the mental health of the patient to have a notice read to him, or to have him appear in open court, then his rights are fully protected by having an attorney receive the notice and put in an appearance on the patient's behalf. This has been approved or enacted by statute in California,[9] Michigan,[10] Nevada,[11] New York,[12] Ohio,[13] Oklahoma,[14] and Wisconsin;[15] and by judicial opinion in Arkansas,[16] Iowa,[17] Massachusetts,[18] Rhode Island,[19] and several other states.

The Hearing.—The point at which a patient is definitely declared committable to a mental hospital is the hearing. In all but four states,[20] a judge or some other nonmedical official makes the actual, official decision that the patient is committed or committable. A single judge is the committing official in 31 states,[21] and a judge sitting with a commission is the committing instrument in Colorado, Florida, Georgia, Pennsylvania, Rhode Island, and Wyoming. A more or less permanent commission is the committing agency in Nebraska, North Dakota, South Dakota, Virginia, and West Virginia.[22] A jury is available at the option of the patient in nineteen states, and in two (Mississippi and Texas) the jury is required of all commitments. However, in Mississippi the jury is reduced to a panel of three [23] so that, for all practical purposes, this may be considered a "commission" rather than a jury.

[9] California Welfare and Institutions Code (1944), Section 5050.7.
[10] Annotated Statutes of Michigan (Supplement of 1946), chap. 127, Section 14.811.
[11] Chap. 257 of the Nevada Laws of 1947, Section 9.
[12] New York Mental Hygiene Law, Section 74, par. 3.
[13] Ohio General Code, Section 1890/25 (1946 Supplement).
[14] Annotated Statutes of Oklahoma (Supplement of 1946), Title 35, Section 62.
[15] Statutes of Wisconsin (1945), Section 51.02, par. 1.
[16] Payne v. Arkebauer, 80 Southwestern (2d), 76.
[17] Chavannes v. Priestley, 45 Northwestern 766.
[18] In re McDowell, 47 Northeastern 1033.
[19] In re Crosswell, 66 Atlantic 55.
[20] In Maryland, Louisiana, Rhode Island, and Vermont the physicians' certificates alone are sufficient to effect commitment, though of course there are judicial mechanisms for reviewing this action. See Flaschner, op. cit.
[21] Commitment Procedures (Topeka, Kansas: Group for the Advancement of Psychiatry, Report No. 4, 1948).
[22] Ibid.
[23] 1940 Laws of Mississippi, chap. 231, Section 4576.

Thus, Texas remains the only state in which every committed patient must have a "trial by jury." In fact, a Texas statute seeking to replace the jury with a commission was held unconstitutional [24] by the state courts on the theory that jury "trial" was provided in the constitution by implication, and that the legislature could not encroach on that constitutional right. The new (1935) Texas constitution does give the legislature power to enact a law governing *temporary* commitment without a jury, and this has been done; but it apparently does not apply to final and permanent orders of commitment.

When the Patient Has Property.—When a psychotic patient has a substantial amount of property, the psychiatrist cannot object to an orderly legal procedure to determine the amount of the property, to name a trustee for it, and to ascertain that the assets of the patient are not squandered. Conversely, where he has little property, it will fall upon the state to feed, house, and treat him while he is in the hospital—a fact which does give the state a moral as well as a legal right to hold a hearing to determine the extent of the patient's assets, and to decide who, if anyone, can be asked to contribute to his maintenance while he is at the hospital. It is this "property" aspect of the case which causes so much of the apparent "red tape" in commitment proceedings.

Emergency Commitments

The routine commitment procedure, with its petition, hearing, and adjudication is too unwieldy for emergencies. A special, streamlined procedure is provided for emergencies in twenty-two states.[25] Sometimes the special feature consists in waiving the judicial hearing; in other states a single physician, instead of the usual two, may commit a patient in an emergency. These commitments are temporary, and before the expiration of the specified period (usually ten days; in some states as few as two, in some as long as thirty, and in Arkansas [26] for "as long as necessary") a formal judicial order must be obtained. States which do not have simplified emergency procedures sometimes permit "observational commitment," which is often less time-consuming than the ordinary involuntary commitment. Jurisdictions which do not have a short-cut emergency procedure but which do

[24] White v. White, 108 Texas 570.

[25] Arkansas, California, Colorado, Connecticut, Illinois, Kentucky, Louisiana, Maine, Massachusetts, Michigan, New Jersey, New Mexico, New York, North Carolina, Ohio, Oregon, Pennsylvania, South Carolina, Texas, Utah, Virginia, and Wyoming.—From the table appended to the monograph by Flaschner, *op. cit.*

[26] Acts of 1943, State of Arkansas, Act 241, Sections 4, 8.

permit temporary observational commitments are: Arizona, Delaware, Florida, Kansas, Missouri, Montana, Oklahoma, South Dakota, Tennessee, Washington, and Wisconsin.[27] This leaves fifteen jurisdictions [28] in which there appears to be no way of short-cutting the formal adjudication even in acute emergencies. Presumably in those states, a violent patient would have to be detained under police auspices until formal commitment is accomplished.

As a matter of fact, detention in jail is permitted in all but 13 states.[29] And police officers are permitted to transport patients in all states except Maryland, Nevada, New York, Oregon, Rhode Island, Virginia, Wisconsin, and Wyoming.[30]

There is a growing tendency to use emergency commitment procedures even when the patient's condition is not, strictly speaking, a "medical" emergency. It is easier both for the doctors and for the family to set up emergency papers and have the patient taken directly to the hospital, than for all the persons concerned to present themselves at a formal hearing. In Connecticut, for example, a survey [31] revealed that 80 per cent of all admissions are effected by "emergency commitment," whereas certainly fewer than 80 per cent of psychotic persons are violent.

Whether a doctor is evading the law by using an emergency commitment for a nonviolent patient depends somewhat on the wording of the statute. If the law specifically restricts the procedure to violent patients, then obviously it is technically improper to certify quiet patients under its provisions. On the other hand, any psychotic patient is certainly potentially violent, and this may be adequate justification in questionable cases. Many of the laws, in fact, do not limit application of the emergency procedure to violent cases, but merely require a simple statement as to why the regular procedure could not be used. Since the regular procedure exposes the patient to an open airing of his mental disease, the psychiatrist can, with clear conscience, state that this procedure would be detrimental to the patient's health,

[27] Flaschner, *op. cit.*

[28] However, in *The Mental Health Program of the 48 States* (Chicago, 1950) the Council of State Governments calculates that there is some workable provision for temporary hospital detention in all jurisdictions except Idaho, Indiana, Iowa, Mississippi, Nebraska, North Dakota, and West Virginia.

[29] Jail detention is forbidden in Connecticut, Delaware, Maine, Maryland, Massachusetts, Minnesota, Mississippi, New Hampshire, New Jersey, New York, Oregon, Tennessee, and Vermont, according to the Council of State Governments (see footnote 28 above). However, this ban is of doubtful effectiveness because force often has to be used to hold a very disturbed patient, and in the absence of suitable hospital facilities, there would appear to be no alternative to a jail cell.

[30] See footnote 28, this chapter.

[31] Connecticut Committee to Study State Hospitals, *Report to 1947 General Assembly.*

and would certainly make it more awkward to effect his admission to a hospital if the hearing were an essential prerequisite.

Voluntary Admissions

All but six states [32] provide for voluntary admission to a mental hospital. The actual procedures vary so much that no single explanation will cover all jurisdictions. For example, some states (South Dakota, Tennessee, and Washington) [33] limit voluntary admission to paying patients. Others report that their hospitals are so crowded that, in practice, voluntary patients are simply not admitted. Some do, some do not, require a medical certificate in support of a voluntary application. In all states a voluntary patient must be released on his own request, but usually the release may be delayed several days (in some states up to sixty days) and in the interim the hospital authorities obtain formal commitment if this is necessary.

The chief legal problem concerning voluntary admissions is that of the patient's competence to sign his own application. Many voluntary applicants are psychotic, and the question arises as to whether the patient's signature on his application has any legal value. In most states, if the application is made by a guardian, the procedure is considered a commitment, not a voluntary admission. In three states,[34] however, the guardian may sign an application on behalf of the patient, and if the patient does not object, this is booked as a voluntary admission. A somewhat similar procedure is available in Illinois [35] where a guardian may, in effect, "make a contract" with the superintendent of the hospital to have the patient treated there without commitment. With psychotics under the age of twenty-one, a special problem is presented since in some jurisdictions minors cannot make valid "contracts." Where a voluntary admission is construed as a contract, a minor cannot sign himself into a hospital unless the state has a provision [36] whereby his parent or guardian may make such "contracts."

In Canada, the viewpoint—even among psychiatrists—seems to be that a psychotic patient should not be allowed to sign admission

[32] Alabama, Florida, Georgia, Mississippi, Missouri, and North Dakota. See *Commitment Procedures* (Topeka, Kansas: Group for the Advancement of Psychiatry, Report No. 4, 1948). In *Mental Health Program of the 48 States,* New Mexico and Tennessee are also listed as having no voluntary hospitalization, though in Tennessee, at least, paying patients apparently can seek voluntary admission.

[33] Flaschner, *op. cit.*

[34] Arkansas, Ohio, and Utah. See *Commitment Procedures* (Topeka, Kansas: Group for Advancement of Psychiatry, Report No. 4, 1948).

[35] Annotated Statutes of the State of Illinois, chap. 91½, Section 4/1.

[36] Arizona, California, Delaware, Michigan, Nevada, New York, Oregon, and Wisconsin have such provisions according to Flaschner, *op. cit.*

papers to a locked-ward hospital. In this connection, the following remark [37] from a distinguished Canadian psychiatrist (Dr. George H. Stevenson of London, Ontario) is significant:

> People who are mentally sick enough to need to come to a mental hospital should not be allowed to sign application forms if they are going to be deprived of their liberty by all the restrictions placed on them in the mental hospital.

Most psychiatrists in the United States, however, would reject this, since a patient may have insight enough to recognize his need for hospital care. As Flaschner [38] puts it: "A person who is a fit subject for mental hospital treatment and who would not object to hospitalization should not be denied the easiest method of admission."

Terminology

Psychiatrists often wonder why words like "insane," "commitment," "lunatic," and "asylum" cannot be abandoned in favor of less offensive terms like "mental illness," "admission," and "hospital." Ten states [39] have already replaced the older words with the more acceptable ones. Legislators are generally in agreement with the desirability of this change of words. However, in some areas, this would require the rewriting of hundreds of statutes and rulings, and might cast legal doubt on, or require the re-adjudication of, thousands of determinations already made. If it is legally possible [40] to effect the change, the word "parole" should be replaced with "trial visit" because of the penologic implications of "parole." "Certification" may be used in place of "commitment," "retarded" instead of "feeble-minded," and "mentally ill" in lieu of "insane."

The Proposed Model Commitment Law

Psychiatrists are sometimes asked to advise legislators about proposed changes in state commitment laws. In this connection, the Federal Security Agency in 1950 released a proposed draft of a model certification law. The Agency summarizes [41] the proposed statute as follows:

[37] George H. Stevenson. In Daniel Blain (ed.), *Better Care in Mental Hospitals,* (Washington, D. C.: American Psychiatric Association, 1949), p. 40.
[38] *Op. cit.*
[39] Connecticut, Illinois, Louisiana, Nebraska, Nevada, New York, North Carolina, Ohio, Oregon, and Pennsylvania. Flaschner, *op. cit.*
[40] For further review of this point, see *Commitment Procedures* (Topeka, Kansas: Group for the Advancement of Psychiatry, Report No. 4, 1948).
[41] *Press Release* (Washington, D. C.: Federal Security Agency, September 5, 1950). See page 377, this volume, for the text of the model law.

Basic elements of the model law are: (a) maximum opportunity for prompt medical care; (b) protection against emotionally traumatic or degrading treatment; (c) protection against wrongful confinement and deprivation of rights. Major principles of the law are:

Provision should be made for voluntary hospitalization. This should be easily and promptly available. Laws should give patients access to an approved mental hospital in the same manner as to a general hospital. Such procedure should tend to dissipate the age-old concept that mental disease is something remote from physical disease. (Barriers to voluntary hospitalization are not only legal but also economic. Although 41 states now permit voluntary admissions, in 1949 only about 10 per cent of patients were admitted under this method. Some areas take only paying patients on a voluntary basis; others are short of hospital beds and can take only cases serious enough to need involuntary commitments.)

Hospitalization proceedings should involve a maximum reliance on medical judgment. The basic question in deciding whether a person should be hospitalized is his health and his medical needs. The model law follows the current trend of placing major emphasis in any admission procedure on the conclusions of qualified physicians who have examined the patient.

Hospitalization procedures should be free of the characteristics of criminal proceedings. Today the mentally ill person may be arrested by a sheriff with a warrant, charged with insanity by a judge, detailed in a jail pending the hearing, tried in open court before a jury, remanded to jail pending a vacancy in a mental hospital, and finally transported to the hospital by a sheriff. While this procedure in each detail may not be followed by any jurisdiction, it represents a pattern of existing practices which are especially objectionable. The model law would eliminate these concepts and practices. The terms "mental illness" and "patient" replace such terms as "insanity," "lunacy," and "inmate." "Commitment" is replaced by the more general term "hospitalization." Hearings and medical examinations are required to be conducted with utmost regard for the emotional welfare of the sick person. Detention in jail is permitted only in an extreme emergency when confinement is necessary and there are no alternative facilities; health authorities are responsible for arranging that medically trained attendants take the patient to the hospital, when escort is necessary.

Provision should be made for temporary involuntary hospitalization without the necessity of court proceedings. While the model law encourages voluntary admission, not all persons who need mental hospital care will seek it. Whether for temporary observation or in an emergency, it should be possible to hospitalize a mentally ill person promptly and without unnecessary emotional strain on either patient or family. Emergency commitments are both advisable and necessary. The procedure should be simple, readily accomplished and not require a trip to the court house.

Opportunity should be given for prompt judicial proceedings. Deprivation of liberty or property is a legal problem. Commitment involves not only medical care but deprivation of personal liberty. Accordingly, when involuntary hospitalization is authorized on the basis of medical certification alone, there should be opportunity for prompt recourse to judicial proceedings. Involuntary hospitalization for an indeterminate period is so grave an exercise of authority that ultimate responsibility should rest with an arm of the state customarily exercising a judicial function.

Provision should be made for continuing review of the mental condition of hospitalized patients and for conditional release and discharge as warranted by their condition. Too often the fear of irrevocable confinement has delayed bringing the patient under hospital care until the illness has developed to the point where the only prospect is long-term, expensive custody. The model law provides for regular re-evaluation of the patient's condition, release as soon as possible (often preceded by conditional release for out-patient care), and prompt court review of the hospitalization order upon request of the patient, his family or friends.

Patients while in a hospital should be protected in the enjoyment of personal rights to the extent consistent with required detention and treatment. Except when necessary for the welfare of the patient, a mental patient may not be deprived of the right to have visitors or communicate with people outside the hospital. Nor, under the model law, may mechanical restraints (such as straitjackets, straps, etc.) be used except when medically required and on specific written order of the hospital head. Adjudication of incompetency, involving loss of personal and property rights, while often needed for protection of the sick person and his family, is properly separated from the problem of admission to a hospital and considered a separate legal question.

Commitment Check List

Physicians entering a new state, or beginning—for the first time—to sign commitment papers, would do well to obtain from the secretary of state in the state house or state capitol a copy of the commitment law. Since legal language is often as obscure to the doctor as medical terminology is to the lawyer, the physician should have a lawyer friend translate the statute into colloquial English. The next step is to consult with an experienced psychiatrist to obtain from him the actual day-to-day technique—which may be surprisingly different from the formal procedure laid down in the law. One common difference is that in states which have short-cut procedures for emergencies, the tendency is to use the emergency procedure wherever possible. The inexperienced physician will check the following points before beginning to sign commitment papers:

Is a state license required? Do I have a state license? Are hospital interns and residents permitted to sign papers even though unlicensed?

How long must a physician be in practice before he may sign papers? Does this mean, "How long since he became a doctor?" Or does it mean, "How long since he was licensed?"

What is the rule about the committing doctor's relationship with a patient? For instance, may a doctor sign a paper committing his own brother-in-law?

May a doctor on the staff of a state or private hospital commit to that hospital a patient who came there first on a voluntary basis? May he take a call to a new patient's home and there sign a commitment paper?

Must a notary public be present during the psychiatric interview? Must he be present when the doctor signs the commitment paper? Or only when the doctor signs the affidavit attached to the paper?

Must the physicians examine the patient jointly? Or on the same day?

What is the time limit for a valid commitment paper? May a doctor sign a certificate today if the relative signed the petition a week ago? Three weeks ago?

Is there any rule as to who signs first—the applicant (petitioner) or the doctor?

Is this an emergency commitment, an observational commitment, or a formal ("permanent") commitment paper? What does this mean in terms of the doctor's obligation to appear in court or at a quasi-judicial hearing later? If two doctors sign, do both appear? Or only the first to sign? Or how is this determined?

The experienced psychiatrist knows, for his own state, the answers to *all* these questions. While the timid doctor is sometimes afraid to sign a commitment paper for fear of possible malpractice action or other legal complications, the fact is that over 200,000 patients [42] are committed annually. This represents about 400,000 signatures—and very few of these signatures ever lead to legal difficulties.[43]

[42] *Unconquered Frontiers* (New York: Psychiatric Foundation, 1948).

[43] Certain other medico-legal aspects of commitment are reviewed in Chapter 13 (Competency, Contracts, and Guardianships). In particular, see the material beginning on page 196, with reference to the effect of commitment on civil rights, and the effect of release on the restoration of such rights.

Chapter 13

COMPETENCY, CONTRACTS, AND
CIVIL RIGHTS OF THE MENTALLY ILL

A diagnosis of mental illness may mean that questions will be raised about the patient's right to drive a car, cast a ballot, sell his house, or make a contract. These questions all turn on whether the patient is "competent."

In this connection, "competency" is mental capacity to carry on one's own everyday affairs. Competency is the reciprocal of "responsibility." The latter reflects a duty or an immunity; "competency" implies a right or privilege. Thus, one has a duty to obey the law and, ordinarily, a person is "responsible" (that is, answerable or accountable) for violation of the law. However, under the circumstances detailed in Chapter 1, a mentally ill person might be "irresponsible," that is, "not accountable" for his crime; or, to put it another way, he is relieved of this "duty."

Competency will here be considered under seven headings: (a) appraisal of competency, (b) competency to make contracts, (c) effect of adjudication of incompetency on the patient's civil rights, (d) the legal adjudication of incompetency, (e) the patient's liability for suit, (f) guardianship, and (g) competency of witnesses.

Appraisal of Competency

As a practical matter, competency is simply the absence of incompetency. The formula has to be stated in this retrograde fashion because there is a primary presumption that every adult is competent. Unless incompetency can be *affirmatively* demonstrated, a person is presumed to be able to do his own business. It would be difficult to prove that a subject is competent by demonstrating that he has good judgment. But that is not the problem. The burden of proof is on him who would declare the adult *incompetent*. He must show the bad judgment and demonstrate that it is due to a mental disorder. If he fails to prove that, then by default the subject is found competent. Thus, the problem is always one of showing incompetency, or of neutralizing evidence suggesting incompetency. Few of us could pass a test designed to prove that we consistently make judgments with wisdom and deliberateness. However, if anyone challenges our right to vote or to sign a contract, he must prove our incompetency.

Competency to make a will was discussed in Chapter 7. Competency to enter into a marriage relationship or to apply for annulment of marriage was reviewed in Chapter 5.

In general, the determination of incompetency is a three-step procedure. It must be shown *first* that the subject has a mental disorder; *second* that this mental disorder causes a defect in judgment; *third* that this defect in judgment, as a practical matter, causes a specific incapacity with reference to the matter in question. These three criteria will now be reviewed in that order.

Mental Disorders Causing Incompetency.—The subject must have a specific mental disorder affecting his ability to reason, before he can be declared incompetent. Usually this means that the doctor must show psychosis, mental deficiency, or an organic cerebral disorder, but in certain special cases, epilepsy or psychoneurosis may also justify a finding of incompetence. These special cases are:

a) *Epilepsy.* Ordinarily, epilepsy does not affect competency. (If the epileptic also happens to be a mental defective, incompetence can be adjudged as for the mental deficiency.) The exception would be an epileptic who suffers from frequent prolonged confusional states following a seizure, or the one who has psychomotor attacks during which he is amnesic or confused. It would be proper to question the competency of an epileptic who, during frequent and extended periods of postconvulsive confusion, wanders away, is robbed of his money, or shows grossly irrational behavior. A similar disability would apply to epileptics who have frequent and prolonged psychomotor fugues. During such periods, the patient might not know what he was doing. In any individual case, the determination turns on how prolonged and how frequent these periods are.

b) *Psychoneurosis.* In most psychoneurotics, competency is not impaired. However, if the patient is subject to frequent periods of hysterical amnesia or dissociation, his competency might be questioned, at least with respect to transactions during such periods. It is sometimes contended that a neurotic's business contracts should be voidable because of his impulsiveness, poor judgment, or emotional instability. However, this position is generally untenable, since the impulsiveness, poor judgment, and instability of the neurotic are comparable to similar traits in "normal" people.

c) *Alcoholics.* In the absence of a special inebriety statute, alcoholism will not justify a finding of incompetency. In a few states, the law recognizes the chronic inebriate as incompetent, and has special legislation providing for the appointment of a guardian for the alcoholic. In most jurisdictions, however, nonpsychotic alcoholism does not impair competency just as it does not impair responsibility. Alcoholism is not considered a "disorder of thinking" or a "mental disorder" as the term is used in a finding of incompetency.

d) *Psychopaths.* Psychopathic personality, in the absence of psychosis, is compatible with competency. Alcoholism and psychopathic personality are considered "character" disorders rather than "mental" disorders; impairments of "will" rather than of "thinking." True, an alcoholic may squander his pay-check and allow his family to starve; a psychopath may lose his weekly salary in gambling every Saturday night and allow his family to be evicted. These, however, are not, in the eyes of the law, evidences of incompetency; they are tokens of "bad character."

e) *Organic Disorders.* An organic cerebral disorder (not amounting to psychosis) may be the basis of a finding of incompetency if it can be shown that the disorder materially affects ability to reason. This would be true, for example, in patients who have been left aphasic, amnesic, and confused following an apoplectic seizure; in patients suffering from extensive traumatic encephalopathy; in those with delirium induced by meningitis or encephalitis.

Impairment of Judgment.—Establishment of the mental disorder is not sufficient to warrant a finding of incompetency. It must also be shown that this mental disorder caused an impairment of judgment. The psychiatrist may be able to show depression, hallucinations, or paranoid delusions without being able to demonstrate a specific judgmental defect. From his point of view, this seems like an absurd demand. He knows that if a patient has a delusion, his judgment is affected thereby; that a man with normal judgment would automatically correct an hallucination, so that the existence of hallucinations necessarily shows some impairment of judgment. He knows that the neatly isolated single delusion is a myth, and that the mind is not divided into separate compartments; that it is impossible to have a disease in one of these compartments without the entire mind being somewhat involved. That, however, is not the legal view.

A patient was drawing a monthly check from his health insurance policy. He was psychotic, and before the first check came in, the family asked to have some responsible relative named as guardian, for fear that the patient would dissipate the badly needed income. Because of the patient's illness the family had no other source of income. A psychiatrist testified that the man had a delusion that he was being persecuted by an unknown nation-wide conspiracy; that constantly, over the radio, he heard veiled threats in the form of remarks which were not understood by anyone else but which represented secret code signals of the enemy. The judge asked whether the psychiatrist could show any specific impairment of judgment. The doctor added that no man with normal judgment would believe these things. The attorney for the patient retorted that this was an isolated delusion not affecting any other part of his mind, that the man showed good judgment in his day-by-day marketing for groceries, and that the psychosis was thus sharply limited in its effects. The psychiatrist denied that a systematic delusion like this could leave any part of the mind unimpaired. The attorney challenged the doctor to show any disorientation, delusion of grandeur, or any other psychiatric symptom except the one fixed delusion.

The court then ruled that the family had failed to show that any other part of his mind was involved, had failed to show a defect in judgment, and that therefore the patient could not be called incompetent. Accordingly he was given control of his own funds. He spent all his money hiring detectives to find out who was behind this conspiracy, and the family was impoverished. After the money was all exhausted the case was reopened. It was now agreed that, in hiring the detectives to trail an imaginary persecutor, he had displayed poor judgment, and accordingly he was now (when there was no estate left to protect) declared incompetent.

The lawyer would say that these were two perfectly reasonable decisions. The burden of proof was on the family to show that the man had poor judgment with respect to money matters. They had failed to demonstrate this, therefore the patient had to be considered competent. Later on they did demonstrate it (by the fact of his squandering the money on detectives); therefore, later on he could be declared incompetent.

Instances of Specific Incompetency.—Once it is shown that the subject has poor judgment due to a mental disorder, it must finally be demonstrated that this poor judgment affects the matter at issue. In the case just cited, the matter at issue was the handling of money. In other cases it might be the right to drive a car, or to negotiate for the purchase or sale of a house, to contract marriage, or to defend a civil suit. The best evidence is a report that, in fact, the patient did do something foolish because of the poor judgment. Often, however, it is important to have the patient declared incompetent *before* he does something foolish. Here it depends on how persuasive the psychiatrist can be in his testimony or report. He might predict that the patient would squander his assets. Some judges would dismiss this as a guess; others, impressed by the doctor's assurance, poise, and firmness might go along with the recommendation. Most of these actions concern the handling of money—either the judicious spending of money, or the prudent making of contracts. On the first point, there are three questions which the psychiatrist should be prepared to answer:

a) Will he squander his money imprudently because of his mental disorder?

b) Is he likely to fall prey to designing persons because of gullibility or suggestibility; and if so, is this gullibility or suggestibility due to his mental disorder, or is it analogous to the poor judgment that any normal person might have?

c) Is he likely to hoard his money and allow his family to do without necessities because of a psychotic fear of poverty, or because of some delusion which will make it impossible for him to negotiate checks? [1]

Competency to Make Contracts [2]

Criteria.—While the doctor thinks of a contract as a formal and formidable legal document, the truth is that most contracts are never put in writing. The patient who asks a physician to give him some medicine for his headache is making a contract. So is the customer who enters a store and says, "Give me a package of cigarettes." A contract is not valid (except for necessities) if, by reason of mental derangement, one of the parties did not know what he was doing. However, the subject's ignorance of what he was doing must be based on mental derangement and not simply on lack of sophistication or technical knowledge. If, for example, a naïve young man is per-

[1] As an example: a patient received an insurance company check every month and carefully placed it in a cigar box. When the matter was investigated, he had 24 unendorsed, unnegotiated checks in that box. His reason: it was all a plot to get his signature, and he was outsmarting his enemies by refusing to write his name on the back of the checks. Meanwhile his family had to go on relief to get food for their children. Here the delusion prevented him from negotiating his checks, and thus he was incompetent. When a guardian was appointed, the guardian endorsed the checks and turned the proceeds over to the wife.

[2] This section represents an expansion of part of the author's monograph, "Orientation to Forensic Psychiatry," *Archives of Neurology and Psychiatry* LVII (June, 1947), 730.

suaded to buy a business for which he is unfitted, he cannot call on a
psychiatrist to help cancel the contract on the grounds that he did not
understand the implications of the transaction. Such misunderstanding arose from ignorance, poor judgment or lack of training; not
from mental disorder. In general, a contract made by a lunatic is
voidable; and if made by a regularly adjudicated lunatic, it is void.[3]

Necessities.—Would this doctrine affect the right of a doctor to
collect for essential medical services rendered to a psychotic patient?
No, because a contract to supply "necessities" to a child or a lunatic
is valid and enforceable. Essential medical service, like food, is universally considered a "necessity."

Drunkenness.—A contract made with a man in an advanced state
of drunkenness cannot generally be enforced against him unless it is
for a "necessity." Simple over-the-counter sales at standard prices
are usually considered enforceable contracts. The psychiatrist will
be asked whether the degree of drunkenness was such as to strip the
participant of any understanding of the implications of the transaction; if it was not, the contract would probably be valid. If it appears
that in an expansive mood, the drunken person agreed to buy a half-
interest in an amusement park, it is probable that the doctor will
testify that the drunkenness adversely affected his ability to understand the implications of that contract. Since this lack of understanding rose from a mental disorder (acute intoxication), it invalidates
the agreement. Only the person who was drunk can petition to have
such a contract cancelled. The sober participant cannot escape from
the contract by pleading that the other was *non compos mentis*.

Psychosis.—If a person is psychotic, but if the casual observer
cannot see that he is insane and enters into a contract in good faith,
the courts may enforce the contract. Whether they will depends
chiefly on whether the deal can be dissolved without any loss being
suffered. For instance, a salesman makes a contract to sell a washing
machine to a lunatic, not knowing that the customer is psychotic.
The purchaser's guardian appeals to have the agreement voided. This
appeal will usually be granted if the washing machine can be sent
back in exchange for the money paid out. However, if a plumber
spends all day fixing the pipes at the request of a lunatic, it is apparent that the contract cannot be set aside without causing a loss to the
plumber. The latter cannot get back his time. In such a case, the
contract would probably be enforced if the plumber acted in good

---

[3] Wadford v. Gilette, 137 Southeastern Reporter 314.

faith. If a patient is obviously deranged it will be assumed that the other participant knew it and that he did not act in good faith.

Mental Deficiency.—It is often easy to persuade a mental defective to sign on the dotted line, and the psychiatrist may be called on to help the patient escape from his ill-advised financial commitment. If a child of the corresponding mental age would not have been able to understand the implications of the contract, the courts will usually set it aside, unless (as sometimes happens) it appears that the patient's maturity and actual experience with the world make him far shrewder than a child of the same mental age. A man of fifty with a mental age of eight, who has been a self-supporting day laborer all his life, is not the same as a normal eight-year-old when it comes to making business agreements. Actually he has a moderate amount of business judgment based on years of experience in selling his labor— something that the bright eight-year-old would lack. Thus the psychiatrist should not depend on the parallel with a child of the same mental age in evaluating contractual capacity. The problem is a pragmatic one, to be decided independently on the facts of each transaction.

I once examined a mature woman with a mental age of seven and a half who was persuaded to buy a 24-volume encyclopedia. The salesman dazzled her with his assurance that the cost was only two cents a page and that she could stretch the instalments over a year. He never told her the actual aggregate cost and she signed the contract because "two-cents a page" seemed very cheap. As the encyclopedia contained 6000 pages, the customer was committing herself to an aggregate payment of $120, or $2.50 a week. It was testified that with her mental age she could not perform the necessary calculation in her head. (She would have had to multiply $0.02 by 6000 and divide the product by 52 to get the weekly payment figure of $2.50.) Her failure to see the implications of her contract was rooted in a mental disorder—namely, mental deficiency. Hence the contract was voidable.

A farmer with a mental age of seven and a half who had been selling chickens and eggs to neighbors for years, could not escape the consequences of an ill-advised agreement to sell eggs at a low price, on the basis of his mental deficiency. In this instance, unlike the encyclopedia case, the patient's entire background indicated that he could understand such transactions.

A general rule about mental age and business capacity is not used. Each case stands on its own feet.

Senility.—A man in his dotage conveyed his house to the seller of oil stock. The children sought to set the contract aside on the ground of lack of contractual capacity because of senility. If the psychiatrist had found evidence of a senile psychosis or senile dementia, the contract would have been voided. But he reported "simple senility," with fragmentary memory defects, childishness, irritability, and a fondness for living in the past. The contract was then held valid. The psychiatrist might find some mental trait short of psychosis which specifically impairs contractual capacity. For instance, if he found that the patient was grossly disoriented, though quite free of delusions, he might testify that a man who does not even know in what century he is living can hardly understand a business transaction. In general, the doctrines applying to senility and wills also apply to senility and contracts, though less mentality is required to make a valid will than to make an enforceable contract. (See Chapter 7.)

Action Not Withdrawable.—Sometimes a mentally deranged person makes an agreement, repents of it, institutes a suit to set it aside, and is then influenced to withdraw the suit. As a general rule, a person having once initiated action on the grounds of his own incapacity, cannot withdraw the petition.[4] There is too much possibility that he was prevailed on to stop the action by someone taking advantage of his mental enfeeblement.

Mental Disease and Civil Rights

The term "civil rights" embraces such privileges as the right to buy, sell and hold property; entitlement to a driver's license; the right to vote, hold office, practice a profession, or engage in a business; the right to enter into a marriage relationship, to institute divorce proceedings, or to sue for damages. In addition, there is a "natural" right which is presumed to pertain to every person as a human being: the right to be protected from assault, insult, and slander. A mentally ill person never forfeits his "natural right" except when he is compelled to accept treatment (electric shock therapy, for example) that might be construed as an "assault" if done to a competent person without his consent. His civil rights, on the other hand, are seriously affected by his being adjudicated "insane."

The prime civil right is, of course, freedom. The formal commitment procedure obviously suspends this right. If a commitment is

---

[4] *In re* Rhode's Estate, 136 Atlantic Reporter 408; also 140 Atlantic Reporter 889.

accomplished with complete conformity to the law, the patient cannot contend that he has been illegally deprived of his freedom. However, any defect in the commitment procedure will lend support to such a contention. If the law says that the examination must have been made not more than ten days prior to the patient's admission to the hospital, then this must be followed exactly. If the patient entered the hospital eleven days after the examination, he may well win his release by pointing out this defect. This seems absurd to the physician, but freedom is so precious a right that the law properly wraps safeguards around it, and demands that any one who seeks to impair that right must carry the burden of proof and proceed with scrupulous conformity to the law.

While there is considerable state-by-state variation, in general a *formal adjudication* of insanity [5] has the following effects on a patient's civil rights: It takes away from him the right to consent to or refuse to consent to the adoption of his child; it casts doubts on (though does not automatically invalidate) his right to make a will (see Chapter 7 for details); it deprives him, as a rule, of the right to vote or hold office; it suspends his driver's license; in most states it vacates his license to practice medicine, law, or any other learned profession; it impairs his right to marry, though usually, if he does marry while psychotic, the marriage will be valid unless specifically set aside (see Chapter 5); it may render him immune to a civil suit for punitive damages based on any personal action of his own (e.g., a suit for slander), but it will not protect him against suits based on defects in his property; [6] on the other hand, it seldom deprives him of the right to initiate a legal action, except where his personal, sworn signature is required on papers needed to institute the suit. An insane person, thus, can generally sue someone who has assaulted him. On the other hand, he can rarely start a divorce action, because in most states this requires him to sign affidavits based on personal knowledge and in those states his affidavit would usually be meaningless. In some of the poll-tax states, a psychotic person is exempt from the payment of poll taxes.

[5] Not necessarily a formal commitment, however. As discussed below, commitment by itself does not, in all states, suspend civil rights. The reference here is to a formal judicial determination of incompetency and not simply to the approval of a commitment.

[6] This sounds a little confusing, and perhaps an example will make it clear. If a psychotic person owns a piece of property, he does not lose ownership, though he may lose control while psychotic. Suppose there is an unmarked hole in the ground, and an innocent person lawfully walks across it and falls into the hole, breaking his leg. That person could sue the psychotic owner and collect damages. Maintenance of the property is a duty of those controlling it; and damages are properly charged to the owner.

One of the valuable rights which psychotics preserve, is the right to apply for a writ of *habeas corpus*. As Judge Waldman [7] puts it,

. . . this is a writ having for its object the speedy release by judicial decree of persons who are illegally restrained of their liberty. It is essentially a writ of inquiry. It is directed to the person in whose custody the petitioner is detained, and requires the body of the person (alleged to have been unlawfully held in restraint of his liberty) to be brought before the court that judgment may be rendered upon inquiries into the alleged unlawful restraint. This writ existed at common law and comes to us as a part of our inheritance from England. Where a patient is detained after he becomes sane, such detention is illegal and may be handled by *habeas corpus,* and a person committed as insane has the right at any time to have his sanity determined on *habeas corpus.*

A writ of *habeas corpus* may be sued out, on behalf of any person confined in any hospital for the insane, in the courts to determine his sanity. The writ is directed to the executive in charge. On the return date the fact of the sanity of the person so detained is inquired into and all parties in interest are entitled to be heard. If the court finds the patient is sane, he may be discharged from the institution. The court may also impanel a jury to determine the issue of sanity.

An interesting, recent case on the rights of mental patients to have the court determine their sanity, was that reported in 140 N. J. Equity p. 371, and decided by Judge Jayne. In 1927 the patient was adjudged insane and committed to the New Jersey State Hospital at Trenton. His aged mother sued out a writ of *habeas corpus* in his behalf in 1947. The court found that in his 20 years confinement, the prisoner, a man of 61, was a quiet patient, nonviolent, not morose, had no hallucinations, needed no therapy, and to quote the court, "this person is not a patient, but a prisoner."

Said the court, "Under existing legislation the lawmakers intended the judicial official to determine from the evidence adduced whether the mind of the inmate is so deranged and disordered that the public welfare, or the welfare of the inmate, requires his continued imprisonment, which inquiry impliedly encompasses the question whether, if liberated, the inmate in the light of the evidence, is reasonably likely to menace the safety of himself or that of the person or property of others. . . . I decline to believe that the Legislature intended to ordain the perpetual imprisonment of harmless and inoffensive individuals merely because they exhibit some type of psychosis catalogued in the science of psychiatry. *I regard the word 'insanity' in the section of the statute by which my action is governed in a proceeding of this nature as a social and legal, rather than a medical term.* Assuredly, there are psychoneurotic and psychopathic states which are distinguished from insanity."

[7] Henry S. Waldman, "Civil and Legal Rights of the Insane," *Bulletin of the New Jersey Welfare Council,* XXI: 6 (June, 1950), 2.

The evidence further showed that prisoner, while in confinement, wrote a book about Christ, containing novel theories about him. The hospital doctors said he was suffering from a paranoid condition.

The court decided if the man was liberated, he would be invigorated and nonviolent, and he found the man sane, discharging him from confinement.

A recent companion case to the foregoing is In re Perry, 137 N. J. Eq. p. 161, decided by Judge Jayne in 1945. Perry was confined to the New Jersey State Hospital in 1944 and a writ of *habeas corpus* was obtained to question his sanity. The court admitted the difficulty of defining insanity, but refused to hold that every type of psychosis had the legal implications of insanity. In *habeas corpus* proceedings the court said the purpose of the inquiry is to ascertain whether the mental condition of the patient is at present such that a continuance of his confinement is reasonably necessary to obtain the objects of the statute . . . which are to protect the public, or the person confined, or both.

The patient was 48 years of age, exhibits noticeable idiosyncracies, is emotional, loquacious and showed aberrant deportment for years. The court refused to hold him to be insane and discharged him. If liberated, he said, the man would not menace others; he has a perception of right and wrong.

Situations like those cited above are irritating to physicians because the judge seems to be making a medical decision. For example, in the first case, the judge said that if the patient were liberated, "he would be invigorated and nonviolent." In the second instance, the court decided that "if liberated, the man would not menace others; he has a perception of right and wrong." These conclusions, from the doctor's viewpoint, represent naïve and amateurish reasoning. On the other hand, it is unfair to analogize this to a judge's decision that a patient has or does not have pneumonia. The judicial determination does not challenge a medical diagnosis: it determines, rather, a sociologic finding—that the petitioner would or would not be dangerous; or that the findings do or do not fall within the legal definition of "insanity." To the physician even this seems to be an encroachment of a lay authority into a medical area. But such is the law, and the experienced psychiatrist knows it and conforms to it.

The Adjudication of Incompetency

Does commitment, by itself, automatically adjudicate incompetency? If a patient is routinely committed to a state hospital, does he thereby forfeit the right to drive a car, cast a ballot, buy and sell property, or engage in business? We know (see Chapter 7) that he does not necessarily lose the right to make a will. But how about these other civil rights?

Legal Effect of Commitment.—Although there is considerable state-by-state variation, commitment *in practice* (not necessarily in theory) often has the effect of suspending these civil rights. That is why there is so much concern about the legal correctness of the procedure.

From a medical viewpoint, there is no necessary relationship between committability and competency. A patient may need mental hospital care without suffering impairment of competency. And a patient might need a guardian without requiring hospital care. However, this distinction is not obvious to lawyers. In at least four states [8] commitment means that a guardian must be appointed—this, in effect, does adjudicate the patient as incompetent. In addition to the four states listed by Flaschner, this seems to be the law in Virginia too, since that state's Commissioner of Mental Hygiene is recorded as having made the following remarks at the 1949 Institute of the American Psychiatric Association:

> . . . Committed mental patients in Virginia have been adjudicated insane, and by that adjudication a patient loses his right to franchise. . . . The fact that we have released them from the hospital does not erase that adjudication. . . . If you can say that he has *recovered from his mental illness,* you can issue a discharge certificate and erase that adjudication. As a matter of procedure, we rarely do that. . . . In the county clerk's office, the adjudication against this patient has not been erased. Because of this, he cannot legally engage in any financial transactions; he is still incompetent.[9]

On the other hand, most states have recognized, or are beginning to recognize, that—as one New York court put it: "Commitment has a distinct object in view: the treatment of the patient and the protection of the public. An order (of commitment) does not effect an adjudication of insanity." [10]

The more modern viewpoint is also reflected in the following comments [11] from the American Psychiatric Association's Mental Hospital Institute:

> DR. ARTHUR P. NOYES . . . Most of the patients in Pennsylvania come to us . . . on the application of a relative and the certificate of two physicians. . . . The person does not lose his civil rights. For example, he may have some real estate that should be sold, and we are asked if the patient is competent. The staff examines the patient and if he seems to be competent,

---

[8] Arizona, Colorado, Indiana, and Washington. See Franklin N. Flaschner, *Yale Law Journal* LVI (August, 1947), 1178.

[9] Daniel Blain (ed.), *Better Care in Mental Hospitals* (Washington, D. C.: American Psychiatric Association), 1949, pp. 39-43.

[10] Flaschner, *op. cit.,* footnote 49.

[11] See footnote 9, this chapter.

he may transact his business. In Pennsylvania, when a patient is discharged, he may transact legal business.

DR. F. W. HAAS: In South Dakota, our Supreme Court has ruled that a man having been admitted to the state hospital has been committed merely as a sick individual for treatment, and that he is *not* deprived of his civil rights.

DR. WALTER RAPAPORT: In California . . . an adjudication of mental illness means only that the person is in need of treatment . . . there is a question whether the persons in our (mental) hospitals lose the right to vote. That has never been determined . . . if they do vote, there is no question of it. . . . They are able to do business provided the party on the other end is willing to take the chance.

The situation in Canada appears to be less favorable to the mental hospital patient. Thus, speaking at the same institute, Dr. George H. Stevenson of London, Ontario, said: [12] "If they are not competent to look after themselves outside the hospital, they are not competent to do business. The idea that a person is allowed to sell real estate while he is deprived of the right to walk the streets, I find difficult to comprehend."

Thus, the effect of commitment on the competency and franchise of the patient would seem to vary from state to state. So far as I have been able to determine, there are only six states in which commitment definitely appears to vacate the patient's civil rights. They are: Arizona,[13] Colorado,[14] Indiana,[14] Tennessee,[15] Virginia,[16] and Washington.[17] In most other jurisdictions commitment is *not* an automatic adjudication of incompetency.

It is necessary to add, however, that a person who does business with a mental patient, does so at his own risk. The transaction could be set aside if the courts found that the negotiator was taking advantage of the patient's illness. For this reason, in practice, most mental hospital patients find that their business affairs are, in effect if not in theory, at a more or less complete standstill. Again, it seems unlikely that any mental hospital would allow a patient to leave a locked ward in order to cast a ballot; so that, in practice, the patient has lost the right to vote even if there is no law that says that commitment means disfranchisement.

Legal Effect of Release from State Hospital.—When a patient who had been committed to a hospital is released by the staff, what

[12] *Ibid.*
[13] See Flaschner, *op. cit.*
[14] *Ibid.*
[15] Bradford v. American National Bank, 158 Southwestern Reporter (2d) 366.
[16] Joseph E. Barrett, *in Better Care in Mental Hospitals* (Washington, D.C.: American Psychiatric Association, 1949), p. 39.
[17] See Flaschner, *op. cit.*

legal effect does this have on (*a*) the presumption that he is "insane," and (*b*) his previously suspended civil rights? The answer depends on three things:

1. At the time of commitment, was there also a finding of incompetency? Was a guardian appointed?

2. In the state concerned, did commitment, in theory, mean a suspension of civil rights? For example, did commitment automatically cancel an automobile driver's license or the right to vote?

3. Was the release from the hospital considered a parole, trial visit, furlough, or discharge? Is the patient still carried on the books of the hospital and accounted for in their statistics? Can he be forced to re-enter the hospital without a new commitment? Do the courts take any judicial notice of the release from the hospital, or was it purely an administrative act?

The general rule is, that when a status is determined by a court it will take another act of that court (or of a court of comparable or higher rank) to nullify that decision and restore the *status quo.* Compare, for example, the practice in Virginia [18] with that in Pennsylvania.[19] The Commissioner of Mental Hygiene in Virginia describes the situation there as follows: "The fact that we have released them from the hospital does not erase the adjudication (of insanity) . . . Because of this, he cannot (after release) engage in any financial transactions because he is still incompetent." On the other hand, we are told: "In Pennsylvania, when a patient is discharged, he may transact business."

In general, subject to statutory or procedural exceptions in certain states, the rule is this:

If commitment is ordered by a court, there must have been an official finding that the patient was "insane." Release from the hospital will not vacate this finding. It means only that the patient is no longer in need of hospital care; it does not automatically erase the finding of insanity, since a person could still be psychotic yet be unable to profit from further hospitalization. Indeed, unless some other judicial proceeding intervened, the presumption would be that the patient was still psychotic.

Thus, in a Texas case,[20] a person committed murder two years after discharge from a state hospital. As there had been no official erasure of the commitment, the court held that the psychosis was presumed to continue, and that it was up to the prosecution in this case

---

[18] See footnote 9, this chapter.
[19] *Ibid.,* pp. 41-42.
[20] Davidson v. State, 4 Southwestern 74.

to prove that the defendant had recovered. (The assumption that the psychosis, once established, continues until otherwise adjudicated is not irrefutable of course; but it is a *prima facie* presumption.)   In this instance, the presumption operated *in favor of* the defendant because it made his conviction for a crime more difficult.   However, the same line of reasoning would also operate *against* an ex-patient if he sought to engage in business or obtain a driver's license.

On the other hand, in some states the form of commitment carries within it a mechanism for erasing the adjudication.   For instance, it might be that by statute, ruling, or procedure the discharge of the patient would be listed in the order, as a factor nullifying the determination of "insanity."   This would have to be determined in each case by reading the actual order of commitment or finding of "insanity."

If incompetency and committability are determined by separate procedures, then—unless there is a specific ruling to the contrary— the release from the hospital would neutralize the commitment order but have no effect on the finding of incompetency.   Another court action would be needed to find the patient competent and discharge the guardian.

If, in fact, the patient did conduct business while in the hospital— did make a will, sign legal papers, etc., then his release from the hospital would not disturb those rights.   There is, however, one caution to be observed under these circumstances: a business negotiation conducted by the patient while he was in the hospital, might (on the patient's initiative, generally) be set aside on the grounds that he did not know what he was doing.   If this happens, the patient's *subsequent* release from the hospital would not serve to re-obligate him, unless he ratified it later.

Another determinant in many states is the nature of the patient's release from the hospital.   Courts generally distinguish between a trial-visit (also called furlough, leave-of-absence, or parole) and a discharge.   The latter carries with it an implication of recovered sanity.   In some states, if the hospital authorities make an affirmative declaration that the patient has recovered his reason, this will restore his civil rights.   In other states, this declaration is evidence, but it must be presented to a court or commission before it can be operative. In still other jurisdictions, the *fact* of absolute discharge from the hospital (as distinguished from parole or trial visit) is sufficient to erase any prior determination of "insanity."   On the other hand, trial visit, parole, leave-of-absence, or furlough from the hospital never automatically restores the status quo except in states which have a time limit.   In some areas, the law says that after a certain period (usually a year) of supervision at home the patient is presumably restored to reason unless the hospital found it necessary to have him return in the interim.

One of the simplest tests is to find out whether the patient could be obliged to return to the hospital against his will without commitment papers. If so, then obviously his status is still that of a psychotic patient. If, on the other hand, it would take a new commitment procedure to compel the patient to return to the hospital, then (until that new commitment is accomplished) he must be considered sane. The power of release, parole, and discharge usually vests in the superintendent, staff, hospital board, or in some central state agency. This authority seldom extends, however, to patients who had been convicted of crime and were committed following conviction; nor to persons who were indicted for crime, but never tried because of mental disease. In these cases, the recovery from the psychosis returns the patient to the prosecutor, prison or court.

The Psychotic's Liability for Suit

A psychotic person is responsible (or his estate or guardian is) for damages to an innocent party, even though he might not be responsible for any crime involved. In legal language, he might not be responsible for a crime, yet could still be accountable for a tort. For instance, if a psychotic person at large assaults an innocent bystander, the estate of the patient could be required to pay the medical and hospital bills of the victim, as well as compensation for lost income during his period of incapacity.[21] This is based on the legal theory that there is less injustice in requiring the patient's family to pay for the damages than in requiring the innocent victim to meet his own bill. The same rule, incidentally, would apply to a child. If a

[21] In an eastern city, a few years ago, a settlement was reached in an action taken by the parents of a slain boy against the parents of the murderer. It seems that an 18-year-old (described as "a psychiatric problem") had killed a 12-year-old boy. The parents of the victim started a civil suit for damages—they set the amount as $35,000—against the parents of the assailant. The theory of their claim was that the parents knew their son was a "psychiatric problem" and failed to supervise him, thus permitting an opportunity for the slaying. The general question of the accountability of mentally disturbed persons is discussed in Chapter 1 of this book. The essential feature in this case was not the criminal responsibility of the slayer, but rather his civil (financial) accountability or that of his guardians, for damages caused by his mental disturbance. This case was settled out of court, presumably because the defendants' own lawyers advised that if they contested the case they would lose it. Lawyers generally agree that parents and guardians *are* civilly liable for money damages if it can be shown that they were remiss in not confining a dangerous psychotic. Of course the guardian's actual negligence must be proved in each case.

toddler breaks a neighbor's window, the parents of the child are legally liable for the cost of repair, even though there is certainly no implication of criminal responsibility with respect to the child. The parents have a duty to take care that their children do not damage the property of others, and if they are remiss in that duty they have to pay for it. Similarly the guardian (or hospital) has a duty to keep the mentally disturbed patient from causing damage, and is accountable if, by reason of negligence, damage *is* committed.

Another example : a psychotic patient is the owner of a store which is being managed by his family during his incapacity. An overhanging sign falls down and injures a casual bypasser. Here too, it would be unjust to deny the victim the right to sue the store—this, in effect, means to sue the incompetent patient.

In some torts, malice or intent is an inherent element. In these cases, the patient might be immune to suit if the court felt that his mental capacity robbed him of ability to form a knowing intent. If, for example, a psychotic person abusively calls another names, it is unlikely that the victim can maintain a suit for slander. Or, if such a suit is successful, the damages would be considerably lessened [22] by reason of the reduction of the elements of willfulness, malice or intent.

In certain suits, juries are permitted to bring in judgments for amounts in excess of the actual damage suffered. These excess amounts are considered as "exemplary" or "smart-money" or "punitive" damages. The theory is that they discourage others from committing like torts as well as compensate the victim of this one tort. Exemplary (or punitive) damages will not usually be awarded against a psychotic defendant [23] though he would still be liable for simple compensatory damages.

As an example of the legal reasoning involved, consider a case where, acting on a delusion, a psychotic person sets fire to a building. The insurance company reimbursed the owner of the building and then sued the estate of the patient. While the patient was not triable for arson (because of his mental illness), his estate was obliged to reimburse the insurance company.[24]

Whether a psychotic person can perpetrate a fraud depends on the specific facts. In the ordinary definition of "fraud" there is an implication of *willful* misrepresentation, and a judge or jury might find that the psychosis made him incapable of willful intent to misrepre-

[22] Yeates v. Reed, 4 Indiana 463.
[23] Jewell v. Colby, 66 New Hampshire 399; Ullrich v. New York Press, 23 Miscellaneous Reports (New York) 168; and other cases.
[24] Mutual Fire Insurance Company v. Showalter, 3 Pennsylvania Sup. 452.

sent. Certainly this would be true where the misrepresentation was part of his delusion.[25]

On the other hand, there is a species of fraud in which the intent of the defendant makes no difference. If in fact there was a misrepresentation on which the plaintiff relied to his disadvantage, a fraud action will hold, even in the absence of any intent. The distinction between the two types of fraud is highly technical, and the interested reader should consult his own attorney for further explanation. Certainly psychotic persons *have* been held civilly accountable for damages arising out of fraud.[26]

Guardianship

Procedure.—If a person is declared incompetent, a guardian will be appointed to administer his estate. In some jurisdictions the designation "conservator," "committee," or "curator" is used instead of the word "guardian." Most guardianship proceedings concern psychotic or mentally defective patients, but in some jurisdictions a guardian may be appointed for a chronic alcoholic, an apoplectic, an epileptic, or a deaf mute. Anyone who has an interest in preserving the estate can petition for the appointment of a guardian. If the owner of a business is dissipating the assets, thus jeopardizing the employment of his workers, the latter can ask the court to name a guardian. So can a creditor who sees the collection of his debt being threatened by the squandering of a psychotic debtor. If a patient in a state hospital has assets, but is mentally incapable of signing the checks needed to reimburse the hospital, the state can petition for the naming of a guardian. Later it will submit its bill to the guardian. Generally however, close relatives are the ones who initiate the proceeding. In some jurisdictions a guardian may be appointed even though there has been no prior adjudication of incompetency, so that the single legal procedure serves the double purpose of (*a*) declaring the patient incompetent and (*b*) naming the guardian. In other states, two procedures are needed—first, a judicial determination of incompetence, and later the designation of a guardian. There are also states [27] where the fact of commitment automatically adjudges the patient as incompetent. Where this is true, the naming of a guardian then becomes an administrative rather than a judicial proceeding. In most states, however, the record of commitment (while it has some bearing on subsequent incompetency proceedings) means

---

[25] For discussion of fraud as basis for annulment of marriage, see page 79.
[26] Spaulding v. Harvey, 129 Indiana 106.
[27] See footnote 8, this chapter.

only that the patient needs hospital care, and does not by itself prove the need of a guardian. A separate and additional proceeding would then be required for the naming of a guardian.

Selection of Guardian.—The court will decide whether the interests of the patient are best served by naming a friend, relative, strange individual or corporation as the guardian. The psychiatrist may be asked his opinion, and in most cases he would have to say that it makes no difference. If the psychiatrist recommends that a relative be named, the other members of the family may consider him "retained" by that relative, with subsequent strain on the doctor's relationships with the rest of the family. If, to avoid this, the doctor recommends that a strange person or a corporation be named as guardian, the entire family may resent it as an implication of the doctor's lack of confidence. Hence, the experienced psychiatrist makes no recommendation as to the identity of the guardian. A corporation (often a trust company or the trust officer of a bank) makes a good guardian in certain respects. It remains aloof from intrafamily quarrels, invests the assets conservatively, resists all efforts to raid the estate, and takes whatever action is needed on rational grounds without being much disturbed by sentimental factors. For example, a psychotic at large may get into difficulties which suggest the need for commitment. Where the wife or father is the guardian there is often a refusal to apply for commitment. ("I just can't do that to my own brother.") A bank trust officer, on the other hand, is more likely to petition for commitment when it is obviously needed without being deterred by this sentimental objection.

On the other hand, there are advantages in naming a close relative as the guardian. For one thing, the guardian's fee is thus saved (or in effect, returned to the estate). Then too, emergency action is quicker, because the home is always "open" whereas a bank or trust company may operate on a forty-hour week and be unavailable in emergencies. There is also less of a stigma to the patient, in obtaining funds from his own family; and a greater flexibility in disbursing the funds.

An incompetent patient had an obscene tattoo on his forearm. He wanted to have it removed because in the summer time he could not wear short sleeved shirts without exposing the tattoo. He felt very conspicuous walking down the street with this design visible. (When he said that people looked at him in an odd way, *that* was no delusion.) The dermatologist, knowing that the patient had several thousand dollars in his estate, was unwilling to remove the tattoo without charge, and stated that his regular fee was $65. The family and the patient considered the procedure necessary and the fee reasonable. However, the trust officer of the bank refused to release the $65 holding that it was a "lot of foolishness . . . just a matter of vanity . . . let him wear long-sleeved shirts or stay home during the summer . . ."

In a situation like this, a relative would have been a more understanding guardian than the corporation. Yet many relatives are unwilling to serve as guardians because they fear that other members of the family will suspect that they are tapping the estate for personal gain.

Jurisdiction of Guardian.—The papers naming a guardian usually indicate whether his jurisdiction is limited to property or also includes guardianship over the person. Sometimes separate curators are named for these two functions. A guardian of the property has general power-of-attorney, conducts the day-by-day routine of the estate, makes contracts, and buys and sells on behalf of the patient, or advances him small sums with which he can make his own personal purchases. A guardian of the person has the power to request commitment to a hospital, or release from a hospital, or to encumber the funds of the estate for medical or hospital care. However, a guardian cannot have a patient placed in a locked ward (beyond the brief, law-allowed emergency period) without a formal commitment process.

The guardian is an agent of the court. He is answerable to the court for the judicious use of the patient's funds. He therefore does not engage in major financial transactions or make very large expenditures without prior court approval. He does not ask for or need a judge's order every time he advances the patient a dollar for a haircut. But if he finds it necessary to mortgage the property in order to get money enough to maintain the patient, he will certainly seek court approval before signing the mortgage papers.

A psychiatrist who deals with an incompetent patient should know the name of the guardian of the person and obtain his written approval before doing shock therapy, lumbar punctures, or any other procedures which might impair body integrity. He sends his bills to the guardian. In an emergency he can render medical care without approval and still collect his bill. But before embarking on an expensive elective treatment program, he obtains the consent of the guardian.

Competency as a Witness

The psychiatric appraisal of the witness represents a new field of forensic psychiatry. The psychiatrist has long been recognized as one who had something to contribute towards an understanding of the *defendant* in a criminal case and of the *claimant* in a personal injury action. The idea of examining witnesses is something new. The field for this type of appraisal is illustrated by the following hypothetical situations:

a) An obviously hysterical girl charges that a man has raped her. She gives much circumstantial detail, some of it sounding fantastic, and identifies her assailant. Is this witness to be believed? Is she, by temperament, inclined to confuse fact with fantasy? Here the defendant's life may turn on the psychiatric appraisal of the complaining witness.

b) A company is charged with income tax fraud. A disgruntled ex-employee is the principal witness. He has been discharged for dishonesty. Are we dealing here with a psychopath, whose testimony would be of doubtful accuracy?

c) Two years after an automobile accident, a case comes to court. One witness is a rambling, senile man. Is his memory clear enough to place much reliance on what he says today about events of two years ago?

Oral testimony is usually the major factor in a court room judgment. Considering this, it is extraordinary that so little effort is made to evaluate the trustworthiness of the witness and his testimony. To give effective testimony, a witness must (1) observe the event intelligently, (2) remember it clearly, (3) be free of any emotional drive to suppress or distort the truth, and (4) be articulate enough to describe it vividly. Obviously, the psychiatrist would be valuable in the administration of justice if he were allowed to measure the witness's competency with respect to these four elements. Thus he might say that a witness was too distracted or too sluggish mentally to have observed details accurately; or that a witness has a senile psychosis which notoriously plays tricks on the memory; or that a witness is a psychopath, inclined to seize popular attention by spinning fantastic yarns; or that a witness has a form of hysteria in which she is highly suggestible and inclined to adopt as the truth whatever someone last told her.

To see why the psychiatrist cannot simply walk into the court room, examine the witness and give his opinion, it is necessary to understand something of the legal framework of "testimonial capacity." ("Testimonial capacity" is competency to be a witness. Unfortunately the phrase sounds much like "testamentary capacity" which means competency to make a will. Because the two phrases are so readily confused, it may be better to use the longer form— "competency to testify.")

As a general rule, a witness is presumed to be competent to testify. If an attorney thinks that a witness is mentally or emotionally incapable of giving useful testimony, the attorney has to prove it. In some states, the fact that a witness was once convicted of a crime may automatically exclude his testimony. Where this rule holds, it is based on a presumption of perjury, not on a presumption of mental or emotional inability to testify. In any event, it does not apply to most emotionally or intellectually incompetent witnesses, because they do not have criminal records.

A hostile attorney may, perhaps, be certain that a witness is incompetent. The testimony may be the result of hysteria, psychopathy, confabulations, mental defect, or amnesia. And a psychiatrist may agree. But if the witness does not voluntarily submit to a psychiatric examination, how can this incompetency be brought to the attention of the court? There is no lawful way in which a witness can be compelled to submit to psychiatric examination. Some judges will not allow a case to proceed if the complaining witness (or in a personal injury action, the claimant) refuses to submit to examination. But this is largely discretionary with the court, except when the nature of the psychiatric disorder is an inherent part of the case. In any event, this does not apply to collateral witnesses. If the witness will not submit to psychiatric examination, the only other way the attorney can bring out the incompetency is to have the psychiatrist sit in the court room and make a diagnosis based either on (*a*) the witness's overt behavior and speech, or (*b*) his answers to questions raised on cross-examination. It has been said that if the psychiatrist sat at the counsel table and told the attorney what questions to ask, the net effect would be the same as if the witness had submitted to a psychiatric interview in the doctor's office. Hoffinger [28] suggests that: "The psychiatrist may direct the cross-examination, thereby approximating a personal interview with the witness." In a desperate situation where injustice would otherwise be done, this would probably be a necessary procedure. However, other physicians frown on a doctor's sitting at counsel table, directing cross-examination; and the public cannot understand how a psychiatrist can make a diagnosis without having "examined" the patient. Actually the procedure is perfectly defensible. Jurors are always making judgments about a witness's credibility and mental state from observing the quality and nature of his answers. A psychiatrist should be able to do this even better. However, because of the ethical and public rela-

---

[28] John S. Hoffinger, *Yale Law Journal,* LIX (June, 1950), 1334.

tions aspects of the process, most psychiatrists are unwilling to offer
an opinion based only on court room cross-examination.

Even if the psychiatrist is willing to make a diagnosis under these
circumstances, there are other hurdles. The court may not allow the
line of questioning necessary for a psychiatric opinion. Suppose, for
example, a senile witness testifies about an event he saw two years
ago. "I saw the Buick swerve to the right. Then the mail truck
came up from the left and a little boy wearing a yellow coat ran
across the street." The defense attorney believes that the witness
cannot possibly remember those details, and to lay a groundwork
for his psychiatrist's opinion, he tries to ask questions dealing with
the witness's memory. The doctor whispers to him: "Ask him
what he had for breakfast this morning." This is a perfectly sensible
question, since loss of memory for recent events is common in senile
psychoses. But if, in this case, the attorney does ask: "Mr. Jones,
what did you have for breakfast this morning?" the chances are that
the query will be excluded as hopelessly irrelevant to the question of
who was at fault in an automobile accident two years ago. Some
judges might on explanation, admit the question as designed to test
the witness's memory. Other judges would refuse. Even if the
question were admitted, it seems certain that collateral questions
aimed at revealing delusions would be excluded. Thus, delusions of
marital infidelity and of filial ingratitude are common in senile dementia. But only the rarest of judges would allow questions on these
points to be directed at a witness who was not a party to the action.

Courts are more familiar with certain areas of psychopathy than
with others. Thus, most judges know that accusers in sex cases are
often hysterical; and that there is such a phenomenon as a litiginous
form of paranoia. Hence, most courts will allow a searching personal
cross-examination in those two situations: where the complaining
witness alleges a sexual crime; or where the plaintiff has a long
record of repeated litigation. In the latter situation, some courts
seem to think that the purpose of bringing out the previous litigation
is to suggest fraud—that is, a sort "business" of collecting damages.
From the psychiatrist's viewpoint the purpose is to show a character
trait—a paranoid drive towards litiginousness. A similar confusion
attends efforts to bring out evidence of previous lies. Courts allow
it on the assumption that it might show previous dishonesty or misconduct; actually the purpose is to reveal a pattern of behavior suggesting, perhaps, the psychopathy of pathologic lying.

The interests of justice would, of course, be best served if a witness could be expected to submit to a psychiatric examination before

any challenged testimony of his could be heard. Hoffinger,[29] who is a lawyer, not a doctor, recommends:

If the witness refuses to submit to the examination, the court could stay the proceedings or dismiss the case or it could bar him from testifying. The only serious objection to compulsory clinical examination is that a witness should not be forced to reveal the intimate details of his life. But here the right to privacy is outweighed by the need for getting at the truth, especially if the fate of an innocent defendant hangs in the balance. And if the witness is normal, his privacy will remain intact, since nobody but the psychiatrist will have heard his life history. Moreover, a witness' privacy is always jeopardized as soon as he takes the stand.

Without the benefit of psychiatric assistance, a jury *may* make the proper evaluation of an abnormal witness' credibility. But its decision is, at best, an intuitive guess. Good luck alone can make it correct. Aided by expert analysis, the jury can make, at least, an informed guess with greater chances for success. Psychiatric diagnosis should be admitted whenever it is offered, whether based on clinical examination or courtroom observation alone.

Clinical Conditions Affecting Testimonial Capacity

Psychoses at one time rendered a witness automatically incompetent to testify. This is no longer true. If the witness is admittedly psychotic, his capacity to testify becomes a separate issue to be determined by the judge when the question is raised. And it must be raised early in the trial. The hostile attorney cannot, at the conclusion of the case, offer proof of the witness's mental disorder, unless he has earlier raised an objection on that ground.[30]

The judge reaches his decision on the basis of his own observation of the witness's demeanor, his own questioning, and—if he desires—on the advice of psychiatrists who have been given an opportunity to question the witness. In practice, the judge usually bases his decision on the witness's understanding of the specific subject matter of his testimony. If delusions do not appear to touch on that, most jurists will accept the witness. The testimony is further filtered by the jury, which has its own opinion as to the credibility of the witness and the weight of his testimony. Unfortunately the jurist or juror is more concerned with such obvious abnormalities as hallucinations or delusions than with the subtler matters of motivation or memory impairment.

The following clinical conditions will be considered:

[29] *Ibid.*, pp. 1340-41.
[30] State v. Teager, 269 Northwestern Reporter 348; also People v. Enright, 256 Illinois 221; and standard legal texts on Evidence.

1. Schizophrenia
2. Senile psychoses
3. Manic states
4. Paranoid states
5. Drug addiction
6. Mental deficiency
7. Alcoholism
8. Psychoneurosis
9. Psychopathic personality

Schizophrenia.—The schizophrenic haunts the frontier between reality and fantasy. His testimony, therefore, is always suspect. This is particularly bothersome when a hearing or trial concerns activities in the wards of mental hospitals. (Example: Trial of an attendant for alleged cruelty to a patient. Many of the witnesses will be schizophrenics. Where does fantasy end and the recital of truth begin?)

Sometimes a schizophrenic will report an event with carbon-paper fidelity. But not often. Schizophrenics have fallible memories, defective observation, mysterious motivations, and frequent paranoid ideas. Furthermore, even if the schizophrenic registered events faithfully, he would often show difficulty in reproducing them in words.

Sullivan [31] correctly points out:

> The schizophrenic uses speech exclusively for counteracting his feeling of insecurity. . . . The schizophrenic's speech shows characteristic peculiarities because of severe disturbances in his relationships with other people. The result is a confusion of the critical faculties concerning the structure of spoken and written language. Some of these peculiarities may be described as regressively related to the speech of very young children.

Certainly one would not feel comfortable at convicting any defendant on the basis of the unsupported testimony of an active schizophrenic.

Senile Psychoses.—The testimony of a senile dement must be weighed against three well-established characteristics: impairment of memory, delusions of ingratitude, and delusions of infidelity. Not all senile psychotics show all three features, of course. But once a diagnosis of senile dementia is confirmed, the cautious psychiatrist

[31] Harry Stack Sullivan, in J. S. Kasanin (ed.), *Language and Thought in Schizophrenia* (Los Angeles: University of California Press, 1944), p. 15.

looks particularly for those traits because of their effect on the credibility of the senile witness.

Manic States.—While the dynamics are different, the manic's testimony often approximates that of the glib psychopath. Pronounced grandiose delusions are usually obvious enough to be self-discrediting. The less acutely disturbed manic may make a plausible but misleading witness. His overconfidence makes him more positive on the witness stand than the facts warrant. His radiant euphoria often makes him a sort of juristic pet, who is challenged only at the peril of the cross-examiner. A frontal attack on the competency of an intelligent, well-preserved manic is almost certainly doomed to fail. In the short run, he can best the attorney at the question-and-answer game. Skilful advocates find it tactically better to let the witness talk on. The manic is more likely to expose his own psychosis, given time enough, than he is to allow himself to be trapped into such exposure by a hostile attorney.

Paranoid States.—The witness suffering from a paranoid state often makes good sense. Even when the delusion system is apparent, judges and jurors are likely to accept testimony that does not seem to impinge on the delusional network. The psychiatrist knows that a delusional system is not watertight, that it reflects a serious disorganization of thinking, and that spurious reasoning is likely to contaminate *all* of the patient's thought processes. The nonpsychiatrist does not know this. If the witness, for example, has an obviously psychotic delusion about politics, his testimony about a taxicab accident is often accepted in good faith. The psychiatrist realizes, however, that a delusion of psychotic intensity is likely to color all of the patient's thinking. Whether the psychiatrist can teach this to judges and jurymen is another question.

Drug Addiction.—There is an impressive amount of law concerning the credibility of drug addicts. Singer and Krohn [32] tell us that "in some courts, the view prevails that the habitual use of a drug or narcotic . . . may be shown for the purpose of affecting the credibility of a witness or the weight of his testimony." In one famous case,[33] the court said: "Habitual users of opium or other narcotics become notorious liars." In another case,[34] the court accepted a practitioner's opinion that "dope addicts are not to be believed." A

[32] H. D. Singer and W. O. Krohn, *Insanity and the Law* (Philadelphia: P. Blakiston's Son & Co., Inc., 1924), p. 347.
[33] State v. Fong Loon, 158 Pacific 233.
[34] Effinger v. Effinger, 239 Pacific Reporter 801.

western court [35] pointed out: "While the testimony of an opium user is competent, juries should be cautioned as to the credence to be given to it." The drug habit has been considered "evidence of moral degeneracy" [36] and, presumably, indicative of lack of honesty, by more than one court. [37]

Obviously, then, the attorney who depends on a witness who is an addict is going to hear a great many objections from his opponent. The decisions are not entirely one-sided, however. There *are* judges who refuse to categorize drug addiction as an automatically disqualifying trait. These courts impose on the objecting attorney the burden of proving that, in this case, and for this particular witness, the addiction did, in fact, impair memory or character. [38] Sound psychiatric opinion would probably support this view. Thus, Pescor [39] finds that, under certain circumstances, a drug addict "can live the life of a respectable, honored citizen." And this, in general, is standard psychiatric doctrine; subject to the proviso that some authorities believe that a "normal" man would never become an addict, and that therefore—as Vogel [40] puts it: "Most narcotic addicts are primarily psychoneurotic or psychopathic; very few are psychotic." This view is not universally accepted, since it could be equally well argued that, under adequate pressure of circumstances, anyone might become a drug addict. So far as testimonial capacity is concerned, the question is surely whether, at the time the events were seen and at the time the witness is testifying, his addiction specifically impaired his ability to observe, to remember or to report. And that has to be determined for each witness individually, and not by any broad assumption that all addicts are automatically defective in observation, memory, honesty, or articulation.

Mental Deficiency.—In daily life, mental defectives are often engaged in humble or menial work, forming an almost invisible background to the activities of others. Their scarcely noticed ubiquitousness results in their being witnesses to all sorts of incidents; and, as a result, to frequent calls for their testimony. Ordinarily there is

[35] State v. White, 10 Washington 611.

[36] Beland v. State, 217 Southwestern Reporter 147.

[37] State v. Prentice, 183 Northwestern Reporter 411. The subject has been reviewed by M. Rossman, *Oregon Law Review,* III (1924), 81, and editorially in the *Southern California Law Review,* XVI (1943), 333.

[38] For example: Katleman v. State, 175 Northwestern Reporter 671; Kelly v. Maryland, 45 Federal Second 782; State v. Gleim, 17 Montana 17.

[39] Michael Pescor, in V. C. Branham and S. B. Kutash (eds.), *Encyclopedia of Criminology* (New York: Philosophical Library, 1949), p. 132.

[40] Victor Vogel, in H. H. Kessler (ed.) *The Principles of Rehabilitation* (Philadelphia: Lea & Febiger, 1950), p. 280.

no mechanism for submitting a witness to an intelligence test. An attorney might object to the testimony if he knew in advance that the witness was defective; or if this became apparent from the first few answers. If he fails to make timely objection, it is unlikely that he could *subsequently* challenge the testimony, since his failure to object would be construed as waiving that right—that is, as "accepting" the witness's competency.[41]

There are two other ways of approaching this: (*a*) to bring out by cross-examination that the witness did not really understand what he testified about; or (*b*) to obtain evidences of mental deficiency from other sources and confront the court with that. For example:

a) A witness has signed, and on the stand is confirming, an affidavit describing details of an accident. The affidavit contains such words as "deponent", "acceleration", "sutures", et cetera. On cross-examination, the witness is asked how far he advanced in school. Fourth grade at age 16, he tells the lawyer. He is asked what the word "deponent" means; or what he meant when he signed his name to a statement referring to "the increasing acceleration of the vehicle." He indicates that he has no idea of what these phrases mean—an admission which is consistent with his meager education. The incompetence of that part of the testimony is thus made apparent.

b) Almost everyone in America now has an I.Q. figure somewhere on record. Such scores are found in school, Army, or industrial records. An attorney might obtain these reports and use them as bases for reviewing the witness's competence.

There is a common belief that mental defectives are highly suggestible and that therefore their testimony might be clouded by suggestions made by friendly attorneys in pre-trial briefings. The suggestibility of defectives is an assumption based largely on deductive reasoning; it seems logical that a feeble-minded person should be easily persuaded. However, one can recall many mental defectives who are stubborn and not open to persuasion. In a particular case, the defective witness might happen to be very gullible. That, however, is something to be determined by an appraisal of the specific witness; not a conclusion automatically derivable from the fact of mental deficiency.

What makes the defective a doubtful witness is (1) his poverty of observation, and (2) his awkwardness in explaining what he does know. Occasionally his simplicity is an asset. Where the event is

41 See footnote 30, this chapter.

one that can be described accurately in a few broad strokes, the defective witness may be a jewel because he is not likely to inject much interpretation; nor does he have any particular tendency to embroider the details. Unfortunately, however, most events are complex, made up of many subtle details. And here the defective's poor observing powers are liabilities. And his inability to paint the verbal picture with any vividness may also prove exasperating to the examining attorney.

Alcoholism.—In appraising the testimonial capacity of an alcoholic, it is advisable to determine which of the following terms applies:

a) The witness was obviously drunk at the time of the event.

b) The witness's sobriety at the time cannot be determined, but his general history and the particular circumstances make it likely that he was drunk.

c) The witness is a periodic drinker.

d) The witness is a "chronic alcoholic" but not deteriorated.

e) The witness is a deteriorated chronic alcoholic.

f) The witness had been drinking prior to the event, and has had previous episodes of pathologic intoxication.

g) The witness has, and presumably then had, an alcoholic psychosis.

In situations (*a*) and (*e*) the witness's evidence is obviously unreliable. In situation (*b*) the psychiatrist would have to report that there is a strong presumption that the witness was drunk,[42] and that therefore neither his observational acuity nor his memory is to be considered dependable. In situation (*c*) the expert would probably say that a periodic drinker is usually "normal" between orgies; and that if all facts indicate that the event was witnessed during an extended lucid period, the witness would have to be appraised as if he were normal. The nondeteriorated chronic alcoholic (situation *d*) is always an uncertain witness. The fact that he is not manifestly deteriorated gives his words a certain plausibility. Psychiatrists know, however, that a chronic alcoholic is an unreliable observer, that he is often at the mercy of mixed and unpredictable emotions, given to periods of mawkish sentimentality, and emotionally unstable. All of this does not add up to testimonial unreliability in all cases;

---

[42] Hoffinger (see footnote 28, this chapter) cites Kuenster v. Woodhouse, 77 Northwestern 165, as ruling that "a general habit of intemperance during a given month may be admitted (into evidence) to show probable intoxication on a certain day of that month." He adds that "by this technic, alcoholism may sometimes be shown despite the general rule excluding (evidence of) the habit itself."

but it certainly makes one unwilling to base a serious determination on the unconfirmed testimony of the chronic alcoholic.

As a practical matter, courts are loath to receive evidence that a collateral witness is a chronic alcoholic. Yet they usually admit evidence of drug addiction. Hoffinger [43] suggests that "the distinction which courts make between alcohol and drugs may be due to the general acceptability of drinking in our community as opposed to the strong moral opprobrium attached to the taking of drugs." Of course, from the psychiatrist's viewpoint alcohol could be as effective as opium in robbing a man of his competency.

Situation (f) poses a peculiar probative problem. In pathologic intoxication the subject does not usually seem to be drunk; yet he has a sort of alcoholic "fugue" and suffers a more or less complete amnesia after regaining sobriety. There is a definite tendency to fill in the memory gap with fabrications, so that testimony becomes unreliable. The difficulty is in establishing the existence of the pathologic intoxication. About the only practical indicator would be the history of drinking before the event, plus a record of previous episodes of alcoholic amnesia or pathologic intoxication.

When the witness has or has had an alcoholic psychosis (situation g), the psychiatrist must remind the court that confabulation is a characteristic of this disease, and that the testimony of a psychotic alcoholic is always tainted with the possibility of fabrication.

Psychoneurosis.—There is a type of anxiety popularly called "hysteria," which obviously impairs a witness's credibility. Individuals may be driven to make false accusations because of some inner psychic need. Whole populations may be caught up in a sort of hysterical contagion. Orenstein [44] cites cases in which, as he puts it, "the acting out of unconscious drives leads to . . . false accusations resulting at times in erroneous convictions of the innocent." Borchard [45] has studied 65 cases in which innocent persons were convicted. In few was there any deliberate fraud for gain; in most, individual or mass "hysteria" was the motive power behind the spurious charges and false identifications. A larger proportion of hysterically motivated charges concerns alleged sex offenses, especially when the complainant is a child.[46] As I have pointed out else-

[43] *Ibid.*, p. 1336.
[44] Leo Orenstein, *American Journal of Psychiatry*, CVII (March, 1951), 684.
[45] E. M. Borchard, *Convicting the Innocent* (New Haven: Yale University Press, 1932).
[46] Loretta Bender and Aaron Blau, *American Journal of Orthopsychiatry*, VII (January, 1937), 4.

where,[47] "for any unmarried girl, a charge of rape is more face-saving than a confession of cooperative fornication; it is certainly easy to understand why a high proportion of sex complaints are rooted in fantasy. There is a similar psychopathology, however, in other areas of crime, too."

Psychoneurosis by itself will not and should not disqualify a witness. One can expect distortions in obsessional states, memory gaps in amnesic and dissociative reactions, undue suggestibility in hysteria, and some blurring at the reality-fantasy frontier among victims of depression, psychasthenia, and other psychoneuroses. But, in general, personality structure and grasp of reality are rugged enough to make the patient a competent witness, though perhaps an ineffective one.

Of considerable interest in the field of testimonial capacity is the problem of mass psychoneurosis. This is a generally frenzied emotional climate, usually following some socially disorganizing circumstance such as a war, an atrocious series of crimes, a plague, or some other challenge to the community's integrity. Everyone feels threatened, rumors spread rapidly, the atmosphere becomes menacing and the only safety would appear to be in rushing deep into the herd, identifying with the popular sentiment, and, when necessary, joining in the hunt for a scapegoat. This seems to be the chronic climate of police states; and even in free societies, small areas of mass hysteria (areas in time, place or subject matter) can develop if tension is severe enough.

Somewhat related to this is the psychology of rumor, a subject on which Hart [48] has written an illuminating essay. Certainly mass hysteria can furnish the courts with multiple accusers and multiple witnesses, all giving false or distorted testimony for the best of motives.

A vivid description of this mechanism is given by Starkey [49] in her account of the Salem witch hunt of 1692. It began with Betty, whose father found, that when he reproved her,

. . . she remained rigid, worked her mouth and gave off curious hoarse choking sounds. This set off Abigail who . . . began to make babbling and rasping sounds. She got down on all fours and ran under the furniture . . . and sometimes fell into convulsions when she writhed and screamed. . . . As

[47] Henry A. Davidson, *American Journal of Psychiatry*, CVII (March, 1951), 687.
[48] Bernard Hart, *Psychopathology* (New York: The Macmillan Co., 1927), pp. 94-124.
[49] Marion L. Starkey, *The Devil in Massachusetts* (New York: Alfred A. Knopf, Inc., 1950).

the news spread, so did the contagion. Mary Walcott and Susanna Sheldon fell into convulsions . . . and these seizures recurred. Then the affliction spread to the home of the Thomas Putnams where both Ann and Mercy Lewis got it. . . . Nor was even this the end. One girl after another succumbed to the malady. . . . Around each assembled a circle of awed watchers.

The nearest physician was Dr. Griggs of Salem Village . . . this odd epidemic was quite outside his experience. It was not his fault that . . . medicine had not yet struggled out of the apathy of the Middle Ages, that it had forgotten what little the Greeks had learned about hysteria. . . . "The evil hand is on them," he said, the medical vocabulary not having yet been enriched by more soothing shibboleths such as psychoneurosis. . . . A few, very few, distrusted this diagnosis. They were irreverent enough to point out that there was something strikingly apt about the antics of the girls, something very like what many young people would have liked to do if they dared. The girls availed themselves of the opportunity of their illness to rebel against every restriction placed on them by adult society. . . . The girls at this point were having a wonderful time. Their notoriety was infinitely rewarding to childish natures beset by infantile cravings for attention.

On the evidence of these girls, twenty women were hanged by the neck until dead. It is characteristic of epidemics of this sort, that the significant "evidence" produced by the hysterical accusers is the sort of evidence against which there can be no answer. As Starkey puts it:

> The most important principle accepted by the magistrates was . . . the admission of "spectral evidence." Thanks to this arrangement, hallucinations, dreams and mere fancies would be accepted in court, not as proof of the psychological condition of the accuser but as proof of the behavior of the accused. This was, as many good men and women were to discover, the sort of proof against which there is no disproof. Let an accuser say, "Your shape came to my room last night" and the accused has no defense. No alibi can be furnished for the whereabouts of one's airy substance. People accused under such evidence were to have only one recourse.

The recourse mentioned was "confession." Self-condemnation in such circumstances is a spurious confession. However, it takes the pressure off the accused; more than that, such confessions may line up the accused with the accusers, that is, with the forces of righteousness. To reinforce their new respectability, the confessors in such situations will name former confederates, some as false as the fantasies of the original accusers. There is, of course, much more to the psychopathology of false confession than this. Thus, Redlich and his co-workers,[50] after an experimental study, concluded that:

[50] F. C. Redlich, L. J. Ravitz and G. H. Dession, *American Journal of Psychiatry,* CVII (February, 1951), 586.

" . . . many of the striking confessions in public trials of police states were obtained from severely neurotic, guilt-ridden and self-punitive persons. Even the less disturbed person with a guilt-producing fantasy will confess if his functions of self-preservation are weakened by prolonged, grueling and humiliating interrogation." A similar mechanism is fictionally explored in Orwell's novel, *Nineteen-Eighty-Four*.[51]

The phenomenon of mass hysteria is of considerable importance to forensic psychiatry. The atmosphere effectively poisons individual objectivity to the point where creditable testimony is hard to get. The psychiatrist could make a significant contribution by pointing out the neurotic wellsprings behind the fantastic testimony given. But amid the tumult the psychiatrist's voice will not be heard unless it is singularly clear, convincing, and courageous.

Psychopathic Personality.—The psychopath is an unreliable witness. In spite of this, his testimony is often accepted at face value. This is so because of:

a) Confusion about terminology.
b) The witness's plausibility, intelligence, and "charm."
c) Difficulty in assembling information needed to make a diagnosis.
d) Lay difficulty in grasping the concept of nonpsychotic psychopathy.
e) The peculiar motivation of the psychopath.

a) The general phrase "psychopathic personality" is used in three different senses. In this book we mean what psychiatrists generally mean—that the psychopath is a sane person of adequate intelligence who is, by ordinary standards, rebellious, dishonest, or nonconformist, who gets into trouble because of this character trait. However, the term is also used as synonymous with pathologic personality—a much broader concept, which embraces the entire field of character disorder. For example, one widely used nomenclature [52] lists eleven diagnoses under the general heading of "Character and Behavior Disorders," and only one of these ("antisocial personality") corresponds with the traditional concept of the

---

[51] George Orwell, *Nineteen-Eighty-Four* (New York: Harcourt, Brace & Co., Inc., 1950).

[52] The nomenclature used by the Veterans Administration from 1947 to 1952. The VA now uses the American Psychiatric Association nomenclature which recognizes 17 diagnoses under *Personality Disorders* including both "antisocial reaction" and "dyssocial reaction." See Statistical Manual of the American Psychiatric Association (Washington, D.C., 1952), p. 38.

"psychopath." Finally, there is the lay concept that a psychopath is someone who belongs in a psychopathic ward. Since psychiatrists are unable to agree on the meaning, the judicial authorities are understandably reluctant to adopt a general rule about the competency of psychopaths.

b) Not all psychopaths are intelligent and charming. But a great many of them are, and these are precisely the ones who can do the most mischief on the witness stand. If the witness has made an apparent success of any segment of his life, the expert will find it hard to label him a psychopath. "How could a psychopath have achieved this status—or this success?" is the question that will be hurled at the psychiatrist, or, more often, silently asked by the judge or juror. Rejecting the psychiatrist's opinion as contrary to common sense, the jurist or jury will then believe whatever the self-possessed, obviously intelligent witness says. The psychiatrist knows that a transitory success, or the appearance of it, is not uncommon in psychopaths. But he will seldom have the opportunity of explaining that to the court.

c) To make a diagnosis of psychopathic personality requires the assembly of a large amount of historical data about the patient. It is not, ordinarily, essential to accomplish a formal personal psychiatric examination—though certainly such an examination would be helpful. But since the diagnosis reflects a life-long pattern, its major determinant is the life history—the story of how, in fact, the subject did get along in and with society. In the absence of reliable psychologic tests (and there are none), this historical analysis of the patient's life is still the keystone of the diagnosis. But in the judicial arena this poses a serious tactical problem. How is the psychiatrist going to get the information; and getting it, how can he persuade the court to accept it? The attorney might, through private investigation, collect enough information to make it obvious that the witness is a psychopath. What then? If the psychiatrist takes the witness stand and gives this diagnosis, he will be asked on what he based his opinion. If he based it on information not in the record, on the assembly of unverifiable facts, not sworn to or officially documented, the conclusion becomes legally worthless. If he bases his conclusion on what the witness actually said in the court room, he will have hard sledding for two reasons: first, because he is, in effect, making a diagnosis without going through the motions of an "examination"; and second, because each item of the material will be subject to ruthless cross-examination on this pattern:

Q: On what do you base the diagnosis, doctor?

A: On the fact that, throughout his whole life, this witness has shown inability to get along in groups, nonconformity, failure to follow-through on any of his plans, and inability to learn from experience.

Q: Well, let's analyze these items. You say "inability to get along in groups." With what groups did the witness fail to get along?

A: First, in high school he could not remain on the football squad and was expelled for getting drunk; second, in the Army, where—

Q: Just a minute, doctor, just because a man got drunk when he was a teen-ager, you brand him as a psychopath! Is that what psychiatry means? One little adolescent indiscretion and you belong in a psychopathic ward! And as for the Army, well, doctor, isn't it a fact that thousands of American citizens had difficulty in adjusting to the regimented life of the Army? Isn't rebellion against that unnatural life really a normal American reaction? Then you spoke of nonconformity. Well, doctor, haven't the greatest contributions to human progress been made by nonconformists?

A: Well, it wasn't nonconformity as such; it was the way he failed to conform.

Q: Oh, then you didn't mean it when you said nonconformity was one of the elements of a diagnosis here. All right, we'll strike that out. How about the next trait . . .

d) The entire concept is difficult to grasp. The word "psychopathy" irresistibly (to the lay mind) suggests psychosis. It implies, to the layman, some queerness of thinking incompatible with intelligence. Since the most unreliable witness is the *intelligent* psychopath, this makes the concept peculiarly difficult to grasp; and the judge will not allow the expert time for a long lecture on the dynamics of psychopathy.

e) A witness who has a personal interest in the outcome of a case might tell a lie—might indeed fabricate a complete story. To the average juror, such conduct is entirely understandable. What the judge and juryman cannot understand, however, is that a witness might spin an elaborate falsehood even though he personally has nothing to gain by the conviction of the defendant or by a judgment for a claimant or for an insurance company. This type of perjury is, of course, psychopathic lying. Sometimes the motivation is fairly obvious to the psychiatrist if not to the layman. Thus, a witness might offer himself for testimony because he enjoys being in the limelight, or because this gives him a way of expressing or symbolizing hostility. Such motivation is not uncommon in psychopaths.

The judge who prides himself on his common sense, the juror who is honest and simple, cannot understand the power of malice. The malevolence which drives a psychopath into a testimonial network of lies is quite beyond the understanding of the psychiatrically unlearned juryman. Often such testimony tends to degrade the witness himself, and then it becomes utterly incomprehensible. "Why would a man manufacture a story that incriminates himself? It must be true." This is the typical reaction of the layman. The strange masochistic component in the psychopath's make-up is beyond the experience of most jurors and seems strange even to a sophisticated judge.

In summary, then, the psychopath is an unreliable witness, but, for the five reasons above indicated, his testimony may be completely accepted by a naïve court. What makes him unreliable is his fondness for psychopathic lying, his use of the witness stand as a vehicle of aggression and hostility, his frequent skill in making a good impression on inexperienced auditors, and his willingness to wreak mischief even at the cost of degrading himself. Hoffinger [53] properly warns us that:

In spite of his disordered personality, the psychopath . . . may appear normal, mild-mannered, and intelligent. His lies are usually told with more conviction than those of normal people. If his lying is exposed, he is capable of quick adjustment, thereby thoroughly misleading the layman. The psychiatrist, however, can separate the pathological liar from the "normal" liar by correlating the psychopath's maladaptive behavior into a diagnostic life pattern.

[53] Hoffinger, *op. cit.,* p. 1330.

Chapter 14

MALPRACTICE AND THE PSYCHIATRIST [1]

Certain malpractice hazards are peculiar to psychiatry. Many psychiatric patients are inherently litiginous. Some patients confuse fact with fantasy, and fantasy often leads to charges of odd behavior. The psychiatrist sometimes takes action which results in a person's losing his driver's license, or his right to dispose of his property, or· even his freedom. Explanations of psychiatric diagnoses to members of the family may possibly lead to charges of slander. The legal problem of consent to a procedure is more complicated in psychiatry than in the surgical specialties, and spinal taps, induced convulsions or shock therapy may be malpractice traps.

The cautious psychiatrist is familiar with the rudiments of the law of malpractice. He also has malpractice insurance. In this chapter the basic elements of malpractice as it applies to psychiatrists are reviewed and exemplified. This will be of interest to the practitioner, and it should also have some prophylactic value. However, neither this, nor any other text, will furnish the answers if the doctor is actually named in a malpractice action. In such a situation he will need a lawyer, not a book.

Following are sixteen fairly common situations—situations with which any psychiatrist can identify. They exemplify the nature of malpractice and the responsibilities of the physician under such circumstances.

A didactic summary of the problem follows each example.

Situations Illustrating Malpractice Problems

SITUATION 1. A resident physician, on the full-time staff of a state hospital, induces electric shock. The patient dies. Since the psychiatrist here is an employee of, and presumably an agent of, the state, can the family of the deceased sue the doctor if they believe his negligence was the cause of the death? Or must they file suit against the state? And

[1] Leslie S. Kohn, LL.B., member of the New Jersey Bar, assisted in the preparation of this chapter.

if they do sue the physician, how far is the state likely to go in defending its employee in court?

Comment: The family can sue the doctor individually.[2] When a person is injured in a bus accident, he can sue the bus driver, the bus company or both. Normally, he files against the company because the company has more money than the driver. However, in malpractice actions it is more common to sue the doctor than the employer. The state will probably furnish defense counsel for the doctor, and may finance an appeal if necessary, and will assemble experts to testify for the defense; but if a judgment is obtained against the psychiatrist, the state will not pay it. The doctor himself will have to pay that judgment, even if it plunges him into bankruptcy to do so. Every physician on the full-time staff of a private or public hospital or agency should have malpractice insurance to protect himself against these situations.

SITUATION 2. A psychiatrist has done some research and discovered that injections of a certain potent extract produce a brief, severe shock, followed by marked improvement in the patient's mental condition. He published a paper about it—the only such article in medical literature. Before he induces this treatment, he has each patient sign a waiver. On his next case, the patient dies because of anaphylactic sensitivity to the extract. Can the family successfully develop a malpractice action against the doctor?

Comment: Probably yes. The treatment was experimental. A doctor who departs from generally accepted methods does so at his own (legal) risk. The waiver signed by the patient is of doubtful protection in this situation, though it is always desirable to have such forms signed. Here its value is reduced by two considerations. "A physician cannot make a valid contract that the patient shall waive any claim for damages growing out of the doctor's want of care."[3] In plain English this means that the doctor would be protected against a charge of unauthorized operation (technically, assault) but not against negligence in carrying out the procedure. The jury in this case might decide that the physician's failure to pre-test for anaphylactic sensitivity was negligent. If they found that the doctor was careless, the waiver would not protect him. A patient cannot authorize a doctor to be negligent.

---

[2] In many jurisdictions the state is actually immune from suit, so that the family can sue the physician, and only the physician.

[3] Ralph Webster, *Legal Medicine and Toxicology* (Philadelphia: W. B. Saunders Co., 1930), p. 43.

Another complication here is the question of the patient's competency to sign any kind of document. (See Chapter 13 for a fuller discussion of competency.) It would be foolhardy for a physician to perform a spinal tap or administer shock therapy without a consent form signed by the patient (if competent), by the guardian (if the patient is incompetent), or by both patient and near relative (if the patient's competency was undetermined).

What constitutes "experimental therapy" is a matter to be determined from the facts in each case. Swetlow and Florman [4] summarize it as follows:

Mere newness of a procedure does not mean it's still experimental. (In one case) . . . the specialist adopted a line of treatment that had just been reported in his specialty journal. Treatment failed. The patient, charging unauthorized experimental therapy, haled the specialist into court. Verdict was for the doctor. Though this treatment was novel, it had passed the experimental stage. Results had been published in a professional periodical. The court observed that practitioners of a reputable school of medical thought are not to be harassed by litigation merely because their ideas are new.

However, before using this decision as a basis for boldness in experimental treatment, the practitioner should heed these further remarks of Swetlow and Florman in the same article:

The trail-blazing practitioner is always courting a brush with the law. Most juries tend toward compensating damage-seeking plaintiffs. Which means that the M.D. who veers even slightly from the straight-and-narrow of established therapy had better be prepared to prove that he used extra care and diligence.

Borderline cases involving reputable physicians present the real posers. What can the well-intentioned medical man, convinced that an experimental approach is warranted, do to protect himself?

Here are four recommended steps:

Get the patient's consent in writing.
Be sure the document he signs makes clear that the treatment is experimental; be sure it states the risks entailed.
Obtain corroboration from other qualified physicians on the advisability of the experiment.
If possible, have one or two other qualified physicians witness any experimental procedure to attest your skill and diligence.

SITUATION 3. The patient contends that the doctor was negligent in that he administered an intravenous barbiturate too rapidly. The doctor answered that no layman has any right to judge at what speed of injection

4 G. I. Swetlow and M. G. Florman, "Your Liability in Experimental Treatment," *Medical Economics*, XXVII: 3 (December, 1949), 54.

the procedure is negligent. This raises the question: how do court and jury determine whether a doctor was negligent? What standards are used?

Comment: The criterion is the standard of skill shown by similar specialists in that community. Usually this is determined by the testimony of another specialist. It is impossible for a lay jury to decide how fast an intravenous barbiturate should be given. Is two cubic centimeters a minute a carelessly rapid injection rate? Only another expert can say. Assume that a psychiatrist is being sued because death occurred during a narcosynthetic session, the allegation being that the doctor's technique was careless. Some other expert must support that allegation before the judge will allow the case to go to a jury. The family will argue that the patient was in good physical health before the injection; now he is dead, so the injection must have killed him. However, this is not enough to support a malpractice claim. The family must prove negligence. They cannot do this unless some other expert, hearing the technique described, testifies that the procedure was carelessly done.

There are, however, situations where the result speaks for itself, where negligence may be tentatively assumed simply by proof of the bare facts. For example, if a patient is burned with a physical therapy machine, it would be unfair to require that the patient *prove* that the doctor was careless. The instrument was entirely in the control of the doctor; the patient cannot be at fault, and the fact that he was burned certainly raises a strong inference of negligence. If a physical therapy machine is properly constructed and properly used, a patient will not be badly burnt. Therefore, as soon as the patient proves these facts (that he was burned and that the machine was entirely in the control of the doctor) he has carried the burden of proof, and it is now up to the doctor to neutralize that inference of his negligence. Here the patient does not need an expert witness, because the facts speak for themselves. The Latin phrase, *res ipsa loquitur* (which means literally "the thing speaks for itself") is applied to these situations—that is, to cases where the defendant (the doctor) has complete control of the instrument which damaged the plaintiff (the patient) so that a tentative inference of negligence is reasonable. Again, if it is shown that a doctor made out a commitment paper without even having seen the patient, it will not need an expert to prove that the doctor was negligent. (In the latter situation, however, the *res ipsa loquitur* doctrine does not apply since there is no "instrument" in the control of the defendant. None the less, the patient meets the legal requirement by providing the facts and it is up to the doctor to cancel out this presumption of negligence if he wants to defend himself.)

SITUATION 4. A psychiatrist devotes several hours a week to a free mental hygiene clinic operated by the city for indigent patients. He is not paid for this. He issues a prescription for phenobarbital, but carelessly writes 1½ Grams instead of 1½ grains. The patient becomes very ill as a result of the barbiturate overdosage and sues the doctor. Can the doctor successfully defend this action by stating that since he rendered the service free-of-charge, he has no financial liability for damages?

Comment: No—this defense is completely untenable. What determines the doctor's liability is his professional relationship to the patient, not the financial relationship. Also see Situation 9 below.

SITUATION 5. Having made a blunder, a psychiatrist worries about possible malpractice action. Several years go by and nothing happens. He finds out that the "statute of limitations" for malpractice is two years in his state. Three years have elapsed. Can the doctor now breathe a sigh of relief, safe in the assurance that the patient can no longer successfully sue him?

Comment: Probably, yes. Ordinarily a suit cannot be filed if a certain period of time ("the statute of limitations") has elapsed since the action occurred. The statute of limitations on malpractice actions varies from state to state—in some states it is one or two years, in some it is five; in others some intermediate figure.

However, in two special situations our hypothetical doctor will still have to worry. If the patient is a child, the statute of limitations does not begin to operate until he is twenty-one years old. If the child was seven years old at the time of the treatment, and the statute of limitations was five years, this patient could start suit any time before he was twenty-six years old—or any time within nineteen years after the treatment was rendered.

Another factor is this: in some jurisdictions, the statute of limitations does not begin to operate until after the patient first discovers the ill effects of the treatment—this may be a long time after treatment was rendered. The rule on this varies somewhat in different jurisdictions. Thus: a patient complains of headache, and the psychiatrist carelessly examines him, fails to look at the eyegrounds, and hastily concludes that the headache is psychogenic. He administers psychotherapy only. The patient continues for two and a half years, by which time it is apparent that he has a brain tumor and has had it all along—only by now it is inoperable. The statute of limitations in that state is two years. The patient charges malpractice, asserting that the doctor was grossly negligent in doing only a cursory physical examination. The physician answers that the suit is outlawed by the statute of limitations since more than two years have elapsed since the allegedly "cursory" examination.

In some states this would be good defense and would bar any action. In others, the courts would hold that the patient could not have been aware of his brain tumor until recently, therefore did not know until recently that he had a basis for action; hence the statute of limitations would begin to run when the patient first discovered his true condition.

SITUATION 6. An insurance company sends a claimant to a neuropsychiatrist. The claimant alleges paralysis of an arm following an accident. Noting the way he dresses and undresses when he thinks he is unobserved, the doctor concludes that this claimant is a deliberate malingerer—a conclusion reinforced by the physician's survey of the patient's history. The doctor then dictates a report to his secretary, stating that this claimant is a malingerer. The envelope is addressed to Mr. John Smith, Chief Attorney, Full Shield Insurance Company. The Chief Attorney's secretary opens the mail, calls it to the attention of the attorney who, in turn, refers it to the adjuster for further investigation. When the case comes to court, the claimant's expert testifies that the paralysis is hysterical. The company's doctor tells the court he thinks the plaintiff is a malingerer. The judgment is for the claimant. The jury or referee apparently accepts the plaintiff's theory that the paralysis is hysterical.

Can the doctor now be successfully sued for slander on the basis of his testimony? Can he be sued for libel on the basis of his report? (See Appendix A for definitions of libel and slander.)

Comment: Probably not, though the neuropsychiatrist here has made himself unnecessarily vulnerable to such action. Usually a statement made in court, in answer to a proper question, if it is made in good faith, is not actionable, though there is some state-by-state variation here, and there may be some jurisdictions where such an action could be prosecuted. The doctor might have difficulty in proving his good faith, if the burden of proof is on him.

The libel action would probably be dismissed except in jurisdictions where the dictating of a report to a stenographer is construed as "publication." In those areas, the doctor might again have to show that he acted without malice and in good faith.

In some states, doctor-patient communications are "privileged," but this would not apply here. The examiner was not a treating physician, and his relationship with the claimant is not the kind of doctor-to-patient relationship contemplated in such a rule.

In cases like this, it is better for the examiner to say (both in his report and on the witness stand) that he is unable to find any disorder or injury to account for the alleged paralysis. That implies malingering without laying the doctor open to any libel or slander action. See Chapter 11 for a further discussion of this point.

SITUATION 7. A neuropsychiatrist employs a nurse in his office. One of her duties is to give hypodermic injections. At the doctor's request, she gives an injection of ergotamine for the treatment of migraine. She is careless about sterilizing the equipment—at least so the patient says— and an abscess develops at the site of the injection. The patient suffers pain and disability and, at his own expense, he has the abscess opened and drained.

Can he now successfully sue the doctor, or nurse, for malpractice?

Comment: He can sue either or both. Since the doctor probably has more money than the nurse, he will almost certainly file suit against the doctor. The physician here is liable because the nurse was his employee, acting under his general supervision.

SITUATION 8. A psychiatrist rents one room in his office to a psychologist. A mother brings a child to the psychiatrist who, after taking a brief history, says he needs some test results before proceeding further. He has the child tested by the psychologist and is told that the patient is an untrainable mental defective. The physician then turns the case over to the psychologist who arranges for the child's ultimate admission to a state school for the feeble-minded. Meanwhile, at the psychologist's suggestion, the child is withdrawn from the public schools. A year later, when the state school has room for the patient, a retest by a state mental hygiene clinic shows that this is an emotional disorder without any mental deficiency. The indignant parents now bring suit against both the psychiatrist and the psychologist. It is established that the psychologist showed poor judgment in his selection of an appropriate test, and poor skill in administering and interpreting the test. What is the liability of the psychiatrist?

Comment: It depends on whether the psychologist is an employee or an independent professional consultant. If, for instance, the psychologist keeps his own fees, sees patients other than those referred by this psychiatrist, pays rent, and in general has his own practice, then he is an independent professional practitioner, and the physician is no more liable than if he had referred a patient to a competent dentist who had pulled the wrong tooth. On the other hand, if the psychologist was an employee, received a salary from the psychiatrist (or received a proportion of each fee he earned) and was carried on the books for social security deductions as an employee, then the psychiatrist would be liable for the psychologist's malpractice.

Even if the psychologist is an independent practitioner, some question might be raised as to the psychiatrist's judgment in uncritically accepting the test results. If the plaintiff could show that this was grossly poor judgment, there might be liability on the part of the psychiatrist, too.

SITUATION 9. A psychiatrist writes a prescription for methyl phenyl ethyl hydantoin for the treatment of epilepsy in a child. He intends to call for 100 milligrams but, through carelessness, he writes for 100 Grams. The child takes the medication and develops marked ataxia and a stubborn skin rash with blood picture changes as a result. The family sue the doctor, who sets up this defense: the pharmacist had a duty to telephone him before filling a prescription for such a staggering overdosage. The pharmacist knows that this is fifty times the average dose for a child. The doctor did write the patient's age on the prescription blank. (Cautious doctors always do this in writing for medication for the very young or very old). Thus the liability is the pharmacist's, not the doctor's. Is this a sound defense?

Comment: No. They are both liable, and the patient can sue either or both—probably successfully.

SITUATION 10. In most states, an abortion is legal if it is necessary to save a patient's life. A gynecologist refers a pregnant woman to a psychiatrist because the patient threatened suicide if she had to go through with the pregnancy. The psychiatrist carefully reviews the history and studies the patient. She never had any psychotic or neurotic symptoms before this pregnancy. He believes that she now suffers from a reactive depression, of psychoneurotic rather than psychotic intensity. He sends the gynecologist a report stating that a continuation of the pregnancy would aggravate the depression and that the suicide rate is so high among depressed women that an abortion is necessary to save the patient's life. The abortion is done. Later the prosecutor hears of this and has both the gynecologist and the psychiatrist indicted. The psychiatrist sets up two defenses; first, that his advice was sound, and that in fact the abortion did save the woman's life; and second, that it was the gynecologist and not the psychiatrist who actually performed the abortion. Is this a sound defense?

Comment: It is a very uncertain defense. Since it is a crime to procure an abortion, most state laws make it a crime to recommend one, or to be a party to an abortion in any sense. If the abortion is found to be criminal in this case, the psychiatrist is at least an accessory. And there are cases [5] which hold that a suicide threat is *not* enough to justify an abortion since, if it were, any woman could procure an abortion by simply threatening suicide. Perhaps the psychiatrist can persuade the jury that in this case, the threat was a real one. But being a defendant in a criminal case is not helpful to the career of any physician, even if he is acquitted. In some states an abortion is legally justified if the procedure is needed to avoid impairment of the woman's health. While this gives the doctor greater latitude, it is probably going to be interpreted very strictly. It may be necessary to show that the pregnancy almost inevitably would cause some profound impairment of health. It would be hard for the psychiatrist to testify, with clear conscience, that a psychosis would be the *inevitable* result of a continued pregnancy. If he can say only that it would be a *possible* result, this would—in all likelihood—be insufficient legal justification. If he can testify that the psychosis would be a *probable* result, his defense would be much stronger.

SITUATION 11. A psychiatrist limits his practice exclusively to psychotherapy. A self-referred patient complains of "nervousness," irritability, and staggering gait whenever he is emotionally upset. He also complains of spots before the eyes and periods when he feels very cheerful without apparent reason. After a year of psychotherapy he feels worse than when he started. He now goes to another doctor who finds a moderately advanced case of multiple sclerosis. The patient now files malpractice action against the psychotherapist, alleging that in not doing a neurologic examination prior to psychotherapy, the doctor showed bad judgment; and in not recognizing a case of multiple sclerosis, he showed lack of skill; and in not investigating further when the patient failed to improve, the physician was grossly negligent. The doctor answers that he does psychotherapy only, that he does not hold himself out as a neurologist, and that the patient was negligent in not going to a general practitioner, internist or neurologist if he felt his physical symptoms were not improving. How sound is this defense?

[5] Such as Hatchard v. State, 79 Wisconsin 357.

Comment: Not very. Any doctor—in fact any kind of professional practitioner—is supposed to know the limitations of his own field of practice. Specifically, he is expected to know whether his own method of treatment was applicable. If it was not appropriate to the case, he is not protected from a malpractice action no matter how skilfully he accomplished that treatment. If a chiropractor tries to treat diphtheria by spinal adjustments, he is legally responsible for the bad result no matter how skilfully he adjusted the spine. He is supposed to know that chiropractic treatments are not appropriate for diphtheria. Since the psychiatrist is a fully licensed doctor of medicine and has "M.D." on his sign, he is certainly liable for the negligence shown in this case. A cautious psychotherapist either does a careful physical examination on every patient, or insists on a clearance from another physician before initiating psychotherapy.

SITUATION 12. A psychiatrist treating a chronic alcoholic, furnishes him with a prescription calling for a hundred phenobarbital tablets, with instructions to take one at night and one after luncheon. He also instructs the patient to consume no alcohol during the course of the therapy. A week later, the patient becomes drunk, then depressed, then swallows a large number of phenobarbital tablets. It takes a police wagon, a stomach pump, a stay in the hospital, and a good deal of unpleasant publicity before the man is back at work. He now files a malpractice action against the doctor, stating that the doctor should have known that drunken persons often attempt suicide, and that it was exceedingly bad judgment to give an alcoholic so many sedative tablets. The psychiatrist's answer is that it was the patient, not the doctor, who was negligent. He points out that the family knew what the tablets were, knew how unstable the patient was, and that they were careless in not locking the barbiturate away. Finally, he answers that the patient was specifically told *not* to drink any alcohol, and its was the patient's gross violation of this instruction that caused all the trouble. Are these good answers?

Comment: A court might—or might not—hold that this patient's own negligence contributed to the damage. In some states "contributory negligence" bars any suit. In such an area, if the court found that the patient was "contributorily negligent," the action against the doctor would be dismissed. However, in many jurisdictions, contributory negligence merely reduces the damages: it does not bar a suit. In those states, judgment could be rendered against the doctor, even with the finding that the patient was negligent, too.

Probably any jury would find that a doctor was careless in letting a known alcoholic keep a large stock of barbiturates in his bathroom.

Alcoholics are notoriously suicide-prone, and a psychiatrist who does not know that is certainly not a skilled specialist. If he does know it, he showed grossly poor judgment in calling for a hundred tablets in his prescription. The argument that the family should have locked the patient away from the tablets is too weak to get much consideration from the court. The patient, by getting drunk, violated the doctor's specific instructions. But to plead this as a defense, in a case of alcoholism, is ineffable naïveté.

SITUATION 13. A husband asks a psychiatrist to examine his wife because, he says, she has delusions of marital infidelity, and has been displaying marked oddities of behavior. The doctor spends an hour interviewing the woman. She tells him that her husband has a mistress and that she often smells a strange perfume on him when he comes home late at night. She has told her children about it, but they make light of it, and she believes that her husband has poisoned their minds against her. The doctor finds her irritable and worried. She is suspicious of the examiner, stating that she suspects that the husband has called him in order to have her "put away," thus giving him a clear field with his mistress. After his interview, the doctor makes out commitment papers, stating that he found the patient irritable, evasive, and suspicious; that she has delusion of marital infidelity, etc.

A few weeks after the wife has been committed to a state hospital, her family retain an attorney who investigates the situation and finds that everything the wife had said was true. The children, devoted to the father, were ready to believe him when he said that the mother's suspicions were part of the "change of life." Study at the state hospital shows no psychosis. The wife is released and starts suit against the doctor, alleging false certification of insanity. Is she likely to recover damages against the psychiatrist?

Comment: Probably not. The physician acted in good faith. He made a careful examination. His diagnosis was wrong; and perhaps a more experienced psychiatrist would have been more careful. But a doctor is not civilly accountable for malpractice simply because of an honest, non-negligent error of judgment. There was no malice, no negligence, and—so far as the doctor was concerned— no fraud here. Contrast this with the next situation.

SITUATION 14. The situation is the same as in the paragraph above, with this exception: The doctor was willing to sign the commitment paper, but at the last minute the husband changed his mind, and no papers were made out. Three weeks later, the husband appears at the doctor's office. He is carrying blank commitment papers with him. The doctor remembers the case well. The husband says that her conduct has become intolerable, that now she thinks the food is poisoned, that she has locked herself in the room and is starving herself. The husband says he asked the police to break in and take her to a hospital. The police say that they want a signed commitment paper. Since the doctor remembers the case clearly, would he please help out in this desperate situation and sign today the papers that he was willing to sign three weeks ago. Anxious to help out, the doctor signs the papers—dating them today, and the husband goes out and has them notarized.

The wife is subsequently released from the state hospital on a writ, is found to be sane, and it is shown that the husband's story of delusions of poisoning and of the locked room was completely false. What is the doctor's liability?

Comment: The psychiatrist is now really in trouble. In the first place, he is open to criminal action on the grounds of perjury. When he signed the commitment paper, he swore that *on that day* he examined the patient. This was not true. He did not examine the woman on that day. The fact is material, the doctor knew it was not true, the patient was injured because of the doctor's perjury. All of which spells out a criminal conviction against the doctor. Even if criminal action is not brought by the prosecutor, the woman herself can successfully maintain a malpractice action. Certainly it was the grossest kind of negligence to have made out a commitment paper without having examined the patient. This goes far beyond an honest error in judgment. In this case, even if, in fact, the woman were psychotic, the doctor would still have been both guilty of perjury and liable for malpractice.

SITUATION 15. A psychiatrist is consulted by a 55-year-old man complaining of feeling depressed, irritable, and worthless. He makes a diagnosis of involution melancholia, writes a prescription for some amphetamine and some endocrine products, and arranges to begin a course in psychotherapy. That evening the patient's wife calls to ask the doctor what he found. The psychiatrist reassures the wife, telling her that the condition is an acute one, and that it will not last. A few days later the patient commits suicide. The wife now files a malpractice action, alleging that the doctor was negligent in not having apprised her of the danger; that had she known that suicide was a possibility she could have, and would have, taken precautions. Is she likely to win this suit?

Comment: Probably not. Lawyers disagree on this situation, and in posing the problem to a group of attorneys I have received varying answers. The principle is simple enough. For the wife to recover damages, she must show (*a*) that the standard practice among psychiatrists in the community is to notify members of the family when a patient is suicidal, and (*b*) that had this doctor apprised her, she could have prevented the suicide. The only way the wife can meet the first requirement is to persuade some other psychiatrist to testify to that effect. And the second point is even more difficult to prove. It might indeed be alleged that if the wife had been alerted to the possible suicide she would so have harassed her husband with amateurish vigilance that his mental condition would have become worse.

Althought not stated in the facts given above, there is another aspect to this case. It may be that it could be shown that it is current psychiatric practice in this community to administer early electric shock to patients in involutional depressions. If this could be proved, then there might be an inference of negligence in that the doctor allowed this potentially suicidal patient to wait several days before beginning definitive therapy. As stated, this was not the widow's contention, so that the doctor need not meet that argument. Most attorneys whom I have consulted about this state of facts conclude that the patient's death and the doctor's alleged negligence are too remotely connected to support a judgment against the physician. On the other hand, the cautious psychiatrist is reluctant to accept for treatment a potentially suicidal patient without letting some responsible member of the family know of the risks.

SITUATION 16. A psychiatrist advises the family to commit a depressed patient. But at their insistence, he places her first in a private room in a general hospital. On his admission note he indicates that she is a depressed patient. At the family's expense and at the doctor's request, the hospital furnishes round-the-clock nursing service. One night the patient eludes the nurse, jumps out of her twelfth floor window, and is killed. The family now sue the hospital, the nurse, and the doctor. With respect to the doctor's liability, the family's thesis is that he should have insisted on a room with barred windows and should not have permitted a potentially suicidal patient to be housed on the twelfth floor.

Comment: The psychiatrist would probably be held "not liable." No substantial negligence on his part has been demonstrated. He had no control over the hospital architecture. He had advised against a general hospital in the first place. A jury might find that the hospital is liable, but probably not. The nurse's liability would depend on a weighing of the evidence as to her negligence. The nurse was not an employee of the doctor, so her negligence, if any, is not imputed to the psychiatrist. Whether she was an employee of the hospital or whether she was engaged privately and independently in the practice of her own profession would have to depend on the facts as to her method of assignment and remuneration. If she was a registered nurse, practicing privately, paid directly by the patient, the hospital would have no liability for her negligence. A hospital would, however, be liable if it were careless in the selection of its own nursing personnel.

Basic Elements of Malpractice

What Malpractice Is.—Civil malpractice is a negligence, carelessness, incompetency, or malice by a physician which results in damage to a patient. To maintain a suit for malpractice, the patient must show that the doctor did something *wrong*. Civil malpractice is what the lawyers call a *tort* which is the French word for "wrong." Sometimes a doctor commits a tort by doing nothing at all—that is, by failing to act when he should. When a patient files suit for malpractice, he is not simply alleging that the doctor did not achieve a promised result. If that is his complaint, he would be charging a breach of contract—which is a different kind of action. There is no necessary implication of "wrong" in a breach of contract. A person may fail to perform as promised because of circumstances beyond his control. But malpractice is something different; always there is an implication that the doctor did something wrong, or that he negligently failed to do what was right.

Standards of Skill.—When he holds himself out as a specialist in psychiatry, the doctor implies that he has certain specialized skills. If he fails to do skillful work and the patient suffers as a result, the patient can file a malpractice action, alleging that the doctor did not exhibit the degree of skill which a specialist ought to have. The specialist is held to a greater degree of skill and judgment than is the general practitioner. To determine whether the doctor did show the requisite degree of skill and judgment, expert opinion is usually needed—unless the ineptness of the practitioner was so gross that anyone could see it. The plaintiff (that is, the complaining patient) generally has to have another psychiatrist testify that the proper procedure would have been so-and-so. If this is not done, there is usually no way in which the plaintiff can prove that his doctor showed incompetence or poor judgment. If the doctor was guilty of gross carelessness, the blunder may have been so obvious that it spoke for itself. And in that case, expert testimony by the plaintiff may not be needed. See Situation 3.

Old and New Procedures.—A doctor is expected to keep up with progress in psychiatry, and at the same time, he is not supposed to do any experimenting on patients, or use any novel methods, except at his own legal risk. A psychiatrist who treated epilepsy with nothing but bromides might be sued by a patient who developed bromidism as a result. Suppose this patient could get an expert to testify that many newer drugs for epilepsy had been widely accepted for the last forty years. The jury might find the therapist accountable for malpractice in that he held himself out as a specialist yet failed to prevent these complications by methods well known in the specialty for many decades. On the other hand, a psychiatrist who devises a new form of electric shock therapy uses it at his own risk. If the patient is damaged, he can sue the doctor and can probably collect monetary damages, because the judge will tell the jury that if a doctor departs from accepted and generally approved methods of treatment, he is financially responsible for any ill effects. See Situation 2.

Gratuitous Treatment.—The financial relationship between doctor and patient has no bearing on malpractice liability. Whether the patient has paid a fee, is being treated gratuitously, or has defaulted on his bill, it makes no difference so far as malpractice actions are concerned. See Situation 4.

Patient's Consent.—When a psychiatrist engages in any procedure which impairs body integrity, he should have the written consent of the patient. A consent form and waiver should be signed before the doctor does a spinal tap, produces metrazol or insulin convulsions, applies physiotherapy, induces electroshock, or injects any drugs intravenously or intrathecally. If there is any question at all about the patient's competency, the cautious practitioner has the guardian or responsible relative join in signing the consent and waiver. This will protect the doctor against a charge of assault or a charge of unauthorized operation. It will not, however, shield him against a malpractice action if he was careless or negligent or if he used an untried or unaccepted procedural technic. See Situation 2.

The following quotation from Raveson [6] is appropriate here:

[6] Harold Raveson, "Ten Ways to Invite Malpractice Action," *Medical Economics,* XXVII: 8 (May, 1950), 78.

The psychiatrist performing shock therapy must not only have consent, but be prepared to show that the patient knew the score when he gave it . . . With an unconscious and unidentifiable patient, the physician may do what-ever is necessary to preserve health or life. Under these circumstances, con-sent is implied. In all cases, the doctor should get broad and clear consent—preferably in writing. If the patient is a minor or an incompetent, the consent should be obtained from the legal guardian.

Statute of Limitations.—A doctor need not worry today about a procedure he performed twenty years ago. The law frowns on the filing of claims on matters as stale as that. To encourage diligence in the prosecution of claims (and to give citizens some assurance that they will not be forever subject to harassment) all states have "statutes of limitations." This means that unless a suit is filed within the specified time limit, it is thereafter barred. For a tort like mal-practice, this period may be one year, two years, or even five years. The period varies in different states. See Situation 5 for further details.

Negligence of Employees.—A physician is civilly liable for the negligence of his employees. A psychiatrist may have on his payroll a nurse, technician, social worker, psychologist, secretary, or another doctor. If any of them injures a patient by reason of carelessness, incompetence, malice, or gross negligence the doctor is liable. The ordinary malpractice insurance policy covers this. Sometimes the question is whether the other person is an employee, an associate or an independent consultant. The court determines that from the facts in each case. For instance, if a psychiatrist rents out a room in his office to a neurosurgeon, the psychiatrist would not be liable for the surgeon's malpractice even if he referred the patient to him. Their relationship is landlord and tenant, not employer and employee. To this there is one exception: if the doctor selected a grossly negligent, obviously incompetent practitioner (or an unlicensed one), he might be held liable. See Situations 7, 8 and 16.

In this connection, Raveson [7] advises: "Most malpractice policies cover the doctor for suits based on an employees' negligence. It's a good idea to check your policy for this at each renewal date. Re-member that, legally speaking, the nurse, technician or assistant is the doctor's agent."

Erroneous or Illegibile Prescriptions.—A pharmacist is expected to know the normal dosage range of a drug, and he should not fill a prescription that calls for a lethal dose until he has first communicated

[7] *Ibid.*

with the doctor.   However, if the pharmacist errs and fills the prescription, this will not absolve the physician.   The doctor could still be held liable for the ill effects of a prescribed overdose or for a mistake made because the practitioner's handwriting was illegible.   See Situation 9.

A physician who telephones a prescription to the pharmacist (or who gives the information orally to the patient, with instructions for her to pick up the medication at the drug store) is liable for any damage done as a result of misunderstanding.   Raveson [8] cites this illustrative case:

> The physician phoned the druggist, asked him to deliver some mild chloride of mercury.   The druggist thought he said "bichloride of mercury."   Since he had no written prescription he did not know the age of the child nor the instructions for using the medication.   He was told to label the bottle: "use as directed."   In the resulting court melee, the jury fixed the blame wholly on the physician.

Criminal Malpractice.—A physician may be faced with criminal prosecution as well as with civil action.   This is so when the negligence was so gross as to amount to a reckless disregard of human safety; or when a criminal law was violated.   For example, a psychiatrist who gave barbiturates intravenously while he (the doctor) was drunk, could well be tried criminally, as well as sued civilly.   Advising a pregnant woman to have an abortion in order to improve her mental health would be another instance of inviting possible criminal action.   See Situation 10 for discussion of this.

Contributory Negligence.—If the patient was negligent, and if this negligence contributed to the damages, the patient is said to have been responsible for "contributory negligence."   In some states, this bars the patient from suing the doctor at all.   In other states, it does not prevent him from filing a suit, but it does reduce the damages.   See Situation 12.   An attorney should be consulted about the effect of contributory negligence locally.

Amount of Damages.—Within wide extremes, the amount of money awarded in malpractice actions is entirely up to the jury.   The damages can be nominal, compensatory or exemplary.

Nominal damages are moral victories for the patient without much financial burden on the doctor.   Thus, the jury could find that the doctor was, in fact, guilty of negligence, malice, or incompetence, but that the patient really suffered nothing thereby.   In that case the

[8] *Ibid.*

jury might set the damages as one dollar—or even as six cents. This would be a *nominal* award. Of course, it is not a desirable outcome for the physician, even though there is no financial loss, because the record will show that he was once considered accountable for malpractice.

Compensatory damages are supposed to compensate the patient for the pain, suffering, damage to reputation, loss of earning power, and actual out-of-pocket expenses incurred as a result of the doctor's malpractice. In some cases, juries give awards in excess of this, either to "punish" the defendant for his malice, or to set an example to discourage others. These are called *exemplary* or *punitive* damages.

Malpractice Insurance.—Many medical societies participate in group malpractice insurance policies. Other things being equal, the doctor is well advised to purchase this kind of protection. It is usually less expensive than individually bought policies, and it generally assures the cooperation of the rest of the local profession in the doctor's defense if the occasion should arise.

Responsibility of the Employed Doctor.—Of special interest to psychiatrists working for state hospitals, private sanitaria, or government agencies is the fact that the patient can sue the doctor even though the physician functions only as an agent of the government or of the hospital. Even if a physician is employed by the federal government (as in the Veterans Administration), or by a state government (as in a state hospital), or even if he is only doing his duty as an Army or Navy medical officer, he is still not immune from personal suit. The hospital, government, or employing agency will generally help him by furnishing counsel (not always, though), by obtaining medical experts to testify for the defense, and sometimes by financing an appeal. But if a judgment is finally rendered against the doctor, he will have to pay it out of his own pocket unless he is insured. It is therefore wise for psychiatrists who work for the government or for a private agency or institution to have personal malpractice insurance.

PART II
THE TACTICS OF TESTIMONY

Chapter 15

THE NATURE OF MEDICAL TESTIMONY

The psychiatrist may be called on in one of three capacities: (1) as an ordinary citizen-witness, to report facts not requiring special knowledge, (2) as a witness to medical facts, and (3) as an expert offering opinions and interpretations.

Nonexpert Witness

Like any other person, the psychiatrist might happen to witness some incident which later features in litigation. His position here is the same as that of any other citizen. If a psychiatrist, while walking along the street, sees an automobile accident, he may be called to tell the court what he saw. Unless, as a physician, he rendered first aid, his status as a doctor has no bearing on his testimony.

Medical Fact Witness.—He may be called on to testify as to medical facts without being asked any *opinions*. For example, he might be brought into a court on a subpoena, and there asked on what days he saw the claimant (or defendant), what his findings were (his objective findings, not his interpretations of them), what his fee was, whether he collected it, what the patient did (but not what the patient said) and what recommendations he made. These questions all call for simple *factual* answers. This is distinguished from a question dealing with the relationship between the accident and the present symptoms (a matter of *opinion,* not fact), or an inquiry as to whether the defendant knew that he was doing wrong (a *conclusion,* not a fact), or a query about the chance of recovery (a prognostic *opinion,* certainly not a fact). The distinction is of considerable practical importance because, if he is called as a *fact* witness rather than as an "opinion" witness, the doctor:

> Can be compelled to testify by subpoena.
> Is legally entitled only to an ordinary witness fee.[1]
> Needs no qualifications other than a license to practice medicine or a medical degree.

[1] In fact, he usually does collect a full professional fee.

Subpoenaed Witness.—A witness cannot be compelled, by subpoena or otherwise, to give opinions,[2] nor would he be acceptable to the court for that purpose unless he exhibited specialized qualifications; and, as an expert (that is, opinion-giving) witness, he is entitled to full professional fees for his time.

A psychiatrist is ordinarily asked to testify as an expert ("opinion") witness and not as a simple fact witness. There are only two situations in which the specialist is likely to be a simple fact witness. One develops when, as a physician, he rendered first aid in an accident case. Later, he might be called on to testify as to whether the victim was unconscious, how long the laceration was, whether it was bleeding, and that sort of thing. All of these items call for simple *factual* answers. The other situation arises when the psychiatrist refuses to go to court, and the lawyer finds it necessary to serve a subpoena. Since an expert cannot be compelled to give *opinions,* the only testimony the attorney can elicit is a series of *facts.*[2]

For example, the psychiatrist feels that the defendant is a psychopath and fully responsible for his acts. He does not want to testify for the state, because that would be contrary to his own patient's interests. And he cannot, in clear conscience, testify for the defense, because he does not consider the patient irresponsible. He thus refuses to come to court, only to be served with a subpoena by the prosecuting attorney. As a subpoenaed witness he has to answer fact questions: When did you see the patient? Who paid the fee? What was your diagnosis? How often did you see him? But if the prosecutor asks, "Do you think that the defendant knew that he was doing something wrong?" the doctor can answer that that is a matter of opinion. Or, a psychiatrist is asked to testify on behalf of, or in opposition to, a patient whom he has been treating for an anxiety reaction. The patient now alleges that the psychoneurosis resulted from an accident. The doctor knows that this is not true, and therefore he will not testify for the plaintiff. Since he does not want to hurt his patient, he refuses to testify for the insurance company. If the insurance company brings him to court on a subpoena, he will have to answer factual questions such as: When did you see the plaintiff? What did your examination reveal? But if asked whether the accident could have caused the symptoms, or whether the patient is likely to recover from his illness once he collects the damages, the doctor can, in most jurisdictions, state simply that these are matters

---

[2] In most, but not in all jurisdictions. In some states, the doctor, once on the stand, can be ordered by the court to give his *opinion* about a case as well as the facts. The psychiatrist should ascertain the local rule on this.

of opinion, and he can remind the court that he has not been called as an expert.

Subpoenaed Witness Asked for Opinion-Evidence.—If a doctor, called in on a subpoena, is asked an opinion-question, he can refuse to answer on the grounds that he was brought to court on a subpoena and is prepared to give *facts,* but that he cannot give *opinions.* Sometimes the judge will support him, sometimes the judge will suggest that the attorney qualify the doctor as an expert and pay an expert's fee, and that the doctor in turn agree to answer. In most states the doctor can still refuse to give his opinion, on the theory that his opinion is, as it were, his own private property. In a few jurisdictions, it is held that once any witness is on the stand, he can be compelled to tell not only all he *knows,* but also all he *thinks* about a case. The psychiatrist should ascertain from the attorney what rule prevails in his jurisdiction. Illinois, for example, is apparently one of the states where giving an *opinion* is held to be as much of a civic duty as giving the *facts.* Thus, in *Dixon v. People,* 168 Illinois 179, the judge said: "It is not accurate to say that mere abstract knowledge . . . is, of itself, property. . . . When a physician . . . is called upon to give his opinion . . . while he is already testifying as a (fact) witness . . . there is no infringment of a property right."

On the other hand, as Webster [3] tells us, "In the federal courts, the practice seems to be that a physician cannot be compelled to testify as an expert unless arrangements have been made to compensate him for his services. This ruling would seem to be the logical one." Of course, if prior arrangement of compensation is essential, the net effect is to make it impossible to subpoena an expert or to ask him "opinion" questions after he has been subpoenaed, since, if he really did not want to testify, he could simply state that any fee offered was insufficient.

Expert Witness

Usually the psychiatrist comes to court as an expert and is thus expected to give not only findings and facts but also opinions, prognoses, conclusions, and evaluations. Whether a particular doctor is acceptable as an expert depends, in large degree, on the discretion of the judge. It is general practice for courts to permit any physician to testify as an expert if he can establish any reasonable claim to specialized knowledge, even though his qualifications might not meet

[3] Ralph W. Webster, *Legal Medicine and Toxicology* (Philadelphia: W. B. Saunders Co., 1930), p. 17.

standards of specialists' organizations or boards. The judge's position is usually this: let the doctor testify—the jury can appraise the validity and credibility of his testimony themselves and compare his testimony and qualifications with those of the other experts. Furthermore, few states have any legal provision for restricting specialized practice. In the eyes of the law, any person licensed to practice medicine at all is fully qualified (legally) to do brain surgery, obstetrics, ophthalmology, or any other branch of practice. For further details about qualifications of the psychiatrist, see Chapter 16.

Fees

An expert witness is entitled to be paid *for his time*. Let it be understood that he is not being paid for his testimony. Every citizen has a duty to offer his services free and freely to the state in the administration of justice. That is why jurors and fact witnesses can be required to attend court for purely nominal fees.

When Subpoenaed.—If a doctor is subpoenaed he could, in theory, be offered nothing except the small subpoena fee.[4] In practice, however, it is customary to offer even the subpoenaed physician reasonable compensation.

As a matter of fact, doctors are rarely called to court on a subpoena because a lawyer is more or less bound by the testimony of his own witnesses, and a hostile medical witness (whose testimony binds the attorney) could be damaging to the development of the case. Most lawyers agree that it is better not to call a physician as a witness at all, than to have him come reluctantly and testify adversely. Subpoenas are sometimes issued to doctors, however, under these three circumstances:

1. When all that is wanted is simple factual testimony (dates, size of lacerations, objective findings) and when the doctor has refused to come to court voluntarily.

2. When a doctor is willing to testify but wants a subpoena to show that he could not help himself. For example, a state hospital may have a rule forbidding its staff physicians to go to court on a private action. In such a case, if a subpoena were issued, the hospital would have no choice but to permit the physician to testify. Or a doctor might feel that in the interest of justice, he ought to testify "against" someone who had once been a patient. To protect himself

---

[4] In some states this might be fifty cents in the county, one dollar outside the county, and an extra fifty cents if the doctor is ordered to bring records. In a few jurisdictions subpoena fees are a trifle higher, but rarely does the nominal witness fee exceed two or three dollars.

against a subsequent charge that he did something contrary to the interests of a patient, he might want to say that he could not help going to court : he was subpoenaed.

3. When, as a result of prior conversations, hostility has developed between doctor and lawyer, and the latter feels an urge to be punitive in the relationship. He might then take delight in compelling the physician to come to court and sit there all day waiting to be called. A preventive of this situation is to avoid being aggressively belligerent to lawyers. If discord does develop, the only thing the doctor can do is to present the problem frankly to the judge—to say that it does not look as if the medical testimony will be needed for several hours, and may the physician return to his office and await a call?

A subpoena is a court order. It must be obeyed under penalty of a fine or contempt of court. That, in fact, is the source of the word "subpoena." The document reads, in most states, "Fail not under penalty or punishment for contempt of court," or words to that effect ; and "under penalty" is the key phrase which, in Latin, is *sub poena.*

Size of Fee.—Size of the fee is generally a matter of negotiation between the doctor and the summoning attorney. In some states, the fee for time spent is determined in the Workmen's Compensation Board by an existing fee schedule.

If the doctor has already been paid for his examination, consultation and treatment, the only remaining fee is that for the time in court. This should be billed at the doctor's regular hourly basis, time being computed on a portal-to-portal basis. That is, he should bill for his time spent traveling to and from the court house, time waiting in the court room, plus time on the witness stand ; in other words, from the moment the doctor leaves for court until his return to his office, hospital or home.

Examinations, consultations, and treatments are billed at the doctor's regular rate. Since this bill may become part of the claimant's or defendant's announced costs, it may be made public.

Contingent Fees.—In personal injury actions, the doctor called by the defendant (usually an insurance company) submits his bill directly to the company, and payment is made by them. The expert called by the plaintiff will submit his bills for hospital, home, and office visits directly to the plaintiff. It is sound practice for plaintiff's doctor to try to collect these fees prior to the court appearance, though of course with indigent patients this may be impossible. Where the patient is indigent, the doctor may have to wait until disposition of the case before he can collect any of his fee. Furthermore, an impoverished patient will have no resources with which to meet the medical costs unless he wins a judgment in his litigation. In this situation, the doctor's payment is contingent on the outcome of the case. This is, therefore, a "contingent fee." Some physicians frown on the acceptance of cases on a "contingent fee" basis because it gives the doctor an emotional investment in winning the case. However, it is a principle of medical ethics that the indigent always have a call on a doctor for his free services. In such situations, the plaintiff is indigent unless and until he wins the case. He is then no longer indigent and can and should pay his medical bill. If all the psychiatrists in a community were to refuse "contingent fee" cases, the net result would be that a poor person who suffered injury would have no redress because he would be unable to obtain medical evidence to support his claim.

In Criminal Cases.—In criminal actions, the district attorney's office (or prosecutor's or state's attorney's office in some jurisdictions) will pay the prosecutor's psychiatrist for his time in examining the defendant and for his time in court. Bills are ordinarily submitted to the county, though this practice varies somewhat in different states. The office which calls for the examination will advise the doctor as to the address to which his bill should be sent. If the defendant has a court-assigned attorney, the defense psychiatrist may be expected to render the service gratuitously unless examination is accomplished by a court order. In that case, the court will indicate the authority to whom the bill is to be sent. In other criminal cases (where the defendant retains his own attorney), the defense psychiatrist's bill should go to the defendant's family unless the defense counsel gives other instructions.

Other Situations.—In other types of litigation the psychiatrist charges for his time on a per-hour basis, according to his regular schedule, and he bills the person calling him into the case.

Travel Time.—Occasionally an expert is asked to travel a considerable distance, involving a total time of two or more days away from his office. It is expected that the summoning party will pay the doctor's first-class travel costs, plus a reasonable *per diem* fee (computed on average meal and hotel costs), plus a negotiated fee for the doctor's time. It is not customary to calculate this on a per-hour basis. Some doctors ask for fees commensurate with income lost by being out of the office for that period.

Salaried Physicians.—Hospital-employed physicians charge fees according to the rules of their institution with respect to the right to engage in private transactions. If the time spent is not charged against the doctor's vacation or leave time, the fee will not be large because the witness is drawing his regular salary, anyway, during that period. On the other hand, if the physician goes to court on his own time (that is, on vacation or leave time, or has leave without pay for that purpose), the fees would be comparable to those paid to private practitioners.

Chapter 16

QUALIFYING THE PSYCHIATRIC EXPERT

How qualified must a psychiatrist be to be accepted by the court as an "expert"? There are two considerations. First, he must have at least a minimum of specialized qualifications in order to get a hearing in the courtroom. If, after preliminary questions, the judge feels that the witness is grossly unqualified, that ends his participation in the case. Second, the judge may allow him to testify, but the jury may not consider his testimony seriously. They may conclude that he is not expert enough to satisfy them: or they may accept the opinion of another witness who makes a more favorable impression. Generally, the judge is inclined to allow any physician to testify as an expert if he has any color of claim to status as a specialist, leaving it to the jury to decide what his testimony is worth.

With few exceptions, courts do not lay down any set rules as to years of experience, limitation of practice, or special certification. In some but not many jurisdictions, special qualifications are set for status as a specialist before Workmen's Compensation Boards. In New York, for example, a psychiatrist submits his qualifications to the Workmen's Compensation Board; after meeting their requirements he is given the code designation SI if he limits himself to neuro-psychiatry, or XI if he is in general practice but is considered as having special competence in neurology or psychiatry. New York is also one of the few states to issue special certificates to psychiatrists. This is the function of the "Board of Psychiatric Examiners" (part of the state's Department of Mental Hygiene), which issues a certificate designating the holder as a "Qualified Psychiatrist." Even in that state, however, a doctor who is otherwise qualified *can* testify before the general courts without possession of this certificate, on the theory apparently, that a party to a suit or a defendant in a criminal action enjoys a constitutional right to have witnesses of his own selection heard on his own behalf.

Elements of Qualification

In general, the qualifications of a particular witness will be determined at each court appearance. The attorney calling him will, by question and answer, elicit his qualifications, and—unless manifestly unqualified—the judge will usually permit him to testify for whatever credence the jury may want to give to his testimony.

When a specialist is well-known in the community, or when his qualifications are clearly superior, it is customary for the opposing attorney to ask that the recital of his qualifications be waived. He will suggest that the witness be admitted at once as an expert. The opposing attorney does not do this out of generosity. He does it because he prefers to keep from the jury an imposing list of qualifications. For the same reason, the summoning attorney usually insists on the expert's being permitted to catalogue his qualifications in open court.

The factors which impress the judge and jury often seem mysterious to the doctor. Jurors, however, are laymen, and judges, though usually more sophisticated than the gentlemen of the jury, sometimes have odd ideas as to what constitutes expertness in a physician. Below are listed some of the items used in qualifying the expert. It must be remembered that, in the last analysis, it is a group of non-physicians (judge and jury) which determines how skilled the witness is: and these factors are therefore to be seen through lay, not professional eyes.

Number of Years of Practice.—To the average juror, this is the most important determinant. Physicians know that longevity is no proof of expertness. But the layman believes that "you can't beat experience" and gives great weight to the doctor's years of practice. In considering the expert's qualifications, jurors tend to lump together total number of years out of medical school without breaking down the time into general and special practice periods. This does not mean that a relatively young specialist is automatically disqualified. But it does mean that when an attorney offers a junior specialist, he must neutralize the prejudice against youth by indicating the intensive nature of his training and experience.

Hospital Connections.—Most laymen, and for that matter, most judges, have a rather foggy concept of the doctor's relationship to a hospital. As they see it, the hospital is the great workshop of medicine; hospital appointments and rank are prime evidences of specialty recognition. If a doctor has the title of "consulting psychiatrist" at a dozen tiny private hospitals, it sounds impressive to the juror to hear this list recited. Likewise, they believe that the highest ranking doctor in the hospital is automatically the finest specialist. Although the superintendent of a state hospital may, perhaps, devote most of his time to problems of personnel, budgeting, and sewage, the jurors will assume that the chief executive of a psychiatric hospital must be the most expert clinical psychiatrist on the staff. Even "courtesy staff" appointments have considerable prestige value in the eyes of the jury. In fact, some laymen believe that being on the "courtesy" staff is greater evidence of expertness than being on the regular staff. A private practitioner of psychiatry may, as every doctor knows, be superior in his skills without having a single hospital appointment. None the less, the admission that the witness does not have a hospital connection, is usually considered damaging in the layman's eyes. That is why some private practitioners mention their sometimes loose connections with small private sanitaria in listing their qualifications. Jurors have little concept of the distinctions between "associate," "adjunct," "assistant," and "clinical assistant" grades. In many hospitals, the title "visiting psychiatrist" may indicate the head of the department, but to the layman's ears the adjective "visiting" has a casual sound that makes the title seem less impressive than, say, "clinical assistant."

Society Memberships.—It is customary for a medical witness to testify that he belongs to the county medical society, *and* to the state society, *and* to the American Medical Association. This sounds like three society affiliations, though, except for dues, it represents a single membership. Jurors pay little attention to this, because the public has some vague idea that all doctors belong to the medical society. If a witness is *not* within the folds of organized medicine, the cross-examining attorney may press him on this, and ask that he explain why.

If the psychiatrist belongs to a local or national psychiatric organization, he will have the attorney bring this out. The layman does not distinguish among the various grades of membership (Associate Members, Junior Members. Fellows, Life Members, etc.). A witness in a higher membership grade might have the attorney ask him to explain what "Fellowship" or "Senior Membership" means, but this is generally considered a vainglorious and somewhat undignified expedient.

Experience with Similar Cases.—Even the experienced psychiatrist is sometimes embarrassed by his inability to cite similar cases. For example, the problem may turn on a diagnosis of true paranoia. The psychosis is so rare, that some busy psychiatrists function for decades without seeing a single case. So too, a practitioner may devote years of activity to psychiatry without once having seen a psychosis with pellagra or with Huntington's chorea. Whether he is testifying that the patient does have this condition or whether he is denying the diagnosis, his position is difficult if he has to admit that he has never actually seen a case. With the rarer disorders it is well for the witness to review his files in advance, so that he may be prepared to answer a question directed at his experience with that particular problem.

Training.—Older practitioners do not customarily enter into the record their specialized background training, since the period is remote, and the value of the testimony inheres more in the expert's current status than in his past training. Junior psychiatrists often have little to present by way of qualification except to list their residencies, courses, and other training items. It is amateurish to recite a list of separate courses, to state for example: "Five years ago I took a course in the psychodynamics of the Superego, and three years ago I attended a series of lectures on 'Progress in Psychiatry.'" If it should turn out that these were brief part-time courses, the judge and jury will get the impression that the witness is trying to pad his experience background.

Papers Written.—If the witness has published three or more papers, it is usually sufficient for him to state (in answer to a query) that he "has made numerous contributions to the literature," or that he "has published several articles on psychiatric topics." If he has written only one or two papers, it is usually best to forget them, unless (as rarely happens) one of the papers was focused squarely on the subject in litigation. It is seldom desirable to cite the articles written, though the witness should have a record of his contributions in the event that he is asked about them in more detail. The summoning attorney should be requested *not* to ask the witness to list his writings. Such a question, if raised at all, is asked by the cross-examining attorney.

Books Written.—The author of a book is in a precarious position. True, the fact of book authorship carries some prestige; but this is neutralized by the certainty that the hostile attorney will tear some phrases out of text which seem to contradict the expert's present testimony. Suppose the author had stated that constitutional factors were important in the development of emotional disorders. If he is now testifying for a plaintiff, the company lawyer will quote that phrase to make negative the expert's testimony that this psychoneurosis was caused by traumatic factors. Such a development usually amuses the jury since, at first, it seems to be using his own words to contradict the doctor. Of course it can be explained, but not without a few moments of embarrassment for the author. A good book must make positive statements; it cannot say "maybe" about everything. And positive statements will rise to haunt the author in subsequent litigation.

Special Certifications.—The qualifying value of an American Board diploma or other special certificates depend on the level of sophistication of the judge and jury. In some areas, no psychiatrist is considered truly qualified unless he is also certified. In other places, an American Board diploma is simply one more qualification, the absence of which may be neutralized by other items. It is considered unsporting for a hostile attorney to ask a diplomate whether he received his certification after examination or by reason of age and experience only. In a New York trial in 1950, expert testimony was given by a psychiatrist of unimpeachable standing who had been practicing the specialty for a quarter of a century. He had applied for his American Board diploma only a few years before, however, and on cross-examination he was asked: Q: How long have you been a psychiatrist? A: Twenty-five years. Q: But how long have you been a *certified* psychiatrist? A: Three years. Q: So you've been a really certified specialist for only three short years! It would have been less embarrassing if the witness, before answering the second question, had asked: "Certified by whom?" He then would have had the opportunity to indicate that he had been a fully qualified specialist for two decades before applying for certification.

When an uncertified specialist takes the stand, it is better tactics to have this fact brought out by the friendly attorney rather than to leave it for cross-examination. In the last analysis, Board certification stands as the simplest and least challengeable of the expert's qualifications.

Teaching Affiliations.—The American public has great respect for the educator, though this is not apparent in teachers' salaries. The assumption is that one is not asked to teach a subject unless he has a mastery of it. Teaching affiliations are, therefore, good bases for expertness. The average juror is not a college graduate and is unfamiliar with the pedagogic hierarchy. So far as he knows, there are only two kinds of teachers: professors and others. The title "assistant professor" is often interpreted as "assistant to the professor" and therefore carries an implication of juniority. A judge or referee will recognize the title, however. The juror does not know whether a "demonstrator" of psychiatry outranks an "instructor" or "lecturer" in psychiatry. Jurors are also impressed with appointments to teach in nurses' training schools. Among doctors, a faculty appointment in an undergraduate college (medical school) is more meaningful than lecturing or demonstrating to practicing physicians. However, to the layman, being a teacher in a "postgraduate" institution sounds more impressive.

Agency Affiliations.—Many psychiatrists have, or can obtain, volunteer affiliation with schools, plants, child guidance agencies, city relief departments, social agencies, probation offices, police departments, and the like. These are evidential of recognition in the specialty, and the examining attorney should be told of these so that the expert may be asked about them when qualifying.

Introduction of Qualifications

In some courts it is the custom simply to ask the witness to state his qualifications; in others, the rule is for the summoning attorney to ask a series of questions to bring out the expert's connections, experience and affiliations. If the first practice is followed, the doctor will begin by stating whether he is licensed to practice, and if so, when and where he was licensed; he will indicate the nature of his practice and whether it is limited to the specialty; he will then recite his hospital, agency, medical school, and organizational affiliations, and stop. If the question-and-answer method is used, the attorney should be furnished, in advance, with a summary of the expert's qualifications. This might well follow the ten paragraphs above, with the addition of an item about state licensing and limitation of practice. The attorney will then ask, for example: Are you a licensed physician? Do you specialize in any branch of your profession? With what hospitals are you connected? How long have you been practicing that specialty? To what scientific organizations do you belong? And so forth.

In preparing for court appearance, the psychiatrist might set up a check list covering the following points. He could write the answers under each item, or make brief notes to remind him of the answers, and attach the list to his clinical record before coming to court.

1. Date of graduation from medical school
2. Place and dates of internship
3. Place, nature and date of residencies
4. Other specialty training
5. States licensed and when

    6. Hospital affiliations
    7. Agency affiliations
    8. Books and papers published
    9. Specialty society memberships
   10. Board diplomas or other special certifications
   11. Specialty training not otherwise mentioned
   12. Experience with this kind of case

It is seldom that a doctor has all these data at his fingertips. A check list like this may save fumbling and embarrassment. It makes it possible for the witness to give crisp, prompt, and adequate answers to any question about his qualifications.

Chapter 17

PREPARATION FOR COURT APPEARANCE

The Pre-Trial Conference

The inexperienced medical witness will want to hold a pre-trial conference with the attorney. Purposes of this conference are:

To obtain further facts about the patient.

To prepare the attorney for questioning the doctor about his qualifications. (See Chapter 16.)

To help frame the hypothetical question. (See Chapter 20.)

To obtain some concrete data about the timing of the case so that the doctor will be able to plan his own time on the trial day and reduce the usually drawn-out waiting period in the court room.

To review any X-ray films, laboratory data, or other medical reports which the attorney may have accumulated in the course of his preparation of the case.

To obtain from the attorney a general picture of the order in which the other witnesses will be presented, so that the doctor will know how many of the medical facts will have already been placed in evidence before he is called; and—incidentally—to ascertain whether the case will be heard with or without a jury.

An attorney is an advocate. He will strive to present the case in the most favorable light, and thus may unintentionally mislead the doctor. As one experienced trial lawyer [1] puts it: "The attorney will assure you that the patient was never sick before he was involved in the accident. Be skeptical about this. Ask questions. Ask the attorney what kind of hypothetical question [2] he is planning, and insist that he include all the pertinent medical facts, not merely the helpful ones. Review the hypothetical question, phrase by phrase. And, finally, when you get on the witness stand, do not be afraid to admit that you and the attorney did have a pre-trial conference. It is perfectly proper."

[1] Leslie S. Kohn, "When You Are Called Upon to Testify." *Medical Economics,* XXIV (March, 1947), 67.
[2] See Chapter 20.

Personal Preparation

Preparation for trial is time well spent. Even an experienced witness reviews the anatomy of the organs involved. He familiarizes himself with the recent medical literature on the subject. He gives particular thought to the points on which he is likely to be cross-examined. (See Chapter 22.) He puts himself in the place of the doctor "on the other side" and tries to see how the picture looks to him. He reviews his office records to be sure that they are not documents to be ashamed of. (See Chapter 18.) When the psychiatric aspect of the issue is highly controversial (and it often is) he checks the literature and notes some citations which support his position. The hostile attorney may cite famous authorities who take a different view, and it is well to be prepared with counter-authorities.

Timing the Trial

The unpredictability of the court calendar sours many physicians on the idea of testifying. They hear stories of being rushed to the court room only to find that three more witnesses have to be heard first. They have had the experience of being told to be in court at 10 A.M.; of arriving promptly, and finding no one there but the spectators; of waiting all morning while a jury is being selected; of being told to return after luncheon; of sitting through the attorney's opening remarks; of hearing four other witnesses testify; and of then being told to come back at 10 A.M. tomorrow.

This poor scheduling is not a matter of malice or whimsy on the part of the lawyers. It is a corollary of the unpredictability of human speech. An attorney may know that his case is the next on the docket. He estimates that the current case will take three days and returns to his office. An hour later he hears that the other case was abruptly terminated by a mistrial. Now he frantically scurries around trying to round up witnesses for *his* case, so prematurely catapulted into the number one position on the docket. Or the contrary may occur. The attorneys in the current case may assure their colleague: "We'll be through by noon." But by noon, when all the witnesses are waiting, the previous case is still droning on. And it may continue for three more days. There is no way of organizing a trial schedule like a railroad timetable.

The plaintiff's or prosecutor's doctor should be on call as soon as he knows that the jury has been sworn in. He may not be needed for several hours but, once the jury is seated, the case is underway. A defense doctor can plan his time a little better. He cannot be called until after the plaintiff (or prosecution) has "rested." The end-point of the plaintiff's (prosecution) case depends largely on how long the defense counsel himself takes for cross-examination. Therefore the defense counsel should be able to tell with reasonable accuracy when his doctor will be needed.

If it looks as if medical testimony will not be reached until some inconvenient time, it may be possible—as a courtesy—to have the doctor heard out of turn. This requires agreement between the two attorneys and the judge. Most judges are willing to accommodate the physician in such a situation. Placing the doctor out of turn poses one special problem, however. His testimony may have been based in part on facts furnished by *previous* witnesses. For example: it is planned to call a fellow-worker who will testify that he had witnessed convulsions. Based on the description so furnished, the doctor will be asked to give an opinion as to the cause and nature of those seizures. If the doctor is called out of turn and testifies before the fellow-worker describes the convulsion, there will be nothing in the record to show that the plaintiff had any convulsions at all: therefore it would normally be improper to ask the expert to indicate the cause and nature of the seizures. To avoid recalling the doctor later, it becomes necessary for the attorney to ask the doctor to give his opinion, subject to the lawyer's showing later (by other witnesses) that the convulsions, in fact, had actually occurred.

Where there is no jury, cases flow much more quickly. No time is needed to select and swear in the panel, and the first witness can take the stand almost as soon as the clerk calls the case. Furthermore, the presentation is not slowed up by the need to protect the jury from hearing inadmissible evidence. Hence, in nonjury cases doctors may expect to be needed earlier than in cases presented to a jury. While the practice varies somewhat in different jurisdictions, in most states the following cases are triable without juries: drunken driving charges, workmen's compensation cases, divorce and annulment actions, criminal cases where the defendant waives a jury, trials of and hearings on juvenile offenders, cases involving custody and guardianship, litigation concerning wills, and—if both parties agree—certain personal injury actions.

Chapter 18

OFFICE AND HOSPITAL RECORDS

The doctor is expected to bring to the witness stand his records of the case. If the patient was seen at home or in a private office, this means that the doctor's record must be withdrawn from the files and taken to court. Some physicians maintain bookkeeping (financial) records for each patient in a separate file. If so, these documents are also brought to court because the amount of the bill, and the date of payment (if any), as well as the source of the payment, may be factors in appraising damages.

Hospital Records.—Hospital charts are usually obtained by issuing a subpoena to the custodian of the record room, except in private sanitaria where the staff physician is expected to obtain the file. Such records are generally admitted into evidence as such, after they have been "identified." Identification is made by testimony of the official having custody of the record, or by the doctor under whose supervision it was prepared. Once so identified, the chart or the appropriate part of it is available to any medical witness who made the entries. X-ray and laboratory reports are supposed to be validated by the technician who did the work or by the radiologist or pathologist. In practice, however, it is customary to accept them for what they are worth if they appear as official parts of an already identified hospital chart, and if the physician who ordered the tests is on hand to testify about them.

Office Records.—The inexperienced witness would do well to follow scrupulously the following advice given by an experienced trial counsel: [1]

In court, your record may be seized and examined by the judge, by either attorney and even by the jury. Moral: have a record so well prepared that you would not be ashamed to have the whole American College of Surgeons inspect it. Sloppy records humiliate the medical witness. You can't give good testimony unless you have an adequate record to rely on. A successful

[1] Leslie S. Kohn, "When You Are Called upon to Testify," *Medical Economics,* XXIV (March, 1947), 65.

medical witness, whose records have always been something to be proud of, tells me that he keeps on his desk a thirteen-point check list. Whenever he sees a patient whose case might reach a judge's docket, he checks his office file against these thirteen points:

1. Every visit is dated. So is every phone call and conference.
2. The source of the patient is honestly written down. If the lawyer originally referred the patient, that is frankly entered in the record.
3. If the case developed out of an accident or a crime, the "how," the "when," and the "where" are completely explained.
4. Hospitalization data are obtained, summarized and incorporated in the office record. In accident and criminal cases, especial attention is paid to presence, depth and duration of unconsciousness, and to the patient's sobriety, and whether he entered the hospital walking, in a wheel chair, or on a litter.
5. The patient's own words are used in writing the history and in recording the subjective symptoms. When a doctor testifies that an illiterate laborer complained of tinnitus and insomnia, even the jury laughs.
6. In all cases, the findings include—at least on the first visit—a note as to height, weight, blood pressure, pulse, and the size and place of scars. For an English-speaking jury, scars are reported in inches, not in centimeters.
7. Findings of the examining physician are carefully separated from complaints. If the word "anxiety" appears in the record, for instance, it must be apparent whether this means that the doctor *found* evidences of anxiety or whether the patient *said* he suffered from anxiety.
8. Any items in the record, not in the doctor's handwriting, are initialled by him.
9. Findings of the radiologist are entered in the record and the doctor indicates whether it was he who ordered the X-ray and whether he actually saw the films himself.
10. When a laboratory test is ordered, this fact is written in the record and dated. When the report is received it is copied into the record and dated.
11. The financial data are either (*a*) copied on the clinical record, or (*b*) attached to the record when it is brought to court. This includes bills sent, remittances received (with dates), and a note of who actually paid the bill.
12. A carbon copy is retained for every record, report and letter sent out. There are no exceptions to this.
13. At least once in the record (or in a carbon copy of the report) a note is entered as to the extent of the disability.

Carbon Copies of Forms.—Physicians are often asked to fill out forms to be sent to insurance companies, accident boards and government agencies. If a simple carbon copy is made, this will be baffling when the doctor later uses it to remind himself of what he said. For example, the form might have a printed question: "Is the claimant a relative of yours?" The doctor types in "No." On his carbon copy, the word "No" stands by itself with no clue as to its meaning. To prevent this, the questions themselves should be typed into the carbon copy.

Use of Records on the Witness Stand.—In court, the doctor ordinarily uses the record to "refresh his memory." He does not read it verbatim. The theory is that he is testifying directly from his recollection of the case, the record serving simply as a springboard for his memory. If he reads a record word for word, it will make the file one of the exhibits in the litigation. The record can then be seized, stamped, and retained by the court. As a matter of fact, even if he merely refers to his notes now and then, the judge or attorney may want to inspect them and will have a right to do so. If the doctor has this possibility in mind, he will not bring slovenly notes to court with him.

The carbon copy of the report to the lawyer forms an excellent basis for answering the questions raised by the attorney on direct examination. Suppose the attorney has in his hand the original of the physician's report. He glances at it and asks, perhaps, "What did you find with respect to the plaintiff's (or defendant's) intelligence?" If the doctor uses the carbon copy of that letter as his source of recollection, he knows that he and the lawyer are both referring to the same item. This device also protects the attorney against being surprised by his own expert's testimony. If, for example, in his report the physician has given an estimate of disability or a prognosis as to outcome, the lawyer knows what answer to expect; and if the doctor uses the carbon copy of his report as a basis for his answer, he will not be in the embarrassing position of contradicting himself.

Chapter 19

DIRECT EXAMINATION OF THE MEDICAL WITNESS

The witness is subjected to two, sometimes three, lines of questioning. First, the summoning attorney asks him a series of questions: this is direct examination. Then the opposing attorney asks him additional questions: this is cross-examination. The judge may, at any time, turn toward the witness and ask a question. Jurors may, but rarely do, ask questions directly of the witness. After cross-examination has been concluded, the summoning attorney may come back and ask additional questions to clear up matters elicited on cross-examination. These supplementary questions constitute "redirect" examination. And finally the hostile attorney may engage in "re-cross" examination. Rebuttal and surrebuttal testimony may also be introduced, as explained on page 310.

The Course of Direct Examination.—Direct examination usually proceeds as follows. The attorney asks the physician his name, address, and professional status. He then qualifies him (see Chapter 16 for details). He asks whether he ever examined the patient and, if so, when, where, and at whose request. He has the doctor report the findings at that examination. The lawyer then frames the history of the case, together with the patient's subjective symptoms, into a hypothetical question. The doctor is asked to assume (*a*) that a patient gave the history detailed in the hypothetical question, and (*b*) that the doctor found in this hypothetical patient exactly what he found when he examined the claimant or defendant. Based on these assumptions, the doctor is then asked to state the diagnosis.

Special Questions.—After the attorney has reached this point, he asks a series of special questions which depend on the type of case and usually take one of the following forms:

In a personal injury action:
> What relationship, if any, existed between the accident as described and the diagnosis you have just reported?
> What is the extent of disability? (or the prognosis)?

In a criminal action:

Was the defendant sane or insane?

Was he in the grip of an irresistible impulse?

At the time of the crime, was he able to recognize that his action was wrong? And if not, why not?

In a will case:

What was his mental condition at the time he signed the will?

Was he capable of knowing the nature and extent of his property?

Did he know that he was making a will?

Did he know the natural objects of his bounty? (See Chapter 7.)

Was his mentality such that he retained his own free agency in disposing of his property?

In a case involving marriage or any other contract:

At the time of the agreement, what was his mental condition?

Did he understand the implications of the agreement?

Was he capable of managing his affairs with ordinary prudence? If not, why not?

Preliminary Briefing.—It is perfectly ethical for the summoning attorney to brief the physician, prior to the day of the trial, by telling him exactly what questions he is going to ask.

Mention of Insurance Company.—In a personal injury action, the claimant's doctor must make no mention of any insurance company. If, for example, he examined the patient jointly with the insurance company's doctor, he must be careful to avoid the phrase "insurance company" in reporting this. If he sent a form or report to the company, he says only that he sent it to "the defendant." The reason for this rule is given as follows:

The idea is that the plaintiff sues the defendant not the insurance company, and that juries are more liberal with a company's money than with an individual's. If the jury knows that the defendant is insured, it may bring a stiffer verdict. So whenever a plaintiff's witness utters the phrase "insurance company," watch for the calling of a mistrial.[1]

In workmen's compensation cases, this rule may be waived in states where, by law, all employers must be insured, and where decisions are not made by a jury.

Brevity of Answers.—The shorter the doctor's answer the narrower the opening for cross-examination. In general, cross-examina-

[1] Leslie S. Kohn, "When You Are Called Upon to Testify." *Medical Economics* XXIV (April, 1947), 112.

tion is limited to subject matter brought out on direct examination; hence, the more the expert talks, the wider the scope for subsequent cross-examination. Psychiatrists are accustomed to lengthy and detailed histories, and often include much irrelevant material merely to lend dimension and depth to their understanding of the patient. However, in the court room, irrelevant material should be excluded unless asked for, since it merely gives the cross-examiner more material with which to try to confound the doctor. The fact that there is a normal vaccination mark on the left arm is certainly part of a complete physical examination. However, it is irrelevant on a matter concerning criminal responsibility, custody of children, divorce, or the effect of a recent head injury. If the doctor mentions it just to be complete, he may be harassed by a cross-examiner who wants to know whether that mark could not have concealed a more recent injury, or whether the patient's brooding about the cosmetic effect of it might not be causing his emotional symptoms—a bothersome and totally unnecessary line of cross-examination which the physician himself invited when he gratuitously described a completely insignificant vaccination scar. If a question can be answered "Yes" or "No", it is good practice to give a monosyllabic answer, though there is absolutely no legal requirement to do so.

Misleading Questions and Answers.—If a question is so awkwardly phrased that the answer will be misleading, the expert can—and should—usually so indicate.

For instance, following a head injury, the physician examines a claimant and notes no positive objective findings. However, on the basis of his psychiatric study, he is satisfied that the patient does have a traumatic neurosis. If the lawyer asks him what he found, the doctor might recite a list of minor findings such as "slightly exaggerated reflexes, sweaty palms, and fine tremors of the eyelids." The attorney should, at that point, offer a hypothetical question which embraces the patient's history and complaints. If, by error, he fails to do so, and asks his witness, "What do these findings indicate?" the doctor is in an awkward position. In all honesty, he would have to reply: "They indicate nothing." This, of course, would be misleading to the court and unfair to the patient. His best procedure would be to say something like: "By themselves, it is impossible to tell what these findings mean, unless the doctor also knew the patient's history and complaints." This serves as a signal—and a perfectly proper one—to the attorney to furnish the hypothesis which includes the history and patient's complaints.

The Hypothetical Question.[2]—Generally speaking, a witness can tell what he saw and found, but not what somebody else told him. This ban on hearsay evidence is logical under most circumstances. To allow a witness to tell the jury what X told him that Y had overheard Z saying to W, would be to open the door to all kinds of unverified and unverifiable gossip and rumor. However, the restriction on hearsay imposes certain limitations on medical testimony. A diagnosis is based in part on findings, but also on history and subjective symptoms; and these are technically classed as hearsay. This is doubly true in psychiatric testimony where, in large part, diagnosis is based on what the patient said. Rigid enforcement of the hearsay rule would thus make psychiatric testimony almost impossible. One method of admitting history and symptoms into the record is the hypothetical question; that is, an acceptable hypothesis which embodies what the patient said and which includes the history. This is presumptively taken as true in order to permit the doctor to make a diagnosis or evaluation. It is up to the attorney to show that, in fact, these things are true.

Statements Made by the Patient.—Another deviation from the hearsay rule concerns statements made by a patient to a *treating* physician. This is based on the somewhat ingenuous theory that when a patient goes to a doctor for *treatment,* he will give a truthful history and a correct battery of complaints, to avoid getting the wrong treatment. On the other hand, when he goes to a specialist primarily for the purpose of enlisting his support in subsequent litigation, there is a possibility that he might exaggerate his symptoms or give a self-serving history in order to bolster his case. Thus his statements to the specialist fall into the "hearsay" category. The medical expert is usually in the second class—the physician visited primarily to lay a foundation for litigation.

For example, a patient may be bothered for years with spells of impulsive behavior. He seeks no therapy until one day he commits an assault, and a criminal charge is made. He then rushes to a psychiatrist for treatment. But the court will assume, with this timing, that he went to the psychiatrist to obtain support for a defense of irresponsibility. Even though the doctor in this instance actually functions as a treating physician, the court is likely to rule otherwise; and the physician cannot testify as to what the patient said. Nor can he give a diagnosis based materially on such statements. The history

[2] Reviewed in more detail in Chapter 20.

and subjective symptoms can be furnished to the psychiatrist in court as a hypothesis, however. (See next chapter.)

Another example: After a head injury, a patient goes to his family doctor for treatment. As the headaches persist, the general practitioner calls in a psychiatrist as a consultant. The latter recommends a therapeutic regime. A year later the case reaches the courts. Even though the psychiatrist thought of himself as a therapist, the court will probably rule that one of the prime reasons for the reference to the specialist was to obtain his services as a witness. The following colloquy is a sample of how that works:

Q: Now, doctor, did you examine Mr. John Smith, and if so when?

A: Yes, I examined him at my office on May 27.

Q: At whose request?

A: He was referred to me by Dr. William Jones, his family physician, who thought that—

Opposing Counsel: I object. This doctor cannot know what Dr. Jones thought; nor does it matter.

Judge: Objection sustained. Please confine yourself to answering questions as asked, doctor.

Q: What did your examination reveal?

A: The patient was complaining of headache and—

Opposing Counsel: I object. What the patient said is obviously hearsay.

Summoning Counsel: Not so, Your Honor. This specialist treated the patient and as a treating physician is entitled to tell us the patient's history and complaints as he received them in the normal course of his treatment.

Judge: Did you treat this patient, doctor?

A: I furnished Dr. Jones with recommendations for treatment and he followed—

Opposing Counsel: Object to this witness's telling us what Dr. Jones did.

Judge: Sustained. Did you personally render any treatment?

A: No, sir.

Summoning Counsel: He directed and supervised the treatment, and as such stood to the patient in the relationship of a treating physician.

Judge: That's a little farfetched, counsel. The admissibility of the patient's complaints turns on whether this specialist was retained primarily as a future witness or primarily as a medical consultant. Doctor, am I right in assuming that you never saw the patient prior to the accident?

A: That's right, Your Honor. But I never gave any thought to possible litigation. As a matter of fact, I—

Judge: This is purely a legal question, doctor, and I'll make a ruling on it. Please don't volunteer anything. Now, I'm ruling that when the patient consulted this specialist, he—and I mean the patient—was aware of the fact that litigation was contemplated and knew that a specialist would be a desirable witness. I take notice of the fact that very few patients with head injuries consult brain specialists except when desperately ill or when litigation is contemplated. Furthermore, this doctor must have elicited a history of the accident. It would be naïve to suppose that he was completely unaware of the contemplated litigation. There is no record of continued direct treatment here such as is the rule in the ordinary relationship between a patient and his doctor. I'll sustain the defense counsel, and ask the witness to confine himself to telling us what he found, and to omit any references to what the patient said, and any diagnosis or prognosis based in material part on what was told to him.

Summoning Counsel: Exception.[3] Now, doctor, when you examined the patient what did you find?

A: His tendon reflexes were exaggerated, his eyelids were tremulous, there was a slight sway in the Romberg position, he seemed ill at ease and anxious, and when my 'phone rang he jumped as if startled.

Opposing Counsel: Object to the last phrase—"jumped as if startled." That's purely a conclusion on the part of this witness who, though he may be a psychiatrist, is not a mind reader.

Judge: Overruled. That the patient jumped as if startled is a matter of common observation and should be considered an admissible objective finding.

Q: On the basis of these findings, doctor, can you make a diagnosis?

A: No.

Q: Why not?

A: Because I would need a history and some knowledge of the patient's complaints before I could interpret those findings and make a diagnosis.

Q: All right; then assume that a man, 56 years old, previously in good health, was rendered unconscious in an automobile accident . . . (etc., this being the hypothetical question).

Dying Declarations.—Another exception to the hearsay rule is that a statement is admissible if made by a person who is dying, who knows he is dying, and who, in fact, soon thereafter does die. Here

[3] This means that he wants an entry made in the record that he takes exception to the judge's ruling. If the case is decided against him, counsel can appeal, and one of the elements of the appeal will then be the contention that on this point the judge was in error.

the theory is that a man who is about to die (and knows it) would have no reason for not telling the truth. Thus, if the psychiatrist is in attendance on a dying patient, he can later quote his statements to the court, provided (*a*) the patient knew he was dying, and (*b*) the patient did die soon afterwards.[4] If the patient recovers, however, the "deathbed" statement becomes mere hearsay and is not admissible.

Diagnosis by Court Room Observation.—Sometimes the psychiatrist, instead of formally examining the party to the suit, is asked to sit in court and observe his behavior. Later, he is called to the stand and asked whether the claimant's (or defendant's) behavior was consistent with psychosis, neurosis, or other disorders. An attorney would not think of asking a cardiologist to diagnose heart disease in such an informal manner. Even with a visible lesion, like a skin rash, the dermatologist is not expected to make a diagnosis by long distance inspection across the width of the court room. Only psychiatrists, of all medical specialists, are sometimes asked to give opinions based on such casual observation. The justification is that psychiatric diagnoses are based largely on what the patient says and does. A party to a suit is a conspicuous person in the court room. He sits well up front, is sometimes on the witness stand, and is generally visible to all the spectators. Furthermore, he is usually ill at ease and under pressure, so that evidence of psychiatric abnormalities may, perhaps, be more noticeable. In one case,[5] this kind of observation diagnosis was even admitted with reference to a witness instead of a party to the suit.

In most jurisdictions, it is within the discretion of the judge to admit or exclude medical testimony based on court room observation

---

[4] This "dying declaration" rule will strike any psychiatrist as naïve. Many a convicted criminal goes to his execution vowing his innocence, fervently (but mendaciously), to the end. I once had a patient who, having found out that he had multiple sclerosis, committed suicide by swallowing a large number of barbiturate-containing capsules. He had an insurance policy which provided double indemnity for accidental death, and he set the stage to make this appear like an accidental overdose. He was stimulated into a brief period of consciousness before he lapsed into his final coma, and in that interval told the intern that he took the capsules by mistake. I am sure he did this to protect his family by securing that double indemnity. Still, the dying declaration was admitted into evidence, because it met the criteria for an admissible deathbed statement. However, the court and jury also felt that this was a gallant lie, and rendered a verdict in favor of the insurance company, holding that the death was *not* an accident.

[5] In United States v. Alger Hiss (1950), the principal prosecution witness was a man named Whittaker Chambers. A distinguished psychiatrist was sitting in the front row during all of Mr. Chambers' testimony, and heard the witness tell his own life history during direct and cross-examination. Later the judge permitted the psychiatrist to take the stand and offer a psychiatric diagnosis on Mr. Chambers based on the doctor's observation of his words, history, and behavior as noticed during the trial.

of the patient. Many judges accept such testimony, reasoning as
follows: Courts and juries are expected to consider the demeanor,
expression, language, and general behavior of witnesses in determining their credibility; and to consider similar factors in deciding
whether a criminal defendant is the kind of person who might or
might not have committed the act. If this is proper when judgments
are made by laymen, it should certainly be proper when the judgment
is made by a psychiatrist who is, presumably, a skilled interpreter of
human behavior.

This may be legally sound; perhaps it is even psychologically
sound.[6] But, in terms of the professional and public-relations standing of the psychiatrist, it is a hazardous venture. When newspapers
report the incident, the public gets the impression that here is a doctor who, under oath, is willing to make a diagnosis without even
having examined the patient. The physician's action *can* be explained
and justified. But in the public forum he has no opportunity to
explain and justify. The newspaper reader leaps to the erroneous
conclusion that the witness must have been venal to offer a diagnosis
which helped his "side" of the case, without even bothering to examine the patient. Furthermore, the medical witness who makes a
diagnosis from court room observation is in a precarious position
under cross-examination. He invites a severe attack on his diagnostic
technics, his partiality, and his good sense.

Admissibility of Test Results.—The admissibility of intelligence
test scores, Rorschach test interpretations, electro-encephalographic
tracings, and similar exhibits is largely discretionary with the judge.
The great difficulty with testimony based on psychological tests is that
the witness finds it impossible to explain his reasoning (from the
tests) to the average jury. Suppose, for instance, the expert says
that, based on Rorschach findings, he believes that the claimant (or
defendant) is subject to periods of impulsiveness and elation. What,
in the test, gave him that opinion? He answers that large numbers
of "confabulatory whole" responses are evidential of such traits. He
is then asked to explain a "confabulatory whole" response, and he
answers that it is an interpretation of the whole blot in terms of one
of its details. He may be pressed to give examples. The answers
sound incredible to the jury. The cross-examiner asks: "Do you

---

6 Probably not, however. The judge and the jurors are essentially impartial, and
what their opinions may lack in expertness they possess in freedom from bias. The
medical witness, however, once he agrees to testify, does identify himself with the
side which called him. To protect himself from this kind of unconscious but inevitable bias, he ought to do his examination under optimum not minimum conditions.

mean to say that just because the defendant looked at that card and said it resembled a bird-cage, you want this jury to believe that that proves he is impulsive or elated?" It is impossible at this point to give the court a complete course in Rorschach interpreting, and the jury and spectators are left with the impression that it is the witness and not the defendant who is impulsive.

Similar hazards face the expert who is testifying on the basis of intelligence-test scores. I recall an action to set aside a contract based on the allegation that the plaintiff was a defective, with a mental age of nine and a half and quite unable to understand the implications of the contract. The expert testified that on the Stanford Revision of the Binet-Simon test, the plaintiff had scored a mental age of nine and a half. On cross-examination the witness was asked to describe some of the tests which the subject failed to pass. For obvious reasons the expert was loath to recite these tests to the jury, but the judge insisted that the jury had a right to know the findings on which the conclusion was based. The procedure then continued something like this:

Q: How did you know that his mental age was under ten?
A: Because he failed some of the tests which a normal ten-year-old child could pass.
Q: What test?
A: Well, for instance, he did not know the day of the month, nor could he repeat four digits reversed and—
Q: Do you mean to say, that if I forget whether today is the 22d or the 23d of the month, that proves I'm an idiot? (Laughter from jury and spectators.)
A: No, but he failed numerous other tests.
Q: Well, you admit that his forgetting the day doesn't prove anything. Now you say he couldn't repeat four digits reversed. Gentlemen of the jury, would any of you care to try this now? I am sure that there are no mental defectives on the jury and—
Judge: Please confine yourself to examining the witness.
Attorney: Sorry, Your Honor, but this ludicrous testimony—well, let's forget it. Now, doctor, what other evidences of idiocy did you elicit?
A: I didn't say he was an idiot. I said he had a mental age of nine and a half which is considerably above the idiot level and—
Q: Oh, I see, a sort of high class idiot, well—
A: No, not an idiot at all. Only a moron.
Q: Only a moron! Well, tell the jury the tests you used to prove that this man was only a moron.

A : A normal nine-year can form a good sentence using the words "boy" and "ball" and "river," but the subject here failed that.

Q : What was his answer?

A : He offered the sentence: "I saw a boy, a ball and a river."

Q : What's wrong with that? He made a sentence using all three words, didn't he?

A : Yes, but simply repeating the words like this is inferior to the average nine-year-old's performance.

Q : Guess I must be an idiot—pardon me, a moron myself. That sounds like a good sentence to me. (Laughter in the court room.) Now what else did this subject fail to do to your satisfaction?

A : It's not to my satisfaction, it's a matter of—

Q : Just answer the question, please. What other tests?

A : He was unable to find rhymes for "day," "mill" and "spring."

Q : Amazing! Does a nine-year have to be a poet before you consider him normal? Is this your science of psychology? He can't find a rhyme for "spring" so you brand him as a moron and help him escape from his contractual obligations?

Judge : Counsel, please save those comments for your summing-up.

Q : My apologies, Your Honor. I should restrain myself, but this line of testimony is so incredibly fantastic that—well, let's go on. What else?

A : He passed the other nine-year tests, and all the eight-year ones. Therefore, so far he has a credit of eight years plus 4 months for the two nine-year tests he did pass.

Q : Four months? Are you psychologists so accurate that you can gage mental age by the month?

A : Not really. It's just that there happens to be six tests to a year, so it's convenient to refer to each test as two-twelfths of a year, which, of course, amount to two months. But it doesn't literally mean "months" in the sense that nine years and four months is any significant degree better than nine years and two months.

Q : I see. You say "months" but you don't mean "months." Very clear. (Laughter from spectators.) Did you try any more tests?

The cross-examination proceeded in this fashion to the amusement of the jury, the glory of the attorney, and the discomfiture of the expert. This does not happen with the more esoteric medical tests—blood chemistries, for example, or electro-encephalographic tracings. It does not happen because laymen find these tests utterly beyond their range of comprehension. But everyone considers himself an expert in human behavior and a shrewd judge of human nature; it is popular opinion that the appraisal of another person's intelligence is a matter of common sense. No layman will dispute the doctor who says that a blood sugar of 200 milligrams is abnormally high. But he will consider himself qualified to dispute the doctor who says that a normal nine-year-old can rhyme "mill" and "spring." Because of this quirk, the expert witness must be careful about talking too freely on the stand. Sound preparation would require that the attorney first have another expert testify that the test used is generally considered reliable. Then he would specifically qualify his main witness as skilled and experienced in the administration and interpretation of that test. Then, he would try to have the test results, as such, admitted into evidence without subjecting the expert to cross-examination on the details of the construction of the test. There is good precedent for this in the way in which courts handle X-ray interpretations or blood tests. The roentgenologist may be cross-examined on other possible interpretations of the same film; but he is rarely questioned about the milli-amperage of his machine, the length of the exposure, or his technique in developing a film. He may be asked whether a certain lesion could be missed by X-ray or whether another lesion could give the same picture. Similarly, the clinical pathologist is seldom asked to detail the steps of evaluating the sugar content of the blood, though he may well be cross-examined as to what other conditions could cause hyperglycemia. A similar plan could be followed with respect to personality and intelligence tests, with the expert subject to cross-examination on source of error and possible interpretive variants.

The Patient as an Exhibit.—The patient himself may be exhibited. Thus, it is legally permissible to demonstrate by tests made in the presence of the jury that areas of anesthesia exist; or the jury's attention can be called to tremors, spasms, and other visible signs. The judge is required to make sure that this exhibit is solely for the purpose of informing, not for the purpose of inflaming the jury. The distinction is sometimes difficult to make. In most states a patient in a lunacy hearing can insist on making a personal appearance, but in some jurisdictions the judge can refuse to let the patient appear if there is testimony that this is harmful. With depressed and paranoid patients, particularly, a personal appearance is dangerous. Allowing a paranoid patient to remain in court while others testify about him is, of course, one way of further intrenching his delusions and may lead to violence. And a depressed patient may be driven to suicide after hearing his mental condition publicly discussed.

Chapter 20

THAT HYPOTHETICAL QUESTION

Nature of the Hypothetical Question.—At least two thirds of medical diagnosis is based on hearsay. Diagnosis is drawn from three components: history, subjective symptoms, and objective findings. The first two of these are technically "hearsay." In psychiatry, there are even situations where the diagnosis is based 100 per cent on this kind of "hearsay." For example, after a man is dead, the family may contest his will on the grounds that he did not know what he was doing when he made the will. No psychiatrist had ever examined the testator during his lifetime; yet one or more specialists will testify as to his mental state. Since none of them had examined the testator, on what can they base their diagnosis? Only on the description of the testator's behavior as furnished by lay observers. Witnesses describe the testator's actions, and then the doctor is asked: Assume that somebody behaved this way. What can you say of his mental condition? Note that the foundation of the question is an *assumption;* that is, a hypothesis. The query itself (beginning "Assume that—") is a hypothetical question.

A more common example is this: The psychiatrist examines an adult and finds mental deterioration. The history is that he was normal prior to a certain date when he sustained a depressed skull fracture, and that he has progressively deteriorated since. The doctor concludes that this is a post-traumatic mental deterioration. In court, however, the examiner cannot swear that this man actually sustained a head injury; nor can he state under oath, as a positive fact, that this patient was normal before the accident. The attorney therefore gives him an assumption as a framework for his diagnosis. He says: "Assume that a man, 26 years old, a high-school graduate, previously in good health, sustained a head injury on such-and-such a date, and that the injury was diagnosed as a depressed fracture of the frontal and left parietal bones with laceration of, and gross hemorrhage into, the cortex of the brain; and assume that on examination this man revealed the findings which you have just reported. Now can you say what relationship, if any, existed between the

injury as described and the findings you have reported?" This too
is a hypothetical question.

Effect of Changing the Hypothesis.—If the hypothesis is changed,
the answer is likely to be changed. This simple fact is the key to
the apparent "battle of experts" which sometimes seems to stultify
psychiatry. For example, in a criminal case, psychiatrists for both
defense and prosecution jointly examine a defendant and find him
surly and mute. He answers no questions, smiles vaguely at the
doctors, and shows manifest irritation at the interview. By itself,
this behavior does not make any diagnosis possible. In court the
prosecution elicits the expert's findings (mutism, irritability) and
then gives him this kind of hypothetical question:

Assume that a boy is expelled from school because of misconduct,
thereafter wanders around the country, being frequently arrested; assume
that on several psychiatric examinations at various places he has been
diagnosed as having a psychopathic personality; assume that he solicited
a ride on a public highway and when the car stopped at a red light, he
proceeded to assault the driver and that this led to his arrest; that he
showed no feeling of remorse or shame; that he just laughed at the police
officers when interviewed in connection with this offense; that on one
occasion he remarked to a cell-mate, "Sure I beat him up. What right
does he have to drive a car when I don't have one?" And finally assume
the findings which you reported at your examination last week. Can you
make a diagnosis, and if so, what?

The expert would say that the person described was a psychopath.
And this would, of course, indicate that he was fully responsible.
The newspapers that day would carry a headline indicating that the
defendant was sane according to this expert.

The next day the defense psychiatrist mounts the stand and after
stating his findings (identical with those reported by the prosecution's
expert) he is given this hypothetical question:

Assume that a boy daydreams so much in school that he is unable to
make progress in his studies and is accordingly expelled. That thereafter
he wanders around the country, giving as the reason a feeling that God
has chosen him to be a wanderer; that he often sleeps in parks and
open fields, telling people that God made the earth as a natural couch;
that because of this he is frequently arrested as a vagrant; that he has
numerous psychiatric examinations as a result of these many arrests;
that sometimes he is called a schizophrenic and sometimes a psychopath; that one day, while riding in a car which picked him up, he heard

a voice telling him that the driver of the car was an emissary of the devil; that he demanded that the car stop immediately, but when he explained why, the driver laughed at him and called him "crazy." That at a red light in the main street of this city, with dozens of vehicles, hundreds of people, and one traffic policeman near him, he began to pummel the driver, screaming that he was flagellating the devil; that thereafter you examined him and found him to be mute. Can you make a diagnosis, and if so, what?

The expert would say that, assuming these facts, he would conclude that the defendant was psychotic. The newspaper headlines would then read: "Jones Insane, Says Alienist." Any casual reader, comparing this headline with yesterday's, would naturally assume that at least one of the psychiatrists was either venal or incompetent. Yet both were honest, their different answers being due simply to different hypotheses.

An even more common example could be drawn from the tort law. Here the claimant's expert would get a hypothetical question which indicates that the patient was in good health prior to the accident and completely disabled after the injury. He would have to testify that, if this is true, the accident was the precipitating cause of the disability. The defense psychiatrist, however, would receive a different hypothesis. He would be told to assume a number of symptoms prior to the accident, and would also be told, in all likelihood, that recently the claimant has been engaging in vigorous play or exercise. If this assumption is correct, then obviously the role of the trauma is considerably less than under the first hypothesis.

Basis of the Hypothetical Question.—The attorneys cannot manufacture a hypothesis out of whole cloth. However, they are *not* required to include every item of the evidence and history in their assumption. (Obviously not, since it would be impossible to frame a hypothesis that would include *everything*.) On the other hand, the attorney is not permitted to insert assumptions that are totally unsupported by the evidence. If the evidence shows that the claimant was unconscious for five minutes, the attorney cannot frame a hypothesis which assumes that he was unconscious for five hours.

Tentative Hypotheses.—In cross-examination of the prosecutor's (or plaintiff's) expert, the defense counsel is in a peculiar position. He may have in his file evidence to justify a radical rewriting of the hypothesis. Yet he has no opportunity of introducing that evidence until after the prosecution (or plaintiff) closes his case. For example, in a personal injury action, the plaintiff has testified that, ever since the accident, he has been confined to the house. The hypothetical question given to the doctor naturally includes this assumption. Part of the question reads: ". . . and assume, furthermore, that ever since this accident the victim has been confined to the house . . ." The doctor's answer is based, in part at least, on this assumption, too. But the insurance company has witnesses who, when their turn comes, will testify that within the past few weeks the claimant has been seen dancing in a public hall, driving a car, and attending a baseball game. The defense counsel, cross-examining the doctor, might say: "But assume that since the accident, instead of being home-bound, the plaintiff has been driving a car, dancing in public, and attending ball games." If he asks this question, the plaintiff's attorney will object that nothing in the evidence supports such an assumption. At this point only two courses are possible: either (a) the company attorney withdraws the question, waits for his half of the case, introduces the evidence, then recalls the doctor and asks him the modified question; or (b) he asks the judge to allow him to modify the hypothesis, subject to his supporting it later by evidence introduced in his half of the case.

Situations like this are fairly common. To avoid recalling the doctor for his cross-examination, most judges allow the defense counsel to give the expert a modified hypothetical question, subject to "connecting it up," that is, contingent on the attorney's eventually proving that the modification in the hypothesis is justified. In the example cited above, the cross-examination would be allowed to proceed as follows:

Cross examiner: Doctor, you have testified that, assuming that this plaintiff is still confined to the house, the psychoneurosis has to be classed as severe. Now, I ask you to assume for a moment that, instead of being bound to his home, this plaintiff is able to drive a car, and only recently was seen dancing at the Cake Mixer's ball in Krueger's Auditorium. Assuming that—

Plaintiff's Attorney: I object. Counsel has no right to include in any hypothesis an item for which there is not one shred of evidence. Nothing in the record so far indicates any attendance at any balls or any driving of a car. The hypothetical question as modified is grossly improper.

Cross-examiner: I haven't had the opportunity of introducing any evidence yet. I ask the court to admit this, subject to my connecting-up.

Judge: Allowed. It is understood, of course, that if defense counsel fails to prove the attendance at the ball, the driving of the car, and the nonconfinement to the house, the doctor's answer must be stricken out. All right, doctor, now answer the question as modified by defense counsel.

Doctor: If I am to assume that since the accident, this patient has been driving a car and attending public functions, then I'd have to say, were that true, that the psychoneurosis would not be so severe as I had first appraised it.

Plaintiff's Attorney: But doctor, can't a psychoneurotic enjoy an occasional car ride, dance, or ball game?

The Hypothetical Man.—An attorney can create a non-existent hypothetical man by simply selecting the facts which support his concept and ignoring others. The court therefore can insist on the inclusion of at least a minimum of facts in the hypothesis.

For example, an old man wills his estate to his housekeeper, and his children contest the will on the grounds that their father lacked testamentary capacity. No psychiatrist has ever examined him, so all diagnoses here are based 100 per cent on hypotheses. Some witnesses describe psychotic behavior, some describe fragments of normal behavior, some describe eccentric but nonpsychotic behavior.

If all this evidence is now in the record, the attorney for the housekeeper would, in all probability, not be allowed to make up a hypothesis by simply assembling the favorable descriptions. The judge could, and probably would, insist that he include in his description, some of the statements showing odd behavior too. For example, Mr. A. testifies that he used to play chess with the old gentleman once a week and his behavior then was always normal. Mr. B. reports that the testator always slept with an umbrella under the bed for fear that the house might catch fire during a rainstorm and he hated running out in the rain without an umbrella. And Mr. C. testifies that the subject would frequently engage in loud conversations with his long-dead wife. The attorney for the housekeeper would, of course, like to frame a hypothesis that would include only Mr. A's testimony and others like it, and ignore completely the statements of Mr. C. suggesting auditory hallucinations. And the attorney for the sons would like to offer a simple hypothetical question based on Mr. C.'s testimony, such as: "Assume that a man of seventy-two would imagine that he heard his long-dead wife conversing with him, what would you say about his mental condition?"

The court could insist that the attorney for the housekeeper include Mr. C.'s testimony, and the attorney for the sons include Mr. A.'s testimony in their respective hypotheses. The doctor should expect to be offered a hypothetical question which includes all of these. For example, suppose the psychiatrist was testifying for the sons, attempting to set aside the will. Naturally he would be given Mr. C.'s testimony showing the hallucinations, and he would say that people of normal mentality do not hear imaginary voices. But he should be prepared to answer a question based on Mr. A.'s testimony too; to answer, for instance, this question: "Could a man suffering from an arteriosclerotic psychosis play chess once a week with normal interest, attention and skill?" The query is not particularly difficult; but the doctor should expect to be asked something like this.

Assumption of Material Not in the Hypothesis.—The doctor's diagnosis and evaluation must be based exclusively on (*a*) material in the hypothesis, (*b*) his own findings *as recited in court,* or (*c*) a combination of these. If he includes any other material in reaching his opinion, his entire answer may be stricken out. For example, in the doctor's office, the patient says that he was taken to the Hunterdon Hospital immediately after the accident, that he had an X-ray there, and that the X-ray showed a "depressed fracture of the right parietal bone." The psychiatrist does not personally call the Hunterdon Hospital or inspect their records. He naturally assumes that this is true, and his diagnosis and prognosis are based on several factors, of which this is certainly one. In court, he is given a hypothetical question which makes no mention of the fracture. And the fracture, let it be remembered, is not one of his own "findings." He gives a diagnosis and evaluation in court, but he includes in his opinion the assumption of the depressed skull fracture. This is improper. At cross-examination, he will be asked to support his diagnosis or appraisal, and inevitably the assumed skull fracture will come out. This will nullify every bit of his testimony.

In such a situation the witness will do one of two things: either he will rethink his conclusion and give the reply appropriate to the limited facts furnished; or, before giving a full answer, he will say: "It depends, in part, on whether he had a skull fracture." This answer serves to remind counsel of the skull fracture, just in case the attorney had forgotten it. And if in fact there was a fractured parietal bone, the attorney will promptly add this to the hypothetical question.

Supplementary Hypotheses.—In some courts the expert is permitted to add items to the hypothesis by asking if he may make certain additional assumptions. For instance, before testifying that under a certain hypothesis the diagnosis would be a traumatic psychoneurosis, the doctor might want to ask: "And may I also assume that the plaintiff does not have high blood pressure?" In many jurisdictions, this kind of cross-questioning by the witness is not permitted, but in some states, particularly in their less formal tribunals, the judge will allow it.

Modifying the Hypothesis.—On cross-examination the opposing counsel may properly ask the doctor whether his conclusion would be affected if certain items were added to, or subtracted from the hypothesis. Thus it would be proper for counsel to ask:

1. The hypothetical question given by counsel asked you to assume, among other things, that the patient was unconscious for twelve hours after the accident. Now I ask you, doctor, if you were to assume that he was not unconscious at all, but that immediately after the injury, he talked and walked in a normal manner—if you assume that, would your opinion and conclusion be changed?

2. You have stated that the headache was due to the concussion incurred on October 20. Now I ask you to add one more assumption: assume that on January 2 of the same year—some nine or ten months *before* the accident—this claimant applied for benefits under a health insurance policy, asserting at that time that he had migraine. Add that to the hypothetical question and tell us whether that would change your opinion.

Inconsistent Hypotheses.—An internally inconsistent hypothesis may be and should be, rejected by the doctor. The court will support him in this. For example in a long hypothetical question (and sometimes such a question takes an hour to read) it may be stated at first that it is to be assumed that the subject never went beyond the sixth grade in school; and towards the end of the long hypothesis may be an assumption that he is a high-school graduate. More commonly, there may be a hypothetical question which includes the formal statement that "he was previously in good health;" and a little later in the hypothesis is the statement that "except for a chronic mucous colitis and a recurrent migraine, he had no gastro-intestinal or head symptoms prior to the accident." Obviously, the doctor cannot be asked to assume both good health and the existence of two chronic diseases. When such a question is asked, the witness may point out the discrepancy and ask counsel which of the reciprocally exclusive assumptions he is to make.

The Pyramided Hypothesis.—The pyramiding of one hypothetical question on top of another is generally not permitted. For example, a surgeon received a hypothetical question and, basing his reply on that, he rendered a diagnosis of concussion of the brain with fracture of the right temporal bone. Next a psychiatrist was called, and he was asked, "Assume that this patient had a concussion of the brain and a fracture of the right temporal bone, and that it was so diagnosed by a competent surgeon, and assume. . . ." In a situation like this, the judge would probably intervene and point out that a hypothetical question must be based on facts and not on opinions which themselves were rooted in another hypothesis. As one court neatly put it:

The opinion of an expert witness cannot be based upon opinions expressed by other experts. Facts, not opinions, must be assumed in the (hypothetical) question. If it were otherwise, opinions might be built upon opinions of experts and the substantial facts thus driven out of the case.[1]

Group Hypotheses.—The rule just stated does not necessarily exclude a group hypothetical question offered as a time-saving device. Thus, three or four experts may be available to testify on one side of a case. Each will receive the same hypothetical question. If it is a long question, the court may allow the attorney to call the doctors to the rail and read the question to all of them at once. (One of the doctors, though, would probably be sitting in the witness box at the time.) Then as each doctor takes the stand, he can be asked. "You recall the hypothetical question, read in your presence, to Dr. Jones? Well, I want you to assume the same hypothesis yourself at this time." Whether this will be permitted is discretionary with the judge. Some courts will insist on the question being re-read verbatim even though it takes an hour or two, and even though the doctor has already heard it several times.

The Enriched Hypothesis.—If a medical witness is supplementing the hypothesis with facts he has acquired independently, he has a duty to indicate the basis of his answer. For example, a hypothesis has been framed which describes vaguely some odd behavior. The psychiatrist has actually examined the patient but has not detailed his findings. After hearing the hypothesis, he gives a diagnosis based on the assumptions plus his findings. Perhaps he was able, in per-

[1] Louisville, New Albany, and Coryden Railway v. Falvey, 104 Indiana 421.

sonal interview, to elicit hallucinations, but this was not included in the hypothesis. The doctor includes the hallucinations in his own reasoning, however, because he knows for a fact that the patient has them. The doctor can ask, before giving the diagnosis, whether he is also to include his own findings. If told Yes, he can give the full answer. More likely, however, he will be told first to state what those findings were. No less an authority than a Chief Justice of the United States Supreme Court has stated:

The opinion of a witness from facts that he failed to disclose is inadmissible. If he knew anything about the mental condition of the deceased which aided him in arriving at a conclusion, that knowledge should have been developed.[2]

Hypothesis Based on Court Room Observation.—May a doctor sit in court all through a trial and be asked to take as an assumption everything he has heard, and then to give an opinion? (Of course *opinions* expressed by witnesses would have to be excluded, since it would otherwise be a pyramiding of hypothesis on hypothesis.) Some attorneys and judges argue that this is permissible,[3] since, if it were forbidden, the same effect could be achieved at a tremendous waste of time by giving the doctor a hypothesis which consisted simply of the entire trial record. However, it is an unsatisfactory procedure from the viewpoint of the doctor. In the first place, it requires his presence in the court room sixty seconds out of every minute and sixty minutes out of every hour. If he steps out of the room for a moment, the entire structure of the hypothesis may be challenged, because maybe, during that moment, he missed something important. Then, too, it requires the doctor to listen attentively to reams of testimony, much of which has no relevance to the medical question at issue. Furthermore, it lacks the sharpness of focus afforded by the concentrated, fact-packed hypothetical question. And it requires the doctor to determine what, in each witness's testimony, was opinion, and what was fact. This is necessary because he has to assume the facts but exclude the opinions, in constructing the platform for his opinion. A witness may have said: "The patient appeared nervous." Is the doctor to include this in his thinking? Or is this merely an opinion? Occasionally an attorney invites a psychiatrist to sit all through a trial, to note the statements and attitude of each witness, and then to testify as to what his diagnosis would be, assuming that everything he heard was correct. The experienced psychiatrist will decline the offer for the reasons indicated.

[2] Raub v. Carpenter, 187 United States 159.
[3] People v. Lowhone, 296 Illinois 403.

Advantages of the Hypothetical Question.—The hypothetical question has been subjected to much adverse criticism—chiefly on the grounds that it seeks to straitjacket into a few paragraphs an entire life history, and to restrict the psychiatrist to an opinion based on these few paragraphs. Since each attorney selects the most favorable item for his hypothesis, the result is to create a ghost man—a severely sick one on one side, and a blatantly healthy one on the other. The hypothetical man does not exist. The psychiatrist is giving an opinion based on the description of a fantasy. However, no alternative seems workable.

On the asset side, it is to be noted that the hypothetical question is a great boon to the medical witness. It relieves him of the need to determine which set of facts is true. It affords him maximum professional freedom, since it allows him to give a purely professional answer without worrying about the accuracy or partiality of witnesses. It makes his life easier, because he gets a history stripped to the bone, with all extraneous matter excluded and the issue thrown into sharp focus. And it permits him to adhere to the truth regardless of which side is adversely affected. This is made possible by the fact that when the attorneys, according to their respective interests, substantially modify the hypothesis, the doctor can appropriately modify his answers to accord with each new set of assumptions.

Chapter 21

THE TRANSLATION OF
TECHNICAL TERMS

In the courtroom some doctors use medical jargon because they automatically think in technical terms; some because they believe that the scientific words are more precise; and some are driven—consciously or otherwise—by a desire to impress the jury. Such words as "affect" and "etiology" spring naturally to the lips of the psychiatrist, though they are generally misunderstood by judges and jurors. Technical terminology can destroy a doctor's usefulness in the courtroom, lead to a bewilderment of the jury (and therefore, sometimes, to a miscarriage of justice), and may even make the doctor an object of ridicule. The jury is amused to discover that the "contusion" to which the witness solemnly testified, is, after all, only a bruise; and that the "ecchymosis of the peri-orbital region" is jargon for a black eye. When (usually on cross-examination) they learn the truth, the jurors feel that the doctor has been putting on airs.

It is true that scientific terminology is more precise than lay language. But such preciseness is often gained at the cost of clarity. Thus, there may be a shade of difference between "the cause" of the psychosis and the "etiology" of the psychosis. But the difference is so subtle that it has no substantial meaning in a courtroom. For all practical purposes the words are synonymous.

Similarly, the word "affect" is not completely congruent with the word "mood," but, as used in a public forum, "affect" does mean "mood." To report that the patient exhibited a "flattening of affect" is to say that he seemed emotionally blunted, or that his mood did not seem to fluctuate normally. The latter phrases are homely ones, well understood by a judge or by a juror of average intelligence. Even if "flattened affect" has a faintly different tinge of meaning, the layman will never grasp the intended difference. The alleged precision of the scientific term is often spurious.

Double Meaning

This problem of translating medical jargon into plain English is one that haunts all medical witnesses. In psychiatry it is doubly vexatious, because many psychiatric terms are only special modifications of ordinary English words. Consider a word like "ego" which has a broad meaning in general English and a specialized one in psychiatry. The word "psychosis," according to a well-known general dictionary, means "any mental process" though, of course, the specialist uses it in a much narrower sense. So with "affect" and "libido" and "catharsis" and "maniac" and "psychopath" and "complex" and "association" and "analysis" and "adjustment" and "anxiety" and "compensation" and "melancholia" and "hysteria" and "incompetent" and dozens of others. Let the reader define each of these words in its specialized psychiatric sense; and then let him turn to a standard nonmedical dictionary and read the first definition there. The difference between the general and the special meaning will be striking. When the psychiatrist speaks, he means one thing; but the jury hears something else. To the psychiatrist the word "hysteria" suggests a convulsion, a blindness, or a paralysis; to the layman it suggests a temper tantrum. To the juror nothing is more obvious than the fact that the word "psychopath" means "insane" because, after all, a psychopathic ward is for insane persons. Yet psychiatrists who quarrel as to the meaning of that word "psychopath" are generally agreed on one point: whatever else it means, it does *not* mean "insanity." Thus this word used by the expert is given an almost opposite meaning when heard by the layman. The plaintiff who is "anxious" to get a judgment, obviously (in lay eyes) suffers from "anxiety" to win his case. Yet the psychiatrist has a much narrower definition of "anxiety" than that.

The Process of Clarification

The psychiatrist unaccustomed to public appearances must bewilder, amuse or mislead his auditors when he uses words which mean one thing to him but something quite different to the layman. Several methods are available for clarifying these words. He can, wherever possible, furnish his reports in lay language. Or he can use the technical term and follow it up immediately with an explanation. Or he can prime the attorney to ask him to explain certain words. For example, it is generally agreed among psychiatrists that the phrase "mental disease" will be reserved for psychoses. Reciting

his opinion about a severe psychoneurotic, the expert might testify:
"I found no evidence of mental disease." To the jury, this is a clean
bill of mental health. If the patient has a severe psychoneurosis, this
would be a most misleading impression. The simplest procedure
would be to testify: "I found no evidence of insanity." Or if the
record already reads "no evidence of mental disease," the doctor can
add, "by which I mean, no evidence of insanity." Or (if he can
depend on it) he might wait for the attorney to ask: "When you say
no evidence of mental disease, do you mean that the patient was
mentally normal?" This would, of course, give the opportunity to
explain that the subject had a "nervous" or "emotional" disease
rather than a "mental" disease.

Consider the following testimony: "The patient showed marked
psychomotor retardation and considerable inhibition of speech; affect,
however, was flat, and not in accordance with the apparent retardation; the ego was functioning poorly as shown by numerous instances
of lack of contact with reality. This was evidenced not by disorientation but by judgmental defects. His personality is constricted
and there is preoccupation of a dysphoric nature. Some ideas of
reference were implied though no frank delusion-formation was
evident."

This is just jargon. Even to psychiatrists, a word like "dysphoric"
is practically obsolete. A medical witness should know better than
to offer this kind of testimony to a lay jury. If his compulsion to
pronounce these words is irresistible, he might, at least, define them
as he goes along. The same thoughts could be expressed in lay language—perhaps with less precision, but with more clarity, by some
phrasing like this:

"His voice was low and monotonous. He spoke little, and volunteered nothing. It was practically necessary to drag words out of
him in order to get an answer. Yet he did not seem especially depressed or worried. Rather, his mood was one of blank dullness:
he was neither elated nor dejected. He felt that people were referring
to him when they spoke with each other privately, but he did not show
any clear-cut delusions about this—just vague ideas that he was the
subject of other people's conversation. . . . The patient knew the
day and the year and he knew where he was, but he had a rather
foggy grasp on the finer details of what was going on around him.
He displayed poor judgment, too." (Give example.)

The only technical term here is "delusion" and that is a word that
has accepted legal standing. The adjectives "elated" and "dejected"
can be understood in their lay senses. References to the "constricted

personality" were omitted.   Some mention, in simple language, might be made of the preoccupation and dysphoria.

Before going to court the witness would do well to review his proposed testimony in order to eliminate words which will not be understood at all—or misunderstood.   As some help in this, the following two lists are offered.   The first gives words which the layman thinks he knows but which he usually misunderstands when he hears a psychiatrist use them.   The second is a list of words which the average juror cannot understand at all without some definition or explanation.

Index Expurgatorius [1]

List 1.   *Words which the intelligent layman thinks he knows— but which he usually does not know:*   These are standard English words which the psychiatrist uses in a specialized sense.   (See glossary at end of book.)   In giving testimony he must be careful not to use these words without making it clear that they have specialized meaning.

Adjustment	Erotic	Moron
Affect	Extrovert	Negativistic
Analysis	Fabrication	Obsession
Anesthesia	Fugue	Oriented
Anxiety	Hallucination	Paranoiac
Association	Hypnotize	Pathological Liar
Catharsis	Hypochondriac	Phobia
Complex	Hysteria	Psychoanalysis
Compulsion	Identify	Psychopath
Concussion	Illusion	Psychosis
Conversion	Incompetent	Retardation
Delirium	Infantilism	Shock Therapy
Delusions	Inferiority Complex	Stream
Dementia	Libido	Transference
Deterioration	Mania	Trauma
Ego	Mannerism	Waxy Flexibility
Electric Shock	Melancholia	

List 2.   *Words which the layman knows he does not understand:*   These words annoy him.   Where possible a rough equivalent should be given, either instead of, or in addition to, the technical term.   A

---

[1] This caption is a good example of what *not* to do. Many readers will have to look up this phrase in a dictionary, and this means that I have aired my learning at the cost of irritating the reader. An item on the *index expurgatorius* is a work which is forbidden until amended. So with the words in these two lists. But it is bad writing and worse speaking to use phrases which are as obscure to the average auditor as this one.

good test of the psychiatrist's ingenuity is to see if he can describe a case without using any of these words.

Abreaction	Euphoria	Oedipus Complex
Alzheimer's	Globus Hystericus	Paranoid
Ambivalent	Hebephrenic	Psychasthenia
Amnesia	Id	Psychodynamic
Aphasia	Idea of Reference	Psychometric
Catatonic	Intelligence Quotient	Psychomotor
Confabulation	Introverted	Sadistic
Constitutional Psycho-	Involution Melancholia	Schizoid
path	Korsakow's Syndrome	Schizophrenia
Dementia Precox	Narcosynthesis	Sensorium
Disorientation	Neologism	Verbigeration
Etiology		

Clarification in Action

Perhaps the psychiatrist's report reads that "during the narcosynthesis, the patient exhibited considerable abreaction." It would be fatuous to read it that way to a jury, though I have heard it done. It is better to describe the procedure of narcosynthesis and the kind of emotional discharge which took place. "A lump in the throat due to a nervous spasm of the gullet" may not be elegant scientific English, but it conveys a better picture than "globus hystericus." A word like "verbigeration" may be graphically described.

The psychiatrist knows just what he means when he says "I administered electric shock," but to the jury it sounds like some kind of malpractice. The claimant's doctor may testify that the patient "exhibited anxiety" in his office. On cross-examination, the opposing attorney is almost certain to say, "Wouldn't anybody be anxious about the results of an examination when he is suing for $50,000?" This makes the jury laugh and for the moment the psychiatrist appears to be the butt of the laughter. Of course he can explain later that he was using "anxiety" in a special sense. It is better to avoid giving such an opening by describing the manifestations of that anxiety—the furrowed brow, the sweaty palms, the shaky hands, the vaguely expressed fears, the evidences of interrupted sleep, etc. I have heard a psychiatrist testify that the defendant (in a criminal action) was "delirious," only to hear the prosecution retort: "Delirious with joy at your findings, I am sure." Here again, it is better to describe the excitement, the visions, the confusion, the screaming, the noise, the agitation, rather than to use the correct but easily misunderstood word "delirium."

Something more is involved here than a battle of wits or an exercise in semantics. Psychiatry must make itself understood by the public, not only in the courtroom but also from the lecture platform and in the schools. The witness who learns the craft of expressing himself in vivid and not-easily-misunderstood words has enormously enriched his potentialities for public education.

Chapter 22

CROSS-EXAMINATION

Reluctance to submit to cross-examination is the conscious or unconscious reason for the refusal of many doctors to testify in court. This is sometimes a fear of being made uncomfortable or even ridiculous; and sometimes it is simply that the physician is so accustomed to *ex cathedra* statements to the public that he feels any cross-questioning is an indignity. However, medicine is a social science; and of the fields of medicine none has more impact on the public than psychiatry. What the psychiatrist does requires community sanction to an even greater degree than the activities of other physicians. This is because, of all medical specialists, the psychiatrist is one who handles society's trouble-makers, the one who is most often asked, in effect, to deprive a person of his liberty, his franchise, control of his own funds, and custody over his own children. In view of the serious social implications of psychiatry and of the dependence of mental hygiene activities on social support, the psychiatrist has a peculiar duty to submit his credo to public inspection. And cross-examination in the courtroom is one of the instruments with which the doctrines of psychiatry are put to the test of public acceptability. Cross-examination will here be considered in five areas: [1]

1. Criminal cases: cross-examination of the defense expert.
2. Criminal cases: cross-examination of the prosecutor's expert.
3. Personal injury cases: cross-examination of the claimant's expert.
4. Personal injury cases: cross-examination of the defense expert.
5. Cross-examination through the use of books and articles.

Examination of the Defense Psychiatrist in a Criminal Case

In a criminal case the defense psychiatrist has been put on the stand because the attorney expects him to testify that the defendant has a mental disease as a result of which he did not realize that the act was wrong. The district attorney in cross-examination, is likely to take the position that the defendant has only "put on an act" which

---

[1] Much of this material is an expansion of the author's article, "On Being Cross-Examined," *American Journal of Psychiatry*, CVI (December, 1949), 424.

fooled the psychiatrist. He will emphasize the fact that a psychiatric diagnosis is usually made by the patient's words and actions rather than by objective findings. "How do you know he had delusions?" the prosecutor might ask. Generally it comes down to the fact that the patient told the doctor that there was a plot against him or that people were looking at him in a suspicious way or something of that sort. The cross-examiner will then come back with: "In other words, doctor, you find he has a delusion because he told you so himself."

This kind of cross-examination comes as a shock to the inexperienced witness. He has been trained to attach great importance to the history and complaints given by the patient, and to his behavior and actions. Now a lawyer comes along and sneers at that and says, in effect, "You're a dupe for taking these at face value."

Perhaps the best way to handle that is to insist that the diagnosis is based on *total* examination, to point out that the patient's words are inherently consistent with a well-recognized psychotic pattern, that his behavior fits the same pattern, that his appearance likewise gears into the picture, and that the *totality* of these findings, not any one of them, spelled out the diagnosis. The cross-examiner may now try to break these points down one by one. The experienced witness may admit that any *one* finding is insignificant, but every time he says this he repeats that the combination of the findings and not the separate findings made the diagnosis.

For instance, the cross-examiner will ask how the witness made the diagnosis of mania. The answer is that it was based on euphoria, talkativeness, grandiose delusions, and flight of ideas. He then asks: "Does the fact that the patient felt happy mean he is insane? After all, numerous people feel happy much of the time. And surely talkativeness does not prove a psychosis," and so on. If the doctor passively agrees that each item is insignificant, he is, in effect, saying that the diagnosis is based on a sum of six or seven ciphers. He will want to explain that, while many people feel happy, they do not normally feel happy in jail; or at least not as happy as this man was; and that, in any event, it was not the euphoria which was significant but the euphoria in combination with everything else.

Occasionally an attorney barks out a short question and then demands: "Answer Yes or No." The witness is not bound by this. He has the right to explain what he means, and if the attorney insists on a one-word answer, he can turn to the judge and say that a simple "Yes" or "No" would be misleading. His Honor will almost certainly tell the doctor to explain or amplify.

Examination of the Prosecutor's Psychiatrist

Testifying for the state in a criminal action the psychiatrist will probably say that the defendant has no psychosis; or that, if he does have a psychosis, it has not deprived him of his power to realize that the act was wrong. The defense attorney usually attacks this testimony on the basis of the adequacy of the examination. If the examiner spent one and a half hours with the patient, he will ask if a ninety-minute examination is enough to tell all about a patient's personality. The doctor will have to answer that it is enough time in which to recognize a psychosis. If he asks whether the witness could swear that the man did not exhibit psychotic behavior the day before or the day after he examined him, the witness will have to concede the possibility, but in the same breath will doubt the probability. In any event, he is testifying to the defendant's condition when he examined him. That is all anybody can ask.

Another area for cross-examination by the defense counsel is this: He will perhaps describe the gruesome circumstances under which the crime was committed and ask whether a person with a normal mind could do that. Or he will tell about the defendant's underprivileged childhood (or conversely his overprotected childhood) and suggest that no person who had had that kind of childhood could now be normal. He will quote a low I.Q., or evidence of depraved or vicious habits, or anecdotes of behavior oddities, and ask if all that does not indicate something wrong with the defendant's mind. He may even have unearthed the fact that the defendant was once called a psychopath and ask whether "psyche" does not mean "mind" and whether "path" means "disease," therefore "psychopath" means he has a diseased mind.

None of these queries is difficult to handle. With a little reflection the expert can work out the appropriate answer to each. The trouble is that unless he anticipates this line of cross-examination, he may be caught off guard, sitting in the goldfish bowl of the witness stand, without time to do any reflecting. That is why it is worth while to list these common questions; the witness can anticipate them and be prepared for them when they come.

Examination of a Claimant's Psychiatrist

In a personal injury action, if a psychiatrist has been called to the stand by the plaintiff, it is because he is prepared to testify that the accident caused certain damage to the nervous system, either mechanically or through its emotional impact. Where there is

obvious structural injury the dispute will center around the permanence of the damage. This kind of cross-examination is not difficult
to meet, since there will be objective findings to support the diagnosis
and prognosis. A question which may bring grief to the witness
concerns how many similar cases he has seen with this grave prognosis. If he says that the present psychosis was caused by the head
injury, he may be asked whether recovery is not to be expected.
If he says it is unlikely, he may be challenged to cite cases in his own
experience in which the psychosis was permanent. Here too, if the
doctor expects this, he will be prepared to meet it.

A different problem arises when the disorder was due to the emotional effects of the accident. The expert will be asked how he
knows the patient really has the psychoneurosis, since objective findings may be nil. Conversion reactions are the commonest of the
traumatic neuroses, and these are the disorders where we do have
objective findings like hypesthesia, tubular vision, lost pharyngeal
reflexes, and the like. Of course, a cross-examiner may suggest that
these symptoms were malingered, but the doctor is on safe ground
emphasizing that these are the classical stigmata of hysteria and
that malingerers do not usually select just these few isolated findings.
In the pure anxiety reactions following trauma, the diagnosis is
supported by evidences of the anxiety and with an insistence on the
psychiatrist's special skill in recognizing anxiety when he meets it.

However, the insurance company lawyer is not through yet. He
has two other lines of attack. One touches on the relationship between the accident and the neurosis; the other concerns the permanence of the damage. He may present evidences of emotional conflict
in the patient long before the accident: marital discord, worry about
his job, etc. He will then ask why these could not have caused the
psychoneurosis. To this it may be said that these factors *were* contributory, but that the accident was the precipitating cause. Otherwise we would have to assume a prodigious coincidence; and we do
not believe in coincidences so extraordinary as to suppose that a man
happened to be on the verge of getting an acute neurotic reaction
anyway, and that by coincidence he just happened to suffer an accident at the same time.

Perhaps the trial does not come up until a few years after the
accident. The patient is still in a wheel chair with hysterical paralysis. The defense attorney will remind the jury of the many healing
shrines throughout the world, or of the numerous successful instances
of faith cures. He will describe the piles of crutches at each shrine,
or the anecdotes of the beneficiaries of faith healing, and point out

that these patients can get completely well. Why then, he will ask, does the expert say that this disability is permanent? One answer is that we know these miracles do occur, and maybe there will be a miracle in this case too; but that it is poor medical judgment to depend on miracles. In nonhysterical types of traumatically induced psychoneuroses, the witness may want to remind the court that the patient's age, the present duration of the symptoms, and the poor emotional background (which the defense attorney himself has stressed) all conspire to make this a case with a poor prognosis.

Suppose the psychiatrist is prepared to testify that the claimant is seriously, perhaps totally, disabled. Just before he goes to court, he hears that for months the patient has been driving himself around in his car. That happened to me once, many years ago, and I hastily withdrew from the case. I felt that I would be in trouble either way. If I said he was seriously disabled the company lawyer would ask if he could drive a car. Suppose I said, "Yes." Then he cannot be so severely disabled. Suppose I said, "No, he cannot drive." What would happen to my credibility when they proved that he was driving a car? Accordingly I abandoned the case. One of my more courageous colleagues remained with it. The cross-examining attorney approached and said: "Now, doctor, I have just one little question, which you can answer very simply. Is this man able to drive a car?" His answer was: "Not if I'm a passenger in it, he isn't."

Looking back at it, I see that this was the intelligent way of meeting that line of cross-examination. The answer admitted that he was technically capable of driving, but suggested that, because of his disability, he would be a bad driver. It implied that he could never hold a job where driving was required.

A favorite cross-examining device is to ask the plaintiff's expert what else could cause the symptom. For instance, the lawyer asks: "You have testified that this headache is an aftereffect of the injury. Now, doctor, as an expert neuropsychiatrist, tell the jury what else could cause the headache." The physician could oblige and recite a long list of conditions running alphabetically from arteriosclerosis to yellow fever. The lawyer will keep prodding: "What else?" Then he will say with a smile, "That's all." Of course, the implication is that, when 65 other things could cause headache, the witness is presumptuous in blaming the accident.

One way to meet this situation is to say, "What else could cause headache? You mean in this case, or in other cases?" If the lawyer says, "I mean in general," the judge or the plaintiff's attorney will intervene and say, "We're not interested in other cases." If the lawyer says, "In this case," the answer, if it is true, can be: "In this case, nothing else could have caused this headache."

Examination of the Defense Expert in a Personal Injury Action

The expert for the defendant in a personal injury action must expect that the claimant's attorney will try to prove that the examination was inadequate. Suppose the doctor testifies that he found no serious effects of the injury. "Ah," says the attorney, "but what did you find when you examined the olfactory nerve?" The doctor probably has not tested smell. Few neuropsychiatrists do. "Do you mean to say," says the lawyer, "that you didn't even examine the *first* cranial nerve?" It sounds as if the doctor must have done a very inadequate examination if he did not even get started on the cranial nerves. Of course, once you think of it, the answer is obvious. The accident could not have caused olfactory loss, or the patient made no complaint of it.

However, to be on the safe side, the experienced examiner follows a standard neurologic and psychiatric form, and omits nothing from the examination. Naturally, there are always tests in the footnotes that no examiner will have time to do. If a lawyer asks whether the witness tested for Gerhardt's Syndrome or found a positive Soderbergh's sign, he can say that he never heard of it. The lawyer cannot prove that either of those is of any importance or that American doctors have ever heard of them. See pages 344 to 353.

The insurance company expert frequently underplays the disability and implies that there is a volitional element in the prolongation of the symptoms. This opens the door to cross-examination on motives. "Do you mean to tell this jury, that a man would refuse to return to a $75-a-week job in order to draw $25 a week compensation?" The psychiatrist knows that this is a perfectly possible mechanism; but it sounds incredible to the jury. Experienced defense witnesses, therefore, do not emphasize the motivation factor so much as they emphasize their belief in the transiency of the symptoms. It is hard to neutralize this by cross-examination, because it is largely a matter of opinion and prophecy.

Cross-Examination Based on Medical Literature

Sometimes a witness is confronted with a book and asked how it happens that he disagrees with the distinguished author. Since a book cannot be cross-examined, it is not good legal evidence. But if the witness admits that the writer is an authority, some judges will allow the book as a basis for examining the witness. Take an example. The doctor has testified that this psychosis or psychoneurosis was due to the trauma. The insurance company says it was inherited because the plaintiff had an aunt who was known throughout the neighborhood as an eccentric. On cross-examination, the witness has denied the hereditary factor. The lawyer now approaches, holding a slim fabrikoid volume. He asks: "Do you consider Edward Strecker and Franklin Ebaugh as authorities in the field of psychiatry?" Of course the answer is, "Yes." He then introduces the book and reads a statement on page 6: "No one can doubt the importance of heredity as a factor in the production of mental disease."

There are several ways of meeting this challenge. The witness can ask in what year the book was published. In this example, the lawyer has cited the 1925 edition. Even if he should be citing a 1950 text, the witness often looks relieved and says that psychiatry has made a lot of progress since that book was written. Or he asks to examine the entire paragraph, and often finds (as he would in this instance) that the sentence is torn out of context and that the whole burden of the paragraph was actually to underplay heredity. Or he could point out that the distinguished author's remarks are true *in general* but that no two cases are alike, and *in this case* the witness is certain that heredity played no role, however important it might be in other cases.

Books can be found which will support any point of view. An attorney will look for a book containing a statement favorable to his side. Most lawyers seem to dig up only rather old books, so that generally the doctor can depend on the obsolescence of the volume to relieve him of appearing to disagree with an authority. Usually, however, the best way of neutralizing a book is to state frankly that opinions in a book are always general, that in practice every patient must be considered individually, and that few people in real life conform to textbook pictures.

It comes as a surprise to some psychiatrists to learn that medical books and articles are inadmissible, as such, in evidence. As Singer and Krohn [2] put it, there are four good reasons for rejecting books: (1) Medical progress is so rapid that even last year's book may be obsolete by now; (2) the book is usually a compilation of other authorities' reports and, therefore, from the legal viewpoint, a book

---

[2] H. D. Singer and W. O. Krohn, *Insanity and Law* (Philadelphia: P. Blakiston's Son & Co., Inc., 1924).

is essentially hearsay; (3) the author did not write his text under oath; and (4) the author is not available for cross-examination.

If the witness himself is the author of the book, he can be confronted with the text and asked to explain how it appears that he is disagreeing with himself. (Some courts, though, will not permit an author to be cross-examined on his own book, holding that the inadmissibility of books is an invariable rule.) [3] This can usually be answered either on the basis of progress in medicine since the book was written, or in terms of the general nature of statements in the book, whereas this case is an exception.

When a medical witness finds himself confronted with a book, it is only because he himself has opened the door to it. He can exclude any article or text by simply stating that his opinion is based on his own study and experience and not on any particular book. If asked whether a certain writer is a recognized authority, he can answer, "In some things yes; in others, no." If the expert will maintain this position, there is no way of confronting him with apparent contradictions from any book or paper. The cross-examining attorney may be very persistent and ask whether the expert's study did not include certain volumes. This is asked in the hope that the witness will name one particular book which he acknowledges as one of the sources of his own knowledge. Then the lawyer may produce the text named and use it to contradict the witness. The expert avoids this by stating that he has studied many books in his specialty, and that his opinion in this case is not derived from any one particular volume. Once he testifies that his opinion (even "in part") is based on a particular book, then he can be vigorously cross-examined against that text to measure his recollection. Even then, the only effect of such cross-examination could be to show that he had misquoted. That will not by itself destroy the credibility of his testimony, though it may leave a bad impression on the judge and jury.

Sometimes a witness is more or less compelled to cite books. This occurs when the expert on the other side has quoted a well-known author to bolster his own statement. If the jury is left with the belief that this represents standard psychiatric thinking, the other expert in self-defense may have to cite contradicting authorities. In one case, the insurance company contended that the child's neurotic symptoms were due to overstudy and not to the emotional effect of a boiler explosion across the street. The company psychiatrist cited an old book which did emphasize the role of "overstudy" in producing neurotic

[3] Mix v. Staples, 17 New York Supplement 775.

symptoms. The claimant's psychiatrist knew that that was an obsolete thesis. But it was the only "famous" authority cited to the jury, and it was apparent that they concluded that this must be standard psychiatric doctrine. This implied that the plaintiff's doctor was heretical when he said that the boiler explosion could have played a role. In that situation, the doctor asked to be recalled to the stand (as a "rebuttal" witness), re-affirmed his position, and when asked to support it, cited many other and more modern textbooks. This is, in general, a risky procedure, because it is so difficult to argue with a book. But in situations like this, it may be necessary.

Generally, the witness can avoid being asked why he disagrees with eminent authorities by simply not recognizing any book at all as the source of his opinion.

Chapter 23

COURTROOM ETIQUETTE

In the courtroom the expert witness appears on a well lighted stage. The judge and attorneys represent the higher echelons of his community; the jury and spectators are a cross section of the people among whom he lives. In many trials his testimony will be broadcast through the newspapers. The doctor's community standing may be conspicuously affected, for better or for worse, by his activities in the courtroom.

For an expert witness in any medical specialty, this is a sobering thought. A reputation may be enhanced or destroyed, not so much by the scientific accuracy of the testimony, as by the doctor's general demeanor in the forensic limelight. The psychiatrist has even more at stake than his medical brethren have. This is so for three reasons: *first,* the psychiatrist's work is more sensitive to the climate of public opinion than is the work of the ophthalmologist or the pathologist; *second,* psychiatric testimony deals with material which is often highly dramatic, and always in an area where every layman considers himself something of an expert; *third,* the public is always suspicious of "brain-specialists," always eager to grasp at any evidence that the psychiatrist is himself an eccentric or at best a dilettante in the never-never land of mumbo-jumbo. To himself in particular, to his specialty in general, the psychiatrist thus owes a peculiar duty: a duty to reflect the psychiatrist as an individual who is honest, objective, and equally free of cant and clownishness. The doctor who values his community standing and the general status of his art will avoid the one extreme of sounding like a stuffed shirt, and the opposite extreme of seeming to be a courtroom tout. There is great temptation in both directions. The psychiatrist of one temperament will use the witness box as a lecture platform, spout solemnly to the judge and jury, explode indignantly when questioned, and retire from the stand, having left an impression that he is but a pompous pedant. His colleague of the opposite temperament will soon become friendly with the attorneys and attendants, call them by first names, spend hours in courtroom corridors exchanging gossip, and await with painfully obvious interest, the verdict in any case in which he has testified.

So much for the preaching. But how about the practice?

Making an Entrance.—Ordinarily a medical witness is not present when the case opens. When he enters, therefore, the trial is in process. As he opens the door of the courtroom, he becomes a magnet for spectators and jurors. If he is just a casual bystander, eyes quickly turn away from him. But as the psychiatrist in the case, perhaps a key witness, presumably an interesting one, he is conspicuous. It takes a certain amount of poise to carry off with grace an entrance as public as this. Sometimes a doctor, flushed with his own importance, or pressured by a need for saving time, will barge down the center aisle, brusquely open the rail gate, tap the lawyer on the shoulder, and whisper hoarsely, "I'm here." The motive of this exhibition is understandable: he wants to be sure that the lawyer will call him as soon as possible, rather than allow him to wait while several lay witnesses (the ones whose time is *not* valuable) drone on.

Discourtesy and exhibitionism are never apparent to the practitioners. The physician just described would deny that his behavior falls into either category. He would be wrong. If the judge does not publicly reprove the doctor for such brusque behavior, he will none the less remember it. From the bench it seems boorish.

Notifying the Attorney.—How to notify the attorney that the doctor has arrived depends somewhat on the architecture of the courtroom, on whether the lawyer knows the physician by sight, and on whether he has an aide at the counsel table with him. Usually counsel sit with their backs to the entrance door. The doctor could walk softly to the nearest attendant, whisper his name, and ask the attendant to pass the word along to the attorney. Sometimes the witness has assured the lawyer that he would be in court at a certain hour, and if he arrives on time he need not do anything. The attorney will look for him, or even stand up between witnesses and ask "Is Dr. A. in the courtroom?"

Informal Tribunals.—In the workmen's compensation bureaus of some states, the atmosphere is informal. Personnel speak casually, sometimes flippantly to one another. Robes, flags, and other symbols of majesty are absent. In this environment the doctor is not likely to affront judicial decorum.[1] And in some cities the police (magis-

[1] This is not a safe general assumption, however. In many of these less formal tribunals, the presiding magistrate may maintain a high level of decorum and dignity. If he is a stranger to the court, the doctor assumes that it is a place of formal protocol until he learns otherwise.

trates') courts are highly informal tribunals, too. But in other jurisdictions, even these courts are places of protocol.

Order in the Courtroom.—The upper courts (at the county, district or higher levels) are almost invariably arenas where dignity is a
prized quality. The judges—even the few who are not themselves
models—are quick to resent any implication of flippancy, discourtesy,
or disrespect. The need for maintaining the proper air is sometimes
a tribulation to the energetic, easily bored doctor. He is sitting on
a hard bench, completely uninterested in the testimony of the witness
ahead of him. He has a newspaper folded in his arm. It is a great
temptation to glance at the headlines. And perhaps the pages can be
turned without the usual tell-tale rattle of rustling paper. But it is
a temptation to be resisted. From his elevated perch, the judge can
see any newspaper-reading spectator, and he construes this as contempt for the court.

Or perhaps the doctor has slipped into a seat next to one occupied
by a fellow-witness whom he has already met. It is a chance to
exchange whispers about the progress of the case. This too is an
opportunity that must be foresaken. That preliminary *sotto voce* instruction to the attendant was all right. But a whispered conversation
soon furnishes an audible background to the trial that will bring an
irritated rap from the judicial gavel. During the brief waiting period
(it may seem hours but will probably be only minutes), the expectant
witness must behave with the motionless taciturnity of a Trappist
monk.

Mounting the Stand.—When the doctor mounts the stand, the
judge—out of courtesy for a fellow professional man—will often say
"Good morning" or "Good afternoon." No doctor will have any
difficulty in making the reply courteous. It may be mentioned,
though, that "Good morning, Judge" is suitable for the golf course
rather than for the courtroom. In the special environment of the
courthouse, the experienced doctor says "Good morning, sir." For
some strange reason, the vocative "Judge" in the courtroom itself is
often as grating to the jurist as "Hello, Doc" is to the physician.

His Honor.—As everyone knows, the conventional appellation to
the judge is "Your Honor." However, it is gauche to add "Your
Honor" to every clause in answering the judge's questions. And
there will be questions from the bench! While some witnesses are
questioned only by the two attorneys, the psychiatrist is almost always
in receipt of one or more direct questions from the judge. As an

intelligent and sophisticated citizen, the judge likes to keep abreast of modern psychiatric thought, and he frequently questions the expert—sometimes rather tangentially—on the content of his evidence. So the "Your Honor" appendix to the answer may be replaced by an occasional "Sir" without anyone suffering pain.

The Fade-out.—If the case is nearing its close, if the physician has already allocated the rest of the afternoon to it, and if he has any personal, financial, or professional interest in the outcome, it is a great temptation for the doctor to linger after he has left the stand. However, unless he has been instructed specifically to remain, the experienced doctor rapidly and quietly fades out of the scene as soon as he has stepped down from the witness box. Lingering creates two impressions, both of them bad. It suggests that the doctor is not a very busy practitioner, and it suggests that he has some personal investment in the outcome of the case. By contrast, a prompt departure from the courthouse emphasizes the fact that he is disinterestedly willing to let justice take its course; and, incidentally, that he has other work to do.

APPENDIX

Appendix A

LEGAL LEXICON FOR DOCTORS *

The physician's lot will be a happier one if he is familiar with the lawyer's concept of the words and phrases below. This lexicon does not give technically precise legal definitions. Indeed some of the explanations will appear to attorneys as quite lacking in that verbal exquisiteness in which lawyers like to indulge. However, such lexicographical nicety is unnecessary, since there is no reason for the medical practitioner to have that rich familiarity with legal language which refined definitions would give. What is offered here is a battery of *operational* definitions: explanations of what the words mean in actual use.

Admission against interest. A statement made by a party to litigation which would be helpful to his opponent at the trial. For example, the claimant contends that the accident caused his present headaches. However, in giving his medical history he tells the physician that he has had headaches all his life. Obviously, if this bit of history becomes part of the trial record, it will help the defendant in the suit, not the claimant. Such a statement is an admission against interest. In criminal cases, the examining physician may elicit, from the defendant, statements that may be damaging to his defense; for example, a confession to the crime, or a statement that may neutralize a claim of self-defense. These, too, are admissions against interest. The circumstances under which witnesses may testify about such admissions are determined by rules of evidence. Yet when an admission against interest *is* admitted at a trial, it naturally tends to damage the party's case.

Arraignment. The point in a criminal procedure (usually after indictment but before trial) where the defendant is asked whether he pleads guilty or not guilty. Psychiatrists examining criminal defendants are interested in knowing whether the examination is taking place before or after arraignment. It is sometimes simpler to make a nonjudicial or at least nonpenal disposition of a case if the defendant has not yet been arraigned.

Annulment. With respect to law of marriage, a decision that the marriage was never legally valid. Like divorce, it dissolves the marriage. Unlike divorce, however, an annulment does not impose on the husband an

---

* Prepared with the cooperation of Leslie S. Kohn, member of the New Jersey Bar, former editor of the *New Jersey Law Journal*.

obligation to continue to support his ex-spouse. (If the marriage never
existed, he never had such obligation.) In some states, the effect of
annulment is to bastardize the children, because, in a sense, it declares
that the parents were never legally married. In those jurisdictions, annulment is obviously more disturbing to the children than divorce would be.
Psychiatrists are involved in annulment proceedings in two situations:
(*a*) where there is an allegation that one spouse had fraudulently concealed a pre-existing mental disorder or degenerative disease: here the
annulment, if granted, would be on the theory that there was fraud which
made the marriage contract dishonest and legally ineffective from the
beginning; and (*b*) where it is alleged that, because of mental deficiency
or psychosis, one partner did not know what he was doing when he consented to the marriage. See Chapter 5 for further explanation.

Assault. Such conduct as would make a reasonable person believe that
injury will be done. The legal and common meanings of assault differ
somewhat. A violent physical attack would, in plain English, be an
assault. But this is not true in legal English. To the lawyer, the assault
is the threat rather than the actual attack. (The latter is a "battery.")
Technically, the psychological effect on the victim, not the intent of the
assailant, establishes the crime of assault.

Battery. Unlawfully touching another person. A physician who does a
spinal puncture without legal consent is committing a battery.

Bestiality. Sexual contact with an animal, though the indictment in most
states shows the word "sodomy." (See Sodomy, below.)

Blue ribbon jury. A jury made up of presumably superior citizens. Technically this is a "special jury." In some states, a "special panel" of
better-than-average citizens is prepared, and each side strikes off certain
names. The resultant jury in such a case is called a "struck jury."

Burden of proof. The duty to establish a certain legal position as a prerequisite to getting a favorable judgment. In a criminal trial the defendant does not have to prove his innocence, since everyone is presumed
innocent; the state has to prove his guilt. Thus, the prosecution carries
the "burden of proof." Similarly, in a civil action the plaintiff has to
prove the defendant's negligence, so that the claimant here carries the
burden of proof. If a physician is sued for malpractice, the patient must
prove his negligence; the doctor does not have to prove that he acted
properly (though it is a good idea to do so). In criminal cases guilt must
be proved "beyond a reasonable doubt." In civil actions the claim must
be established "by a preponderance of the evidence." These two phrases
are measures of the burden of proof. The Latin term is *onus probandi.*
In criminal prosecutions burden of proof is almost always on the state.
That is, the prosecution must affirmatively prove guilt. The defendant
does not have to prove innocence. If irresponsibility is the defense,
there may be a burden on the defendant to establish his "insanity." This
is because every man is presumed sane, just as every man is presumed
innocent. In some states, however, there is a strong compulsiveness to

the position that *onus probandi* is always on the prosecution; and, since having the appropriate mental state is part of guilt, the state has to prove the defendant's responsibility rather than *vice versa,* if the plea is one of irresponsibility. The weight of the psychiatrist's testimony and the emphasis the attorney may place on it will depend—among other things— on whether it is being used to help meet the burden of proof or merely to help neutralize it.

This question of "burden of proof" may be a life or death matter in capital cases where the psychiatric witnesses are evenly matched. If the prosecution has the burden of proving responsibility *beyond a reasonable doubt,* it does not meet the test in such a case. But in places where the *onus probandi* of the irresponsibility is on the defense, the latter will probably be considered as having failed in that duty when the expert testimony is so neatly balanced.

Burglary. Breaking and entering the dwelling house of another in the nighttime with intent to commit a felony there. This is the narrow and ancient definition. In states using this definition, it is not burglary to break into a house in the day time, nor into a factory at any time. However, in those states other crimes are set up to cover such offenses. In some jurisdictions the definition has been broadened or various degrees of burglary have been set up to include all kinds of breaking and entering. In nearly all states the intent of the defendant is a vital feature of the case, and that is where psychiatric testimony may be important.

Carnal abuse. In some states, any type of unlawful sexual handling or mishandling of another. In such jurisdictions, the phrase is broad enough to cover anything from kissing a little boy to violent rape. Other states have precise and more narrow definitions, generally indicating that the crime implies some contact with, or touching of, the genital or sexual organs.

Civil malpractice. Damaging a patient by reason of negligence, but not necessarily in such a way as to constitute a crime. The latter would be criminal malpractice. For example, doing an abortion in violation of the law is criminal malpractice. Negligently setting a fracture so that permanent deformity results is civil malpractice. The same act may give rise to two legal actions—one civil, one criminal. See Chapter 14, page 237.

Commitment. Restraining a person's liberty by putting him in the charge of someone else. When a judge says he committed six people today, he does not (usually) mean that he sent them to mental hospitals. He means, in all probability, that he sent them to jail or prison. He might use the word to indicate placing a person on probation, since in most courts the form of such a sentence is the defendant's "commitment" to the custody (or charge) of the chief probation officer. Physicians think of commitment as sending a patient to a hospital that has locked wards, and generally of sending him there against his will. (In some states a "voluntary commitment" is a contradiction in terms.) In the "Model Commitment

Law" [1] (see Appendix D) the term "commitment" is not used. It is referred to as "involuntary hospitalization" or as "certification." This is in line with modern mental hygiene concepts, since the word "commitment" does have the implication of imprisonment and is therefore undesirable for use with sick people who have committed no crime.

Contract. An agreement in which it is understood that, for a certain consideration, one or both parties will do (or refrain from doing) certain things. The law makes numerous hairsplitting distinctions in deciding whether a valid contract exists. The physician is not concerned with these semantic refinements. He is, however, interested in knowing when his relationship to a patient is a contractual one, since this has some bearing both on his obligations and on collecting his fee. And the psychiatrist may be asked about a patient's competency to make a contract or to be held for the performance of one. It therefore seems worth while to point out that a contract is not necessarily a formal legal document; it can be simply an informal, oral agreement, or even a situation or relationship in which each party assumes certain obligations to the other. If I enter a store and pick up a candy bar, I am making a contract. This is so because, knowing that it is a store, I know that the merchant is offering to sell, not give away, his wares. And he knows that by my act of picking the candy bar off the rack I am offering to buy it. If the price is plainly marked, all the elements of a contract now exist even though no words have been written or spoken. There is "consideration": that is, my money and his candy bar constitute "considerations." There is "agreement": there is an understanding that, in return for my dime, the merchant will do something—i.e., let me keep the candy. Conversely, in return for the candy bar I contract to do something—i.e., give him the dime. So when a patient calls on a doctor, he is making a contract; when a doctor receives the patient he is confirming the contract. One of the essential elements of a contract is the understanding by each party of what he is giving or losing. This is the basis for efforts to set aside contracts made by mentally ill persons—the contention that the patient did not understand what he was doing. For review of these features of contractual capacity, see page 189. For review of the contractual features of marriage, see page 76.

Contributory negligence. Negligence on the part of the complainant. A suit for damages in personal injury cases is based on the theory that the defendant (person being sued) was negligent. If I am hurt in an automobile accident, I cannot recover damages unless I prove that the driver was negligent. However, if my own negligence was also a factor, then I am responsible for some degree of "contributory negligence." A car has no right to run me down even if I cross against a red light. Still, by doing so I am contributing to the accident. In some states contribu-

---

[1] The official designation is "Draft Act Governing Hospitalization of the Mentally Ill." However, most persons identify this document as the "Model Commitment Law."

tory negligence is a bar to recovery of damages. In other states it merely reduces the amount of damages by the extent of the claimant's negligence. The matter is of interest to physicians chiefly in malpractice actions. If the patient fails to follow the doctor's instructions, this failure may have contributed to the damage. This contributory negligence on the part of the plaintiff (patient) may nullify the entire malpractice action; or at least it will reduce the recoverable money damages. See Situation 12, page 230; also page 237.

Criminal malpractice. Damaging a patient while committing a criminal act. Doing an illegal abortion would be an example of criminal malpractice. Executing a commitment paper without examining the patient is another example. This is malpractice because the doctor's negligence has harmed the patient. It is criminal because the affidavit on the commitment paper is now perjured. The affidavit says that statements on the form are true, and one of those statements was that the doctor personally examined the patient.

Defendant. In a criminal case, the person accused; in a civil action, the person being sued; in a malpractice case the doctor, when the patient is the plaintiff. In hearings which are administrative rather than judicial (for example, in most states, a workmen's compensation claim) the defendant may be called a "respondent" because he answers (i.e., responds to) the questions raised by the claimant.

Disposing mind. Legal jargon sometimes written into a will to indicate that the person writing the will is in the mood to, and has the intent of, making disposition of his property.

Dying declaration. A statement made by a man who knows he is dying, and who shortly thereafter does die. Such statements are given more weight as evidence than are other forms of hearsay, the theory being that a man who is about to die, and who knows it, would have no reason for telling a lie. However, there may be evidence that because of the subject's mental state, character, or temperament he might have a motive for concealing the truth even if he knew he were dying. That is the point where psychiatric testimony might be required. (In most states a dying declaration is not admissible in evidence if it be shown that the person did not believe in God.)

Exemplary damages. Award to discourage others from similar offense. Damages awarded to the plaintiff in excess of the actual damage suffered are known as "smart-money" or "punitive" damages, if the purpose of the excess is to punish the defendant. If the reason for the excessive award is to discourage others, the judgment is called "exemplary damages." In a malpractice action, for instance, the actual damage suffered by the patient might be negligible. The jury could award a substantial amount simply to discourage other doctors from being negligent. Such an award would be "exemplary" damages and the defendant (in this case the doctor) would have to pay them in dollars just as real as the money used to pay for "actual" damage. When the defendant in a tort action is psychotic, the jury does not award "punitive" damages, but only an amount which reasonably covers the damage suffered by the plaintiff. Punitive damages are usually not proper in a civil (non-criminal) suit except when the defendant was motivated by malice.

Felony. Serious crime. In most states crimes fall into two broad classes: misdemeanors and felonies. The misdemeanors are lesser (though not necessarily minor) offenses. In some jurisdictions the classification is "misdemeanor" and "high misdemeanor."

Fraud. Deliberate misrepresentation of some substantial fact which results in harm or damage to another person who relied on the representation. If a man should conceal from his fiancee the fact that he has epilepsy, this would be fraud if the fiancee can show that she would not have married him had she known of the epilepsy. (The latter proof is essential, since otherwise the plaintiff would not have relied on the misrepresentation.) If the man were psychotic there would ordinarily be no fraud, because generally he would be considered incapable of willfully and deliberately misrepresenting. There is also a species of fraud in which the defendant's willfulness is not essential.

Habeas corpus. A writ for bringing into court a person held in custody, so that the court may inquire into the propriety of that custody. Its applicability to mental patients is obvious. See page 194 for further discussion.

Hearsay evidence. Testimony based on what the witness heard (rather than on what he saw or did). When a doctor testifies that a patient paced the floor, this is direct evidence: it is not hearsay. When the doctor summarizes a history (furnished by the patient) that the patient complained of restlessness, this is hearsay. He is relating what the patient said, not what the witness (the doctor) saw. In general, hearsay is a sort of second rate evidence. Courts frown on it, though certain types of hearsay *are* admissible. The doctrine is important to psychiatrists as expert witnesses because much of the psychiatric examination is, after all, observation of what a patient says. If a psychiatrist testifies that the patient has a delusion of persecution this testimony, in a sense, is hearsay. It depends on the patient's having told the doctor that he is being persecuted. For a further discussion of this, see pages 264, 272, and 277.

Hypothetical question. See Chapter 20.

Indictment. A written statement, usually prepared by a prosecutor and approved by a grand jury, charging a person with crime. When he is asked to examine an offender, the psychiatrist wants to know whether he has been indicted yet. If the patient is clearly irresponsible, it is procedurally easier to make a medical disposition before rather than after indictment.

Infant. A person who has not attained "full age." In most states the age is set at twenty-one, so that a twenty-year-old man or woman is technically an infant.

Inquirendo de lunatico. A formal, court-controlled hearing to determine whether a patient is sane.

Inquisition. An official hearing, inquiry, or report, by or before a court.

Joint tort-feasor. One of two (or more persons) being sued as having jointly injured someone by reason of negligence. See Tort, below.

Libel. A letter, publication, or other writing which exposes someone to public contempt or ridicule. To call a man publicly (and in print or writing) an alcoholic, a malingerer, or a drug addict would be to libel him. See page 172. If the defamatory remark is spoken rather than written, it is "slander."

Mens rea. Guilty mind, wrongful intent, or intent to do harm.

Misdemeanor. A crime of lesser gravity than a felony. See Felony, above.

Murder. The unlawful and intentional killing of a human being. If the killing was accidental, it is a homicide but not necessarily a murder. If it resulted from negligence where no harm was intended, it is both manslaughter and homicide, but not necessarily murder. Many states have divided murder into two or more degrees according to the intent, premeditation, or willfulness of the perpetrator. Some states also have degrees of manslaughter, usually contingent on the extent of the defendant's negligence.

Nolle prosse or, more exactly, "nolle prosequi." A formal statement that the prosecutor, complainant, or plaintiff is not proceeding with his claim or charge.

Non suit. An adjudication that the plaintiff's case is not good enough to require the defendant to proceed with his defense. The plaintiff always opens the case, and during his half of the trial he must show at least a presumptive justification for the suit. If he fails to establish a *prima facie* case, the judge will not require the defendant to defend himself. Instead the judge adjudicates a non suit, thus terminating the case in favor of the defendant. In some states a non suit is called an "involuntary dismissal."

Non vult. A plea by a defendant in a criminal action which, in effect, is tantamount to a plea of Guilty, without formal acknowledgment that the defendant has committed the crime. It is a concession that the prosecution's case is so strong that the defendant is unwilling to go to trial.

Plaintiff. The person initiating a civil action. Thus in a malpractice action, the patient is the plaintiff and the doctor is the defendant. In an automobile accident case, the person who was injured is the plaintiff and the driver or owner of the car is the defendant. The plaintiff is also, in certain cases, called a claimant, complainant, libellant, or petitioner.

Privileged communication. A communication which may be kept confidential (or sometimes which *must* be kept confidential) even during a trial when the subject of that communication is itself part of the issue. For example, a lawyer cannot be ordered to take the witness stand and tell the jury what the client told him. Such communications are "privileged." So, except in divorce actions, are communications between husband and wife. In most states communications between a clergyman and his penitent, a doctor and his patient, are similarly privileged. In states where physician-patient communications are privileged, the protection extends only to situations where a *bona fide* relationship of patient and *treating* physician exists. Thus, an insurance company's doctor who examines an injured party on behalf of the company, and who is not asked to, nor expected to render treatment, is not in such a relationship. Communications to him would usually *not* be privileged.[2] Again, when a psychiatrist is asked by the prosecutor or court to examine a criminal defendant, and when the contact is exclusively a diagnostic one, with no treatment being offered or rendered, the conversation between the doctor and defendant is not protected by the privilege rule.

Punitive damages. Damages awarded in excess of the damage suffered, when the jury believes that the defendant was motivated by malice. See Exemplary damages, above.

Rape. Sexual intercourse with a woman under any of these four circumstances: (*a*) by force, against her will, (*b*) while she is under a specified "age of consent"—whether against her will or not, (*c*) by putting her in such fear or fright as to amount to duress, or (*d*) by some kind of trickery or deceit so that she is led to mistake the man for her husband. If the woman is psychotic or mentally defective, it is up to the court to determine whether she was without the capacity to give understanding consent. If the court so finds, the act is rape.

Rebuttal testimony. Additional testimony to refute evidence presented. In a trial, the plaintiff, complainant, or prosecutor presents his case first; then the defense calls his witnesses. Ordinarily the trial is thus made of these two parts. Sometimes, however, the plaintiff or prosecutor wants to refute some testimony brought out by the defense. He can then get another opportunity—this time to introduce "rebuttal testimony." For example, in a criminal action the state might bring in witnesses to show that the defendant committed the crime. Then, to the prosecutor's surprise, the defense calls a medical witness to testify that the defendant was psychotic. The prosecutor then has the right to call in a medical expert to refute this testimony. This third part of the trial would then be "rebuttal." If now the defense wants to neutralize this, there may even be a fourth stage—"surrebuttal" by the defense.

Res ipsa loquitur. A Latin phrase meaning, literally, "the thing speaks for itself." It does *not* mean that the negligence was so obvious that it spoke for itself. It is used by lawyers in a more restricted sense than that. It is part of the law of negligence and, so far as doctors are concerned, is invoked chiefly in malpractice actions. Technically it means that negligence will be assumed when the plaintiff (i.e., patient) was injured by an instrumentality entirely in the control of the defendant (doctor) or

---

[2] If the patient's own lawyer sent him to a physician for the purpose of being examined with the intent of having the doctor testify, then the doctor-patient relationship takes on some of the attributes of an attorney-client relationship. The doctor is, for the occasion, part of the attorney's staff. In some states this would make communications between the party and the doctor "privileged."

his agent, and when the use of that instrumentality does not ordinarily cause such damage. The classic example is the sponge left in the peritoneal cavity. The patient cannot directly *prove* that the surgeon was negligent. Here the instrumentality (the sponge) was entirely in the control of the surgeon (or the nurse or assistant as his agent). A sponge is not ordinarily left in the abdomen. Therefore, the fact that the sponge was left behind in this case raises a presumption of negligence which the surgeon must rebut. *Res ipsa loquitur* applies, since its two conditions were met. On the other hand, a deformity following the setting of a fracture does not raise any presumption of negligence. For one thing, the patient had some control of his limb motions (hence it was not entirely in the control of the doctor) and, for another, it cannot be said that deformities do not usually result from fractures. Thus neither element of *res ipsa loquitur* applies. The electric shock machine, the use of needles for insulin injections and spinal taps, and the application of physical therapy modalities are situations of interest to the psychiatrist where *res ipsa loquitur* might apply.

Respondent. The person who "answers," the defendant. In many states the employer (or his insurance company) in a workmen's compensation case is called a respondent. In some jurisdictions the party answering the action in a custody or divorce case would be called a respondent.

Self-incrimination. A statement which tends to incriminate the speaker. There are constitutional provisions in most states forbidding compulsory self-incrimination. Thus, a confession extorted by third degree methods would be an instance of compulsory self-incrimination. In many jurisdictions, it is assumed that when a policeman, detective, or person clothed with apparent legal authority questions a suspect, the latter is so cowed by the questioner's authority, that he feels "compelled" to answer. That is why police officers so often tell a suspect that whatever he says may be used against him. It is to put him on notice that he does not have to answer at all, and to remove the subsequent charge that the person's answers represented compulsory self-incrimination. The psychiatrist, particularly if representing the prosecutor, may sometimes be challenged in court on the theory that he "compelled" (by his air of authority) the defendant to tell things that were later used against him. Courts generally rule that statements made to a prosecutor's psychiatrist are *not* in the category of compulsory self-incrimination. (See the first section of Chapter 2.) However, to be on the safe side—ethically as well as legally—the psychiatrist should make it clear to the defendant, in advance, that he does not have to answer any questions.

Self-serving statements. A statement made by a party to a suit which has the effect of helping his own "side." Naturally most litigants will utter many such statements when on the witness stand. The driver, defending an auto accident case, will say he was driving slowly, while the pedestrian who is suing him will say that he (the pedestrian) had the green light. Each party has thus made a self-serving statement. And,

just as naturally, juries do not consider a self-serving statement necessarily true. One party might get a self-serving statement into the record
by having another witness (not the party himself) utter it, and this
might sound better to the jury. For example, the pedestrian-plaintiff
who was injured in the accident tells the doctor that he (pedestrian)
had the green light. The doctor, when testifying, tries to give a medical
history and mentions that his patient was crossing with a green light.
Thus the doctor is being used to put into the record a self-serving statement on behalf of his patient. It is because the ordinary medical history
is entirely in control of the patient that courts are reluctant to let expert
witnesses read such histories to the juries. They represent ways of getting self-serving statements into the record under circumstances more
favorable than if the plaintiff himself had uttered them. Generally, a self-
serving statement made out of court is not admissible as evidence when
someone (other than the person who made the statement) is testifying.
Under such circumstances, the self-serving statement, no matter how
honest the witness, is a species of inadmissible hearsay evidence. Also see
Hearsay, above.

Slander. A spoken libel. It is making an oral statement within the hearing
of a third party, which holds someone up to ridicule, contempt, or scorn.
It is spoken defamation. If a doctor tells someone else that X is a drug
addict or a syphilitic, this is slander. There are special circumstances
under which it is safe to make such statements, but the ground-rules here
vary considerably from state to state. Unlike libel, slander is not, by
itself, a crime. But it may be grounds for a suit for damages. See
pages 172 and 226.

Sodomy. Sexual perversion. The vocabulary of this subject is confused.
Sometimes sodomy means any kind of sexual relationship other than the
conventional one. Sometimes sodomy means a homosexual relationship
only, and excludes cunnilingus. In other jurisdictions, the term is limited
to buggery and excludes fellatio; sometimes *vice versa*. Statutes and
courts are often squeamish about defining the word with vividness, so that
about the only possible general statement would be that sodomy is sexual
perversion.

Subpoena. A writ ordering a person to appear in court (usually as a
witness). A subpoena to a witness usually includes a statement to the
effect that "You will appear before the court . . . at such a time and
place . . . fail not *under penalty* . . . of a $100 fine" (or some other
penalty). The document may be written partly in Latin, and the phrase
"under penalty" is Latinized to "subpoena."

Subpoena ad testificandum. A subpoena which orders a person to court
for the purpose of giving testimony.

Subpoena duces tecum. A subpoena which requires the witness to bring his
records as well as himself to court for the purpose of testifying. If a
doctor is handed an ordinary *subpoena ad testificandum,* he is under no
legal obligation to bring his records with him. However, the court may

frown on his trying to furnish details of the case without refreshing his memory by looking at his records. Hence many physicians make it a practice to bring records to court even if the subpoena is of the *ad testificandum* rather than of *duces tecum* variety.

Testator. A person making a will and bequeathing an estate.

Tort. A violation of a legal duty resulting in damages, which gives the injured party the right to sue but which does not arise out of a breach of contract. Injuring someone with your automobile is a tort if your negligence was a factor in the injury. (It is also sometimes a crime, but that is another matter.) The driver is not under any contract to refrain from injuring anybody, but he has a duty to drive carefully. If he negligently injuries someone, that person can sue, charging that the driver committed a tort. If a doctor undertakes to cure a patient and fails to do so, the patient can sue for breach of contract. If the doctor negligently injures the patient, he has committed a tort, and the patient can sue for malpractice—which is a tort action—instead of on the theory of a broken contract.[3] Wheras "intent" is an inherent part of a criminal act, it is not necessarily part of a tort. A psychotic person—or, for that matter, a child—is responsible for his torts, in the sense that he (or his parents or guardian) must compensate for damages; though he would probably not be responsible for a crime arising out of the same act. In one case, for example, a psychotic adolescent killed another boy. The patient was not guilty of the crime of murder or manslaughter because of his mental condition. But his parents had to pay money damages to the family on the theory that their negligence (or the patient's negligence, with them as his guardian) caused the damage and constituted a tort. A workmen's compensation claim is not, in these times, considered based on a tort. Thus a single event may lead—potentially at least—to several different kinds of suits. A man driving his employer's truck is in an accident with a car driven by a drunken driver. There is a criminal action against the latter, an action by the victim in tort, and an action by the victim against his employer in workmen's compensation. Much of the psychiatrist's court experience will be in tort actions, because of the frequency of head injury in accidents, or because of the frequent allegation of "nervousness" following injuries.

Tort-feasor. One who commits a tort.

Undue influence. The substitution of one person's desires for the real desire of the testator, as applied to wills, or to changes in the beneficiary of a life insurance policy. In a broader sense, it is the sort of influence which law and morals would condemn as improper. For instance, if, as a price for relieving the pain of a dying man, a doctor were to influence the testator to name him as his beneficiary, the influence would be clearly "undue." But if, because of the physician's devotion to duty, the testator

---

[3] A sensible doctor does not promise a cure, hence he enters into no contract. Ordinarily, therefore, an aggrieved patient has no basis for claiming breach of contract.

changed his will in the doctor's favor, the influence which effected the change would not be considered "undue." Undue influence is the kind of influence which comes from the outside (as contrasted with motivations which originate within the patient's own mind) and which is applied unfairly with the intent of benefiting the person who exercises the influence. Questions arise most often when someone in constant attendance is made the beneficiary of a changed will. One wonders then whether this person took advantage of the testator's illness, gullibility, or suggestibility. The evaluation of influence is a function of the court, not of the psychiatrist. The latter may contribute by indicating whether the testator was the kind of person who would readily fall prey to a designing individual, whether he was gullible, suggestible, competent, or easily influenced.

Appendix B

PSYCHIATRIC GLOSSARY FOR LAWYERS

This is a workaday lexicon, explaining briefly the operational meanings of psychiatric words likely to appear in medico-legal reports or in court testimony. A few neurologic terms have been included. The explanations and definitions are admittedly homely, and sometimes scientific preciseness is sacrificed for clarity. No attempt is made to offer a complete glossary of psychiatry. Words that are seldom encountered in medico-legal practice have been omitted. Necessarily, some concepts have to be explained in terms of other technical concepts.

Abasia. Inability to walk. Usually (though not necessarily) abasia refers to hysterical* inability to walk.

Abreaction. Bringing-up, expressing, releasing, or reliving a repressed emotion.

Acute brain syndrome. A temporary, diffuse impairment of brain tissue function.

Acute hallucinosis. A form of poisoning by alcohol in which the patient' hears voices.

Adjustment. Adaptation to environment; or to a specific field of environ ment, such as "marital adjustment" (getting along with one's spouse), o "vocational adjustment" (getting along with the job), etc. Poor adapta tion would, accordingly, be termed "maladjustment."

Affect. Emotion or mood. More exactly, the feeling tone which the patien appears to experience in connection with the mood. For example, the doctor may report that the patient exhibits a "blunting" or a "flattening" of affect. This does not necessarily mean that the patient experiences n emotions; it does mean that the patient does not display much emotiona coloring, that his mood seems dull and flat and fails to show the normally expected ups and downs.

Aggressive reaction. A personality disorder (not a neurosis or psychosis) characterized by resentment, irritability, or temper tantrums as a result of inability to cope with frustration.

Agorophobia. Unreasonable fear or anxiety* developing while in open spaces.

---

* Throughout Appendix B the asterisk denotes that the word it follows is defined in its alphabetical place in this glossary.

315

Alcoholic psychosis. Insanity due to alcohol.

Alcoholism, acute. Drunkenness; more specifically, drunkenness complicated by poisoning due to absorption of the alcohol.

Alcoholism, chronic. The habit of taking more alcohol than the person can handle; chronic poisoning because of absorption of excessive alcohol over long periods of time; or repeatedly demonstrated inability to absorb moderate quantities of alcohol without developing symptoms.

Alienist. Obsolete synonym for psychiatrist.

Alpha waves. Regular electric discharges obtained by an electro-encephalogram* from normal parts of the brain.

Alzheimer's disease. A form of dementia* due to organic brain disease.

Ambivalence. Contradictory attitudes, generally love and hate, experienced toward the same object at the same time. You can hate one near and dear to you much more vigorously and with much greater bitterness than you can hate a stranger. If so, your total attitude toward that person would be ambivalent.

Amnesia. Loss of memory. (Not to be confused with aphasia*.)

Anal erotic. A character or temperament characterized by orderliness, miserliness, and obstinacy.

Analgesia. Impaired or absent sensitivity to pain. (Strictly speaking, impaired or reduced sensitivity is hypalgesia*, the term "analgesia" meaning actual loss of pain sense.)

Analgesic. A drug which reduces or abolishes pain.

Analyst. A practitioner who treats emotional disturbances by means of psychoanalysis*. If the practitioner is a physician, then he is a psychiatrist as well as a psychoanalyst. If the practitioner is a psychologist* or social worker, then he is a lay analyst.

Anesthesia. Loss of sensation. In neurology, the word is usually applied to specific skin areas, the doctor speaking, for example, of "anesthesia of the right hand," meaning loss of sensation in that area. If sensitivity is impaired but not lost, the proper word is hypalgesia* or hypesthesia*.

Angioneurotic edema. Acute swellings in various, localized skin areas. Classified by some physicians as a form of allergy, it is generally considered, by psychiatrists, to be a psychophysiologic* skin reaction. Also called Quincke's Disease.

Anisocoria. Unequal pupils.

Anorexia. Loss of appetite.

Anorexia nervosa. A hysterical* loss of appetite, or a severe impairment of appetite due to emotional factors, usually leading to malnutrition or emaciation.

Antisocial reaction (Antisocial Personality). A personality disorder (not amounting to a psychosis or psychoneurosis) characterized by chronic antisocial behavior, unresponsiveness to punishment and inability to profit by experience. This is substantially the pattern of the antisocial psychopath*. In the 1952 nomenclatures the term is, for the first time, distinguished from "dyssocial reaction*." The basis for the distinction is that the individual with the dyssocial reaction manifests loyalty to his own code and own group, though not to normal society. Antisocial reaction implies lack of loyalty to any code or group.

Anxiety. A sense of fear, poorly understood by the subject, which arises without apparent cause, or for which the apparent cause is trivial. This is in addition to the obvious dictionary definition of "anxiety." It has overtones of "impending" danger rather than present danger. It is often diffuse, poorly localized, and vague, but always distressing. In some patients anxiety is "converted" into a physical symptom which protects the patient from the source of future fear. For example, a hysterical blindness (a conversion hysteria*, therefore) would protect the patient from seeing anxiety-provoking sights. If the world is too much for him, the patient might develop a vague anxiety whenever he goes out of the house; or, instead, he might develop a hysterical paralysis of the legs so that he could not go out of the house. In the latter case the patient would exhibit no frank anxiety at all, since he is fully protected from threatening situations because of the paralysis; or, as some psychiatrists believe, because all the anxiety has been "converted" into a physical symptom.

Anxiety hysteria. A form of hysteria* in which anxiety* is a prominent symptom.

Anxiety neurosis. A psychoneurosis* in which anxiety* is the predominant symptom.

Anxiety reaction. A psychoneurosis* characterized by diffuse anxiety*.

Aphasia. Inability to utter, write, or understand once-familiar words; or any one of these inabilities. The patient with aphasia generally knows who he is (unless he also has amnesia*). However, he has "forgotten" how to pronounce certain words—that is, he has a "motor" aphasia; or he cannot remember the meaning of the words he hears—that is, he has a "sensory" aphasia.

Apoplexy. The syndrome* resulting from sudden hemorrhage within the brain or from an abrupt blocking of a blood vessel in the brain.

Argyll Robertson pupil. Pupils that do not become smaller when a light is flashed in the eye. The pupil will, however, become smaller if the patient moves nearer to the object. This is found in syphilis and in a few other diseases of the nervous system.

Astasia. Hysterical* inability to stand.

Astereognosis. Loss of the ability to recognize familiar objects by touch alone.

Asthenia. Weakness. See Asthenic reaction*; and Neurasthenia*.

Asthenic reaction. A psychoneurosis* manifested chiefly by fatigue, irritability, and rather poorly localized symptoms. Substantially the same as neurasthenia*.

Ataxia. Impaired coordinative control over the arms, hands, or legs. The patient still has power in the limb; what he lacks is exact control.

Athetosis. A more or less continual, slow, worm-like, writhing movement.

Attitudinal pathosis. Symptoms following an accident, in which the chief motive power behind the symptoms is a feeling of resentment or hostility.

Aura. A sensation, pain, or other feeling which precedes a convulsion* and serves as a sort of signal or warning to the patient that a seizure is coming.

Autistic. Dreamy, unreal, imaginary, or self-preoccupied.

Autistic thinking. Fantasy-wishing, daydreaming, self-preoccupied thinking.

Babinski sign. An upward movement of the big toe when the doctor strokes the sole of the foot. It is found in many organic* disorders of the central nervous system and is absent in psychoneurosis*.

Benign stupor. A form of depressive reaction* in which consciousness or attention appears to be markedly impaired, but from which recovery is expected.

Binet-Simon test. An intelligence test, designed principally for use with children or adolescents, in which the subject's performance is matched against normal performances, age for age.

Buggery. Insertion of the penis into the anus or rubbing it between the folds of buttocks. When the penis is that of an adult, and the anus is that of a child, the perversion is called "pederasty."

Bulimia. Excessive, voracious, or insatiable hunger.

Cardiazol. A synthetic, camphorlike preparation used to induce convulsions* in one form of shock* therapy. Cardiazol is also called "metrazol."*

Cataplexy. A prostration or sinking to the floor due to sudden loss of muscle control.

Catatonic. A state found in some forms of schizophrenia,* in which energy seems maintained either at a very high or very low level. In catatonic excitement, the patient exhibits apparently purposeless overactivity. In catatonic stupor, he fails to respond to, or pay attention to, external stimuli.

Catharsis. In psychiatric usage, this indicates a "talking out" by the patient of his problems with resultant emotional relief. Operationally it is about the same as "abreaction."*

Cathexis. The emotional "energy" attached to an idea or to an object; or the focussing of such energy upon some object or idea.

Central nervous system. The brain and spinal cord (representing the axis or core of the nervous system), bracketed together as the "central" nervous system. The nerves running into and out of the spinal cord and brain are, by contrast, "the peripheral nervous system."*

Cerea flexibilitas. A state of muscle tension in which the arms or legs can be placed in, and will remain in, various peculiar positions. Seldom seen except in schizophrenia.*

Cerebral. Pertaining to the brain generally, or to the cerebrum* particularly.

Cerebral arteriosclerosis. Hardening of the arteries of the brain.

Cerebrum. The brain. More specifically cerebrum refers to the major frontal and upper parts of the brain.

Chorea. Involuntary, irregular, jerky movements of the hands, face, and leg muscles. Also known as "St. Vitus Dance."* The ordinary chorea is an acute infectious disease which leaves no emotional or mental residuals. There is, however, a rare form, known as "Huntington's chorea" (or chronic chorea) in which the speech is markedly involved, and mental degeneration often occurs.

Chronic brain syndrome. Any long-lasting disorder due to organic (structural) changes in the brain. A psychosis due to head injury, for instance, could be described as a chronic brain syndrome with psychotic reaction.

Circumstantiality. Speech in which irrelevant details are constantly being introduced, in which the conversation keeps wandering off the point, or in which the point is reached only after enormous, tangential detail.

Clang association. A train of talk stimulated by casual or adventitious sounds or utterances, often based on resonance or rhyme effect.

Claustrophobia. Anxiety* in small, crowded, or inclosed spaces.

Clonus. Rapidly alternating contractions and relaxations of localized muscles, usually in the knee or ankle area.

Coma. Loss of consciousness, usually profound.

Complex. A group of ideas, largely unconsciousness, with a strong emotional coloring. Behavior may appear unreasonable because its motivation is essentially unconscious, hence such behavior could be ascribed to a specific complex; or the behavior might seem reasonable, but its apparent cause could be sheer rationalization. Its real cause might then be a complex.

Compulsion. A repeated urge to do something which the patient himself knows is foolish. Kleptomania,* for example, is a compulsion. In kleptomania the patient has an urge to steal, knows it is wrong, tries to resist the impulse, but develops mounting tension which can be released only by yielding to the urge. Not all compulsions, of course, are "criminal." Most compulsions take the form of performing minor acts, touching certain objects in a ritualistic way, etc. The essence of a compulsion is that it is contrary to the patient's conscious "will." If the patient *wants* to do what he is doing, then his action is not, strictly speaking, a compulsion.

Compulsion neurosis. A psychoneurosis* in which the most obvious symptom is a persistent compulsion.*

Compulsive neurosis. Same as "compulsion neurosis." See above.

Conation. Will or drive. The word is usually used in contrast with "cognition," which means knowledge. Thus, the McNaghten rule uses a purely "cognitive" test; that is, it seeks to determine whether the defendant *knew* that the act was wrong. In states where irresistible impulse is a defense, a "conative" element is added; it then is a matter of finding out whether the defendant *wanted* to do the act and whether the drive was irresistible.

Concussion. A shaking up of the brain with no substantial structural damage to that organ.

Conditioned reflex. A response that results from learning or training, whereby the subject associates a primary stimulus with a secondary stimulus until the point is reached where he reacts to the secondary (previously neutral) stimulus alone.

Confabulation. The type of story-telling which occurs when a patient has a genuine loss of memory and fills in the gaps with fantasies. While in plain English this word means telling lies, in psychiatry it has a more restricted meaning. In true confabulation (as the word is used in psychiatry) the patient usually believes what he is saying. The lies told by the "psychopath,"* on the other hand, are not technically "confabulations" because the psychopath knows that they are lies.

Constitutional psychopath. A psychopath.*

Constitutional psychopathic inferiority. An obsolete term for "psychopathic personality," that is, for the kind of personality possessed by a psychopath.*

Conversion. The unconscious process of converting anxiety* into loss of function or loss of sensation.

Conversion hysteria. A psychoneurosis* in which there is gross loss or impairment of some function, and in which the disorder so protects the patient that there is little or no obvious anxiety.*

Conversion reaction. An alternate term for conversion hysteria.*

Convulsion. An involuntary, massive, muscle contraction.

Coprolalia. A compulsion* to use obscene words.

Cortex. The outer layer of an organ. In the brain, the outer layer is composed of gray matter*; that is, it is rich in nerve cells. The cortex is thus the part of the brain which receives, interprets and originates stimuli. The adjective is "cortical."*

Cortical. Pertaining to the cortex.*

Cranial nerves. Nerves going directly to, or coming directly out of the brain.

Cretin. A mental defective* whose deficiency is due to abnormality of the thyroid gland.

Cunnilingus or Connilinction. Placing the mouth against the female genitalia, particularly if the tongue is inserted into the vulvar orifice. If it represents simple kissing of the vulva as a prelude to normal coitus, it is not generally considered a perversion. However, if this is the participant's primary sexual aim and if this represents the acme of his sexual satisfaction, then cunnilingus is classed as a perversion.

Cycloid. Exhibiting marked, extreme, or frequent swings in mood.

Cyclothymia. Frequent, extensive, and excessive swings in mood. Some psychiatrists reserve the word "cyclothymia" for cases of actual manic-depressive psychosis.*

Delirium. A combination of excitement, confusion, disorientation,* and some sensory disturbance, such as hallucinosis.*

Delirium Tremens. A delirium* due to alcohol or other drug poisoning, or due to dietary deprivation resulting from alcoholism.*

Delusion. An idea which is (*a*) contrary to fact, (*b*) inappropriate to the person's education, intelligence or culture, and (*c*) adhered to in spite of plain evidence that it is false. Many normal persons have delusions. A man may think he is smarter than he is, a woman may think she is charming and beautiful when she is neither. These are delusions. However, in psychiatric practice, the word is generally reserved for false ideas which are more bizarre than those. The three commonest delusions are (1) delusions of persecution, (2) delusions of grandeur, and (3) delusions of personal unworthiness.

Dementia. A gross impairment of mental faculties, such as enfeeblement of intelligence or serious disorientation*, or major loss of contact with reality. In general, dementia occurs more often in organic* diseases of the brain than in psychoses* without known organic basis. In many psychoses there is no dementia at all. Delusions* often exist without dementia.

Dementia paralytica. A psychosis* due to syphilis; also known as "general paresis"*.

Dementia precox. A psychosis* characterized by various degrees of withdrawal from reality, autistic thinking*, delusion* formation, and/or hallucinosis*. Now generally called schizophrenia*.

Depersonalization. Loss or impairment of one's sense of personal identity; or of one's possession of his own limbs or other parts of the body; or a delusion* that one is someone else.

Depression. A syndrome* manifested by sense of inadequacy, "blue feeling," self-depreciation, melancholy, and guilt feelings.

Depressive reaction. A mental or emotional condition, precipitated by some external factor, and manifested by guilt, self-deprecation, "blue feeling," psychomotor* retardation, dejection, or sense of inadequacy. Unless otherwise specified, a depressive reaction is considered to be a psychoneurosis*. If the condition reaches psychotic* intensity, it is called simply a "psychotic depressive reaction."

Dermographia. Sensitivity of the skin to stroking, manifested by the development of raised lines when the skin is stroked with a blunt object. Also called "dermatographia."

Diplopia. Double vision.

Dipsomania. Periodic and compulsive drinking.

Disorientation. Failure to identify the time, place, or persons around. Disorientation may be partial. A patient might know the year and season, but not the month or day of the week; then he would be "partly disoriented for time."

Displacement. Transfer of emotion to an inappropriate idea or object.

Dissociation. In neurology, a breaking down of the continuity or concordance of movements, such as the failure to swing the arms while walking. In psychiatry, a lack of connection. This might be a lack of connection between the patient's actions and his words; or between his apparent mood and his activity; or even a severe splitting of the whole personality so that one part operates more or less independently. A patient who functions in a prolonged period of amnesia* and then returns to normal has been in a dissociative reaction* during that amnesic period, because that part of the personality apparently split off from the rest of him and operated, for a while, independently.

Dissociative reaction. A psychoneurosis* or other syndrome* character- ized by fugues*, amnesia*, or other forms of dissociation*.

Distractibility. Inability or failure to concentrate on a line of thought; a syndrome* in which attention is fluidly diverted by irrelevant thoughts.

Dura mater. The tough, membranous, outer covering of the brain and spinal cord.

Dynamics. An explanation of a present mental condition in terms of the subject's lifelong emotional development. An effort to connect current emotional symptoms with their long antecedent, predetermining, or causative factors.

Dyssocial reaction. A personality disorder (not a psychosis or neurosis) in which an individual, having always lived in an abnormal environment, manifests resistance to, or disregard of, the conventional social code, though he may display considerable loyalty to his own group and to their code of behavior. It is to be distinguished from antisocial reaction.* The new phrase, "dyssocial reaction," is listed in the *Standard Nomenclature of Diseases*.[1]

Dystrophy. Weakness and wasting of a muscle. Also called "dystrophia."

Echolalia. Repetition of the words used by another person. If the examiner says: "How are you?" and the patient echoes, "How are you?" this is echolalia. But if he says, "How am I? Well, not so good," this is *not* echolalia. It is simply rephrasing of the question.

Echopraxia. Mimicry of the movements of others.

E.E.G. An abbreviation for electro-encephalogram* or electro-encephalo- graph*.

Ego. In psychiatry, the part of the personality which is in contact with the outside world; that part which is noticeable to others. It is what the unsophisticated outsider would consider the "real" person. The other parts of the personality are the id* and the superego*.

Electro-encephalogram. The tracing made by the electro-encephalo- graph*.

Electro-encephalograph. An instrument for picking up and recording the electrical activity of the brain.

Encephalopathy. Structural disease of, or damage to, the brain.

---

[1] Published for the American Medical Association by The Blakiston Co., Philadel- phia, 1952. The terms "antisocial" (or "asocial") reaction or personality have long been used in American psychiatry. Dyssocial reaction, however, is not listed in any nomenclature prior to 1952. Criteria for the diagnosis of antisocial and dyssocial reactions are found in *The Diagnostic and Statistical Manual of Mental Disorders* (Washington, D. C.: American Psychiatric Association, 1952), p. 38.

Enuresis. Involuntary discharge of urine. Bed wetting.

Epilepsy. A syndrome* characterized by recurrent periods of unconsciousness. If the episodes are very brief, and if there is no convulsion,* the condition is called "petit mal." If the attacks are accompanied by convulsions*, the condition is called "grand mal." In grand mal, the convulsions* are usually generalized, or at least they involve most of the limb and back muscles. Where the spells are localized to one part of the body, or where there is a progressive spread of the convulsion* through the body, the syndrome* is often called Jacksonian epilepsy*. In Jacksonian epilepsy*, consciousness may be preserved.

Epileptic. Pertaining to epilepsy.*

Epileptic equivalent. Periodic pains or other unpleasant symptoms which are presumed to represent "equivalents" of an epileptic seizure occurring in persons supposed to be predisposed to epilepsy*.

Etiology. As a practical matter, the "cause" of any condition; operationally, the words "etiology" and "cause" may be considered synonymous. (Technically, etiology encompasses a much broader field, since it includes all predisposing factors, as well as statistical information about the distribution of the disease.)

Euphoria. A sense of well-being, expansiveness, and self-satisfaction; generally used when the sense of well-being is not justified.

Exhibitionism. A compulsion* to display the sexual organs.

Exophthalmos. Bulging eye-balls.

Extravert. A person who enjoys being with other people and dislikes solitude. Also spelled "extrovert." Contrasted with intravert*.

Fellatio. A sexual perversion in which the subject gets gratification out of taking someone's penis and putting it into his mouth.

Flexibilitis cerea. A state of muscle tension in which the legs or arms remain in positions in which an observer places them. Seldom seen except in schizophrenia*.

Flight of ideas. Rapid changing in the topics of thought or talk without apparent connection between the consecutive ideas.

Folie a deux. Simultaneous psychosis* in two or more persons, where these persons had been in close contact or under common influence. Usually one of the persons has a psychosis*, and the others develop similar symptoms because of suggestibility.

Fugue. A period of amnesia* during which the patient functions almost as if normal, but about which he has no subsequent recollection. A defendant might assert that he has no recollection at all of the period just before, during, and after the crime. Observers would state that he acted as if he knew what he was doing. If the patient is telling the truth, then this period of time was a fugue. Also see dissociation*.

Functional. A change in the functioning of an organ without any apparent alteration in structure. In many diseases, the structure of an organ is obviously affected. Thus in an ulcer of the stomach, there is visible depression in the stomach wall. In pneumonia, there is a lung area in which inflammatory tissue drives out the air and causes that part of the lung to harden. These are examples of changes in structure. In other diseases, however, a structure seems unimpaired. The function of the organ is altered, but apparently not its structure. In hysterical* blindness, for instance, examination of the eye shows no visible abnormality. Yet the eye does not function. Hence this is a "functional" disorder of the eye. The analogy may be made to a good piano played by an untutored child. Out of the piano comes only discordant sounds. Yet there is nothing wrong with the structure of the instrument; it is simply not being "worked" properly. The discords are due to "functional" change. In the insanity due to arteriosclerosis we know that there is visible change in brain structure. But in schizophrenia* we can find nothing wrong with the structure of the brain. Hence we classify the latter as a "functional" psychosis*. If, because of the emotional effects of an accident, a patient has backache, and if complete orthopedic study shows no change in the structure of the bones, joints, tendons, ligaments, or muscles of the back, we conclude that the function of the spinal column has been affected, but not its structure: hence the backache is called "functional." Also see Organic*.

Ganser syndrome. A state of apparent confusion in which the subject gives silly, or only partly relevant answers. See page 167.

General paresis. A psychosis* due to syphilis; also called "dementia paralytica"*.

Globus hystericus. A sense of having a lump in the throat, often accompanied by a subjective feeling of choking; generally a hysterical* manifestation.

Grand mal. A form of epilepsy* characterized by periods of coma* and convulsions*.

Gray matter. The more cellular of the two tissues of which the central nervous system is composed. The central nervous system* is composed essentially of two kinds of tissue: white matter* and gray matter. Tissue which is made up largely of cells is soft and grayish in color. Tissue composed largely of fibers is firmer and lighter in color. The cortex* of the brain is made up of gray matter. In the spinal cord, on the other hand, the gray matter is chiefly found in the center, and the white matter* is disposed along the cortex* of the cord.

Gross stress reaction.[2] A transient reaction due to an immediate and overwhelming external situation. Psychoses and neuroses are, by definition, excluded from this category.

Hallucination. A sensation without any external object to account for it. To hear voices in a quiet room is to have an auditory hallucination. To see something that isn't there is to have a visual hallucination, and so with the other senses.

[2] This term is a relatively new one in psychiatry. It was first introduced in *The Diagnostic and Statistical Manual of Mental Disorders* (Washington, D. C.: American Psychiatric Association, 1952), p. 40.

Hallucinosis. Having hallucinations*.

Hebephrenia. A psychotic* regression into silly, deteriorated, or infantile behavior. A form of schizophrenia*.

Hebephrenic dementia precox. A form of schizophrenia* marked by silliness, infantile behavior, and deterioration.

Hemi-anesthesia. Loss of sensation over half the body.

Hemiplegia. Paralysis of the arms or legs on one side.

Hippus. Alternate contraction and dilatation of the pupil.

Homosexual. A person whose major or primary source of sexual satisfaction is from contact with others of the same sex. Among females, homosexuality is generally known as Lesbianism*.

Hypalgesia. Diminished sensitivity to pain.

Hyperactive. Overactive, restless, constantly moving.

Hypesthesia. An area of reduced sensitivity.

Hypnosis. Putting a subject to sleep by inducing a trance or an amnesia* by means of psychological suggestion.

Hypnotic. (*a*) a drug to induce sleep, or (*b*) adjective of the word hypnosis*.

Hypochondriacal reaction. A psychoneurosis* manifested by morbid, usually obsessional, preoccupation with the body organs or with general health. Substantially the same as hypochondriasis*.

Hypochondriasis. A morbid overconcern about disease. It is a psychoneurosis*. The person who has this neurosis is a hypochondriac. The diseases which worry the patient are, in a sense, imaginary; but the psychoneurosis is certainly real. The patient really *is* sick; not sick with the tuberculosis which he dreads, but sick with the emotional conflict which produced the hypochondriasis.

Hypomania. A mild form of manic-depressive psychosis* in which the patient exhibits slight elevation of mood, some increase in psychomotor activity*, and considerable talkativeness.

Hysteria. A psychoneurosis* in which there is gross loss of, or impairment of, the function of one or more organs; as, for example, hysterical blindness or hysterical convulsions; also used for conversion hysteria*. The term is also used, somewhat amateurishly, as a synonym for temper tantrums.

Hysterical. Among psychiatrists, the adjective for hysteria*. Among laymen, temper tantrums. A patient can be quiet and still have a hysterical reaction. In fact, because hysteria serves to protect against anxiety*, the hysterical patient is not likely to exhibit much outward disturbance.

Id. The unconscious reservoir of instincts, urges, and drives.

Idea of Reference. Assignment to yourself of a casual incident; a belief that some meaningless occurrence was really directed at you.

Idiot. A mental defective with an I.Q.* under 25; an adult with a mental age under 3.

Illusion. Misinterpretation of an external stimulus. If I see a tree and think it is a man, this is an optical illusion. If I hear a rumble of words and think my name is being uttered, this is an auditory illusion. Compare with delusion* and hallucination*.

Imbecile. A mental defective with an I.Q.* between 25 and 50; an adult with a mental age between 3 and 7.

Insight. The patient's realization of the severity and nature of his mental condition.

Insomnia. Trouble in falling asleep. (Technically: inability to sleep.)

Intelligence quotient. In a child, the ratio between his mental age and his actual age. Thus, if a 5-year-old has the mentality of a 3-year-old, his I.Q. is 3/5 or 60 per cent; expressed as I.Q. 60. If a 3-year-old child has the mind of a 5-year-old, his intelligence quotient would be 5/3 which is 140 per cent; that is, his I.Q. is 140. In an adult, the denominator of the I.Q. fraction is usually taken as 14 or as 16, depending on the test used. Thus, an adult with the mind of a 7-year-old child, would have an I.Q. of 7/14 (or 50 per cent) on certain tests or of 7/16 (that is 44 per cent). Thus, such an adult's I.Q. would be 44 or 50. In general, an I.Q. under 25 suggests an idiot; from 25 to 50 an imbecile; from 50 to 70 a moron; 70 to 80 represents a borderline intelligence; 90 to 110 is the range of the normal; and an I.Q. over 110 reflects varying degrees of brightness above normal.

Intention tremor. A tremor that develops (or is intensified) when the patient starts a voluntary movement. This is *not* an "intentional" tremor: the patient does not shake on purpose. It is called "intention" tremor because it occurs when he intends to make a movement with his hand or arm.

Intravert. A person who tends to be introspective, uncomfortable with people, and moody. Also spelled "introvert." Compare with extrovert*.

Involution melancholia. A psychosis* developing at or shortly after the "change of life" in some women (and occasionally in men) characterized by physical overactivity (such as floor pacing) with emotional depression or grief. Also called "involutional psychosis" and "involutional melancholia."

I.Q. An abbreviation for "intelligence quotient"*.

Jacksonian Epilepsy. Periodic convulsions* localized to one part of the body, or starting in one area and progressing to other parts of the body. Also see epilepsy*.

Kleptomania. A compulsion* to steal, which the patient tries to resist, but which he feels compelled to yield to because of mounting tension. See "compulsion"*.

Korsakoff's (or *Korsakow's*) **Syndrome.** A psychosis*, usually due to alcohol, manifested by confusion, confabulation*, and suggestibility.

Lesbian. A female whose major source of sexual gratification is by contact with other females. Lesbianism is homosexuality* in the female.

Leucotomy. Cutting into the white matter* of the brain with the hope of relieving tension, abolishing pain, or altering behavior; a form of psychosurgery*.

Libido. The aggregate of forces which drive a human being: the motor fuel of the emotional engine.

Lobotomy. Cutting into the brain for the purpose of relieving pain, grief, or excitement; a form of psychosurgery*.

Locomotor Ataxia. An obsolete term for tabes dorsalis*: a syphilitic disease of the spinal cord.

Lues. Syphilis.

Luetic. Syphilitic.

Mania. As used by psychiatrists, the manic* phase of a manic-depressive psychosis*; as used by laymen, either an obsession* or violently disturbed behavior.

Mania a potu. Pathological* intoxication.

Maniac. A nonmedical word used by less literate persons to indicate someone who is violently disturbed.

Manic. That phase of a manic-depressive psychosis* in which the patient is overactive and expansive. In its milder form, it is called "hypomania." A patient afflicted with this form of the psychosis is also called "a manic."

Manic-depressive psychosis. A mental disease characterized by either (a) a more or less prolonged period of depression*; (b) a period of overactivity and euphoria*; or (c) swings between these two phases.

Mattoid. A crank or eccentric. The term is used chiefly in Great Britain. Sometimes it describes a mental defective, particularly one who has occasional areas of good intelligence against a background of intellectual retardation.

Melancholia. The depressed phase of manic-depressive psychosis*. The term may also be applied to involution melancholia* and is sometimes loosely used to indicate any depression*.

Meninges. The fibrous coverings of the brain and spinal cord. The outer meninx is the dura mater; the inner one (lining the brain and cord) is the pia mater; the membrane between them is the arachnoid.

Mental defective. Adjective or noun indicating "mental deficiency."*

Mental deficiency. Low intelligence. Usually an I.Q.* of 60 or less is considered evidence of mental deficiency. In the United States the phrases "feeble-mindedness" and "mental deficiency" are synonyms. In Britain the phrase "feeble-minded" is reserved only for the highest grade of mental deficiency. The conventional adult groupings are idiocy (mental age under 3), imbecility (mental age 3 to 7), and the moronic state (mental age 7 to 12).

Metrazol. A form of synthetic camphor used to induce convulsions* in psychotics* in connection with shock* therapy.

Migraine. Periodic, severe, one-sided headache.

Moron. A mental defective* with an I.Q.* between 50 and 70, an adult with a mental age between 7 and 12. In England a moron is called "feeble-minded"; in the United States the term "feeble-mindedness" refers to any and all grades of mental deficiency. It is incorrect to use the word "moron" to refer to emotional deterioration or to degeneracy of character, unless these are incidental to mental deficiency. A moron is a person with an inferior intellect.

Multiple sclerosis. A disease of the spinal cord of unknown origin involving impairment in motor function of the arms and/or legs.

Mutism. Failure to speak or refusal to answer questions because of mental illness.

Myasthenia. Weakness and ready exhaustability of muscles.

Narcoanalysis. Putting a patient to sleep, or into a semisomnolent state by means of chemical injections, and then analyzing what he says in this dreamlike state. Also see narcosynthesis*.

Narcolepsy. Periodic, brief spells of sleepiness or of desire for sleep.

Narcosynthesis. Putting a patient to sleep, or into a semisomnolent state by chemical injections, then getting him to talk about his problems, or to relive previous painful experiences in the hope of freeing him from the effects of such experiences; and then suggesting to him, while he is still partly somnolent, that he will be free of symptoms.

Negativism. Doing the opposite of what is asked.

Neologism. A new word coined by a patient, having a special or private meaning to him.

Neuralgia. Pain in a nerve or in an area supplied by a nerve.

Neurasthenia. A psychoneurosis* manifested chiefly by fatigue, irritability, and poorly localized symptoms. Also called "asthenic reaction."*

Neuritis. Inflammation of a nerve.

Neurocirculatory asthenia. Palpitations, faint feeling, and difficulty in breathing because of an emotionally induced and temporary disturbance in the power or rhythm of the heart. Also called psychophysiologic cardiovascular reaction, soldier's heart, effort syndrome, psychogenic cardiovascular reaction, irritable heart, and "disordered action of the heart."

Neurosis. A set of symptoms due essentially to emotional conflict. The word has the same meaning as *psychoneurosis**. At one time a distinction was drawn between "neuroses," which were supposed to be mechanical or structural disturbances of organs due to emotional conflict, and "psychoneuroses," which were supposed to be wholly of emotional origin and manifestation. Today the two words (neurosis and psychoneurosis) are treated as synonyms. In his earlier works, Freud spoke of the "actual" neuroses as contrasted with the "psychoneuroses." Anxiety, neurasthenia, and hypochondriasis were considered "actual" neuroses, while hysteria, psychasthenia, and reactive depressions were grouped as "psychoneuroses." We now know that all six disorders are of emotional origin, and all of them may show symptoms which require some change in the structure or function of the organ. For further definitions, see psychoneurosis*, anxiety*, neurasthenia*, psychasthenia*, obsessions*, compulsions*, phobias*, reactive depression*, depressive reaction*, hypochondriasis*, and psychosomatics*.

Neurosyphilis. Syphilis involving the brain and/or spinal cord. Thus, general paresis* and tabes dorsalis* are examples of neurosyphilis.

Neurotic. The adjective of neurosis*. As a noun "neurotic" means a person who has a neurosis. As an adjective "neurotic" means having the characteristics of a neurosis, that is, due to emotional conflict. If a symptom is described as "neurotic," the implication is that the symptom is due primarily to emotional conflict. It is not "imaginary," of course; it is real enough, and is mediated through actual changes in body organs. "Neurotic" in modern usage is a synonym of "psychoneurotic." Some doctors use the word "neurotic" as a synonym for functional*.

Nymphomania. Excessive sexual desire in a female. The corresponding disorder in the male is called satyriasis*.

Nystagmus. Tremor of the eyeballs.

Obsession. An absurd idea which seizes the person's mind and which keeps hold of him even though he recognizes that it is foolish. A compulsion* is really an obsession. So is a phobia*. So is the persistence of a tune, or some fixed thought. If the patient defends the idea as sensible, it is probably a delusion* rather than an obsession. A subject knows that the obsession is foolish.

Obsessive-compulsive reaction. A psychoneurosis* manifested chiefly by compulsions* and obsessions*, substantially the same as psychasthenia*.

Oligophrenia. Mental deficiency*.

Oriented. Knowing the time, or place, and one's own identity. A person is oriented if he knows who he is, where he is, and what day it is. Otherwise he is, to that degree (or in that sphere), disoriented. A person may be "disoriented for time" while being "oriented for person."

Organic. Pertaining to some detectable alteration in the structure, integrity, or mechanics of an organ, causing disease. Also see Functional*.

Paranoia. A rare psychosis* in which the patient has a fixed delusion*, but reasons logically from that false premise, and in which there is neither dementia* nor hallucinosis*.

Paranoiac. A person suffering from paranoia*.

Paranoid. Well organized delusional thinking. Most paranoid delusions* are persecutory, although it would be perfectly proper to describe a well-organized delusion of grandeur (or of unworthiness) as a paranoid delusion too. A paranoid delusion is a systematized, well-preserved, stubborn, long-lasting delusion*.

Paraphrenia. A rather rare paranoid* psychosis* in which the patient has the hallucinations* expected in schizophrenia,* and the non-deteriorating, well-organized delusions* expected in paranoia*.

Paresis. Technically any weakness of muscle (not amounting to paralysis). In practice, the word is psychiatric jargon for "general paresis,"* a syphilitic brain disease.

Paretic. Pertaining to paresis*.

Passive-dependency reaction. A personality disorder (not amounting to a psychosis or neurosis) characterized by general inadequacy, tendency to lean on others, and indecisiveness. The patient's inadequacies are reflected by his own lack of self-confidence and tendency to cling to others. When his reaction is to become stubborn, to pout, to procrastinate, or to obstruct, the condition is Aggressive * reaction.

Pathologic liar. A psychopath* who repeatedly tells lies because of some inner compulsion* even though such lies are easily exposed, and even though they serve little useful purpose.

Pathologic personality. A psychopath*.

Pathological intoxication. An excessive reaction to moderate amounts of alcohol; a period of frenzy precipitated by drinking, for which the subject subsequently has amnesia*. Also called *mania a potu*.

Pederasty. Buggery* with a child.

Peripheral nerve. A nerve coming from the spinal cord and going to a muscle, gland ,or organ; or *vice versa*. (Actually between the spinal cord and the peripheral nerve there is a collection of nerve roots known as a "plexus." Strictly speaking, therefore, the peripheral nerve connects the plexus with the organ, muscle, or gland.)

Peripheral nervous system. All of the nervous system outside of the brain and spinal cord.

Petit mal. A form of epilepsy* characterized by transient spells of unconsciousness without convulsions*.

Phobia. A morbid fear which the patient himself knows is groundless, but which, nevertheless, seizes his mind. This is a form of obsession*.

Phobic reaction. A psychoneurosis* characterized chiefly by phobias*.

Photophobia. Literally, "fear of light"; ordinarily applied to irritability of the eyes in the presence of light.

Pia mater. The thin lining over the brain and spinal cord, which constitutes the innermost layer of the meninges*.

Posttraumatic syndrome. A set of symptoms following head injury. Emotional symptoms, or those produced by emotional conflicts associated with the injury, are more likely to be thus listed than are symptoms obviously due to organic brain injury.

Presenile sclerosis. The "official" designation for Alzheimer's Disease* between 1933 and 1952, in all hospitals using the *Standard Nomenclature of Diseases and Operations*.[3] In 1952, the fourth edition of this *Nomenclature* changed the designation to "chronic brain syndrome associated with disturbances of metabolism with psychotic reaction."

Psychasthenia. A psychoneurosis* characterized by obsessions*, compulsions*, and/or phobias*.

Psychoanalysis. In a broad sense, any analysis of mental mechanisms. By common, though unofficial, agreement it is understood that the word "psychoanalysis" refers to the technique worked out by Freud and amplified by his disciples, followers, and—later—by those who dissented

---

[3] Chicago: American Medical Association, 1933, 2nd ed. 1935. The 3rd ed. (1942) and 4th ed. (1952) were published for the American Medical Association by The Blakiston Co., Philadelphia.

from and varied his original technique. Actually, "psychoanalysis" has three meanings: it is a doctrine, a research tool, and a method of treatment. As a *doctrine,* psychoanalysis is the belief that emotional disorders are due to unconscious conflicts, most of them dating back to childhood. As a *research tool,* psychoanalysis is a method of investigating problems, starting with the assumption that the psychoanalytic doctrine can explain them. For example, a researcher might try to explain war, strikes, industrial rivalry, criminal behavior, job selection, leadership, etc., in terms of the unconscious, childhood-rooted, drives of the people involved; he might, indeed, think of the history of nations as an example of emotional conflicts involving whole groups. Thus he would be using psychoanalytic doctrine as a method of research. As a *method of treatment,* psychoanalysis seeks to cure people of emotional disturbances by ascertaining the unconscious basis of the emotional conflict underlying them, and by allowing the patient to bring some of these factors into consciousness, to react to them, to release repressed emotions, or to live through—emotionally or in fantasy—the old and once-buried problems. In addition to the "pure" or "original" Freudian technique, there are now many other methods, varying in method or mechanics.

Psychodynamics. The study of the emotional and environmental forces which account for the subject's present mental condition. See dynamics*.

Psychogenic. Having a strong emotional component; almost the same as functional*.

Psychologist. A nonphysician trained in the understanding of mental mechanisms. His field includes testing of mental capacities, determination of personality structure, vocational and personal guidance, experimental and animal psychology, and attempts at the correction of intellectual and emotional disabilities by use of psychological methods. A psychologist who has been trained to practice psychoanalysis* is known as a "lay analyst," because he is not a physician and therefore is not a psychiatrist.

Psychology. The body of knowledge studied by a psychologist*; the science of normal and abnormal mental processes.

Psychometric. Literally, "measuring the mind." In practice, applied to intelligence tests. Thus, a psychometrist is a technician who administers intelligence tests.

Psychomotor. The combination of emotional tone and motor activity; thus to say that a patient "exhibits psychomotor retardation" is to say that (*a*) his mood is depressed, and (*b*) he sits or lies quietly, seldom moving. Correspondingly, "psychomotor elevation" would imply physical restlessness combined with elation of mood.

Psychoneurosis or neurosis. A set of symptoms due to emotional conflict. The psychoses* ("insanities") are excluded from the category of psychoneurosis. (Psychoneuroses is the plural of psychoneurosis.) Some psychoneuroses can manifest themselves only through actual mechanical changes in body organs, so that it is incorrect to assume that psychoneurotic *symptoms* are entirely emotional. A physical disease may cause emotional disturbance which, in turn, may cause a psychoneurosis to be superimposed on the physical disease. Conversely, emotional conflict may cause such phenomena as a rise in blood pressure and ulcers of the stomach, so that psychoneuroses may be associated with physical disease. Many classifications of psychoneuroses are available. Traditionally there are six psychoneuroses: anxiety reaction*, neurasthenia*, hypochondriasis*, reactive depression*, hysteria*, and psychasthenia*. Some authorities distinguish between anxiety hysteria and conversion hysteria and some distinguish between "anxiety neurosis" and "anxiety reaction," thus producing one or more classes of psychoneurosis in addition to the standard six types. Also, some prefer to break down psychasthenia* into three separate neuroses—obsessional neuroses, phobias, and compulsive neuroses—thus adding two more subtypes. Certain psychosomatic* entities are occasionally included in the psychoneurosis bracket too: for example, in some classifications, neurocirculatory asthenia, angioneurotic edema, and spastic colitis would be considered as examples of psychoneurosis.

Psychopath. A shorthand term for "psychopathic personality," or, as it is called in some nomenclatures, "pathologic personality." A psychopath is a person who has trouble getting along because of some long-standing personality oddity, but who is not insane and not feeble-minded. There are a dozen kinds of psychopathic personality, but the one that the law is most disturbed about is the "asocial" or "antisocial." This describes a person who, though neither insane nor mentally defective, never seems to be willing to conform to normal standards of behavior; who engages in repeated criminal acts without learning from experience that crime doesn't pay. The intelligent psychopath of this genre often engages in a long career of fraud, trickery, deceit, or other forms of sophisticated dishonesty. And he persists in such antisocial behavior in spite of any efforts at reform, punishment, or rehabilitation. He tries, often with success, to talk his way out of troubles with the law. The less intelligent antisocial psychopath is more likely to engage in crimes of violence. He tries to fight his way out of, or run away from, his difficulties.

Psychopathic. As used in the phrase "psychopathic ward," a generic term for mental or emotional illness (a psychopathic ward is a place for mentally ill patients). Also the adjective of the word "psychopath"* as above defined. Thus, psychopathic behavior, is *not* insane behavior; but a psychopathic ward can house insane patients.

Psychopathology. An explanation of the mental mechanisms which account for a patient's emotional or mental condition.

Psychophysiologic. Describing a reaction which is emotional in origin but "physical" in manifestation. Thus, diarrhea caused by anxiety would be a psychophysiologic intestinal reaction.

Psychosis. In operation, the same as insanity; theoretically, a severe mental disturbance of any sort. Insanity is a legal term indicating some kind of mental incapacity. In practice, however, to call a man psychotic is to

call him insane; and various forms of insanity, such as dementia precox,*
melancholia,* etc., are all psychoses. Judges occasionally split the hair
and say that a certain patient has a psychosis but that he is not insane.
This is what the court does when it orders release from a hospital of a
patient who is admittedly psychotic. The judge, in theory, says that while
the patient has a psychosis, he is not insane. But as a practical matter
what the court really means is that the psychosis (insanity) is not of
such degree as to require confinement. The true distinction is between
certifiable and noncertifiable insanity, rather than between insanity and
psychosis.

Psychosomatic. The combined influence of emotional and physical factors.
Thus, high blood pressure is a psychosomatic disorder because it has both
emotional and physical components. The blood pressure is measurably
high, the arteries become hard to resist the rising blood pressure, and
changes in the size of the heart may then occur: these are mechanical or
physical factors in high blood pressure. However, emotion may raise the
blood pressure; a sudden emotional experience may shoot up the blood
pressure so fast that it causes a blood vessel to burst; and continued
suppressed hostility may cause a slowly mounting pressure: these are
emotional factors. So it is with a great many disorders—they have
both physical and emotional components; they are "psychosomatic" disorders.

Psychosomatics. The doctrine which holds that mind and body are a
unified entity; that emotions influence body structure and body function;
that physical disease influences emotions; that disease is a composite of
both components, so that the emotional and physical factors cannot be
and should not be disentangled. See Psychosomatic*.

Psychosurgery. An operation on the brain done for the purpose of relieving tension or improving behavior. See Lobotomy*.

Psychotherapy. Treatment by psychologic methods. See Therapy*.

Psychotic. The adjective of psychosis*. As a practical matter, "psychotic"
means insane—no more, no less.

Pyknolepsy. Recurrent, frequent, but very brief episodes of mental
blankness.

Pyromania. A compulsion* to set fires.

Quincke's disease. Angioneurotic* edema.

Reactive depression. A depression* due to some external cause. Unless
otherwise specified, a depressive reaction is considered to be a psychoneurosis*. If it reaches psychotic* intensity, it is called a "psychotic reactive depression." The condition is sometimes expressed as "depressive
reaction."

Retrograde amnesia. Loss of memory due to head injury, in which the
period covered by the amnesia* extends to some time *prior* to the injury.
For example if a patient is injured at 9 P.M., and on regaining consciousness, can recall nothing after 7 P.M. that night, he is suffering from a
retrograde amnesia.

Rorschach test. A method of determining the structure of personality by noting the patient's reaction to a set of cards containing standardized ink-blots.

Satyriasis. Excessive sexual drive in a male. The male equivalent of nymphomania*.

Schizophrenia. A psychosis* characterized by various degrees of withdrawal from reality, autistic thinking*, delusion* formation, bizarre behavior, and/or hallucinations*. Also called "dementia precox."*

Schizoid. Having traits similar to those of a schizoid personality.*

Schizoid personality. Long-term difficulty in adjustment* because of unsociability, excessive intraversion*, shyness, autistic thinking*, or seclusiveness.

Senile psychosis. A psychosis* sometimes developing in elderly persons characterized by memory defects, irritability, delusion* formation, and confusion.

Sensorium. The sensory or perceptive mechanism of the body and mind; usually applied to the patient's awareness of his surroundings. Thus, if a patient is disoriented*, it may be said that his "sensorium is clouded," meaning that he is not clearly aware of his surroundings.

Sexual deviation. Preference for a unconventional method of sexual gratification. As used in current nomenclatures,[4] the term is applied to a personality disorder (not a psychosis or psychoneurosis) in which the patient derives major satisfaction from one of the less conventional modes of sexual intercourse.

Shock therapy. Treatment of certain mental disorders by inducing convulsions*, coma*, or other sudden reactions, accomplished by electricity, inhalant gases, or by the injection of chemicals.

Simple adult maladjustment. Development of symptoms arising out of inability to cope with an immediate situation, without evidence of psychosis or psychopathic personality.

Sinistrosis. Emotionally induced awkwardness or incoordination. The term is sometimes used to describe a brooding sense of grievance following an injury, and thus comes close to the concept of attitudinal pathosis*.

Situational maladjustment. Simple adult maladjustment*.

Somatization reaction. A psychoneurosis* manifested by changes in the function (or sometimes the structure) of organs, causing complaints referrable to those organs. See Psychosomatic*.

Somnambulism. Walking or engaging in other activities, while asleep.

St. Vitus dance. Acute chorea*.

Superego. The part of the personality which represents ideals, goals, con-

---

[4] The term is used in *The Diagnosis and Statistical Manual of Mental Disorders* (Washington, D. C.: American Psychiatric Association, 1952); in *International Statistical Classification* (Geneva, Switzerland: World Health Organization, 1948) and in the 4th ed. of *Standard Nomenclature of Diseases and Operations* (Philadelphia: The Blakiston Co., 1952). However, in the first three editions of the *Standard Nomenclature* (1933, 1935, and 1942) it was called "Psychopathic Personality with Pathologic Sexuality."

science, and self-judgment. Only a violation of superego demands produces a desire for confession or punishment. For each person, the superego is the judge, the censor, and the punisher as well as the ideal.

Syndrome. A group of symptoms; an assembly of signs and symptoms which together spell out a specific pattern of disease.

Tabes dorsalis. A syphilitic disease of the spinal cord.

Therapist. One who treats.

Therapy. Treatment. If the treatment consists largely of psychologic methods—interviews, explanations, re-assurance, abreactions*, counselling, psychoanalysis*, etc.—then it is called "psychotherapy." Psychotherapy is *not* a synonym for psychoanalysis*, however. Psychoanalysis* is *one* kind of psychotherapy. There are others, such as: reassurance, re-education, guidance, and the like. The word therapy is often used in conjunction with an explanatory word like "shock therapy" (treatment by inducing shock*), "companion therapy," "bibliotherapy" (advising the patient to read certain books with the hope that this reading will modify his life), "drug therapy," "physical therapy" (use of physical modalities like heat, electricity, massage, baths, etc.), and many others.

Tic. An involuntary twitch.

Tic douloureux. Literally, a "painful tic"*; usually applied to severe, periodic pain in the face.

Transference. Displacement of emotion from one person or idea to another.

Trauma. In *general medicine,* an injury, blow, or hurt. (It may refer to a simple single accidental injury, like breaking a leg in an automobile accident; or it may refer to a slowly absorbed poison or other irritant. Thus if a worker constantly inhales metallic dust, the irritation to his lungs may cause damage to that organ. And it would be proper to describe this as a traumatic damage.) In *psychiatry,* a hurtful or damaging emotional experience. (Sometimes the experience is obviously damaging and the emotional effects are apparent. At other times, the incident appears to be trivial, the effects are unnoticeable, yet in the long run the patient shows the emotionally damaging effects of this "traumatic" experience.)

Traumatic neurosis. A psychoneurosis precipitated by injury, generally by head injury.

Traumatic psychosis. Insanity due to injury to the brain; not now official in any widely used nomenclature, though it is the common term among doctors and lawyers. The official designation was "Psychosis due to Trauma" in the first three editions of the *Standard Nomenclature* (1933 to 1942), and "Chronic Brain Syndrome associated with Trauma with Psychotic Reaction" in the 4th edition (1952), as well as in the classification of the American Psychiatric Association.[5] In the *International Classification* [6] the term is "Psychosis of demonstrable etiology resulting from

[5] *Diagnostic and Statistical Manual of Mental Disorders* (Washington, D. C.: American Psychiatric Association, 1952), p. 20.

[6] *Manual of the International Statistical Classification of Diseases* (Geneva, Switzerland: World Health Organization, 1948), p. 108.

trauma." Some hospital systems call a traumatic psychosis "Encephalopathy manifested by psychotic reaction." The military services [7] uses the term "Encephalopathy due to trauma manifested by psychosis."

Verbigeration. Excessive chatter, often meaningless, repetitive, or irrelevant talking.

Voyeur. A peeping Tom.

White Matter. Brain or spinal cord tissue composed largely of nerve fibers rather than of nerve cells. Also see Gray matter*.

[7] *Basic Diagnostic Nomenclature of Diseases and Injuries,* Special Regulation 40-1025-1 (Washington, D. C.: Department of the Army, Department of the Air Force, and Bureau of Medicine and Surgery, U. S. Navy, 1949), p. 14

Appendix C

EXAMINATION GUIDES

The inexperienced examiner will find these guides helpful as (*a*) springboards for the examination, (*b*) a check list, and (*c*) a framework for the report. Some physicians will want to type the appropriate guide on a card and keep it on the desk during the interview. Others will turn to the guide just before concluding the interview, and review the headings to make sure that there are no major omissions. Some will find it easier to reassemble their notes under these headings and to use the items as paragraphs in the report.

These following guides will not teach a novice how to accomplish the examination. They are predicated on the assumption that the doctor knows how to conduct a conventional psychiatric interview and perform the physical examination, but wants tips on the special focus required.

Seven guides are offered:

    I. Examination of the criminal defendant
   II. Examination of the personal injury claimant
  III. Examination of the testator
  IV. Examination of mute patients
   V. Examination of the allegedly drunken driver
  VI. Examination of the juvenile offender
 VII. Determination of competency

Guide I. Examination of the Criminal Defendant

1. PRELIMINARY READING: Chapters 1, 2, and 3 of this book.
2. PRELIMINARY BRIEFING:

   a) Factual description of the alleged crime.
   b) Probation office record (or background history of the defendant from other sources). Look particularly for:

   (1) Schooling.
   (2) Vocational history.
   (3) Medical history.
   (4) Military history.
   (5) Marital and social history.
   (6) Habits and avocational activities.
   (7) Previous criminal record if any.

   Check on permission to enter jail if defendant is in custody.

3. INTRODUCTION TO THE DEFENDANT AND IDENTIFICATION OF THE EXAMINER:

   a) If examination is to be conducted in jail, try to arrange with warden to have defendant brought to jail infirmary and accomplish examination there. Accept visiting room, if infirmary is rejected.
   b) Have doctor, nurse, warden, or guard (in that preference order) introduce defendant to examiner. (If examination is being made on behalf of defense, counsel is best one to introduce the doctor.)
   c) Tell the defendant:

   (1) That you are a doctor.
   (2) That you are interested in understanding how he happened to get into this difficulty.
   (3) That you will be taking notes.
   (4) That you will make a report to (judge, district attorney, defense counsel or probation officer, as case may be).
   (5) That you may have to testify in court.
   (6) That defendant does not have to answer questions; that if he would rather not have a certain answer written down, he should explain that he would prefer not to answer that particular question; and that it is all right for him to do so.

   d) The record should indicate that the items above, *c*(1) to *c*(6), were explained to the defendant.

e) If a third party remains during the examination, a note to that effect is included in the record.

f) If patient refuses to (or is unable to) answer questions, see Guide IV, this Appendix.

4. THE PHYSICAL AND NEUROLOGIC EXAMINATION: It is generally best to start with this since it is easier for a patient to warm up during this kind of examination than during a formal psychiatric interview. The conventional routine physical examination is done. In addition, check particularly on:

a) Cardiovascular: dilated or sclerotic peripheral vessels, blood pressure abnormality.

b) Ophthalmologic: exophthalmos, dilated, contracted, unequal or fixed pupils; arcus senilis; optic atrophy.

c) Skin: bruises, scars, needle marks, pallor.

d) Endocrine survey.

e) Neurologic findings: tremors, impaired associated movements, scars on tongue, choked disc, incoordination, tics.

5. ASSAY OF INTELLIGENCE: Probation office surveys should include reports of intelligence tests accomplished previously in school, in the armed services, or in connection with employment applications. Examiner should be prepared to do simple psychometric test, in any event. If more thorough study by psychologist is possible it should be obtained. A raw I.Q. is not sufficient. It is essential to know something of the type of intelligence, too. Is current intelligence consistent with school and vocational history or has there been deterioration? Is subject "word-minded," "thing-minded," or "idea-minded?"

6. FORMAL PSYCHIATRIC EXAMINATION:

a) Behavior, general attitude, cooperativeness.

b) Clarity, brightness, awareness.

c) Psychomotor activity: restlessness; speed of thinking; productivity articulateness; coherence; general pressure of thought, speech and action.

d) Mood: its depth, appropriateness, and stability.

e) Orientation and general contact with reality.

f) Memory for recent and remote events, and for details for the alleged criminal act.

g) Delusions and hallucinations; are they easily elicited? Is patient's behavior consistent with these symptoms?

h) Insight. Does offender consider himself a "mental case"? Does he justify his actions? Any sense of guilt, shame, or remorse?

i) All this, of course, superimposed on what the psychiatrist considers a good general psychiatric examination.

7. APPRAISAL OF PERSONALITY:

a) Seclusive or extroverted.

b) Moody or stable.

c) Ambitious, self-satisfied, or crushed by sense of inadequacy.

d) Energetic or lazy.

e) Amiable, sullen, friendly, unfriendly.

f) Mature or immature.

g) Impulsiveness, spontaneity, caution, deliberateness.

Note: This is not, of course, a model for the study of personality. If projective tests can be administered, this should be done. If not, the psychiatrist tries to determine what he can of the offender's previous or "normal" personality. These seven items constitute a skeleton on which this survey can be erected; they do not spell out the sum total of personality appraisal.

8. SPECIAL TESTS AND PROCEDURES: Occasionally one or more of the following might be desirable:

a) X-rays, including air encephalograms.

b) Electro-encephalograms.

c) Spinal fluid studies.

d) Blood studies.

e) Metabolism tests.

f) Special psychologic tests.

g) Hospital observation.

h) Interviews under narcosis. (See page 37.)

9. PATIENT'S KNOWLEDGE THAT THE ACT WAS WRONG: This is usually the crux of the psychiatric inquiry. The answer cannot be neatly spelled out by a series of infallible test questions. However, these points may help:

a) Does he say that he now thinks that the act was wrong?

b) Did he attempt to run away from the scene of the crime?

c) Did he attempt to conceal or destroy his identity (as by erasing fingerprints, using an alias, or conjuring an alibi) ?

d) Did he voluntarily surrender to the police?

e) Did he use every available means to avoid apprehension?

f) Was the act planned or impulsive?

g) Was an escape plan formulated in advance?

h) Did he intend—was he capable of intending—that his act should have those consequences?

i) Was he in the grip of a powerful impulse? If so, would that be most accurately described as:

(1) A psychotic kind of impulse?

(2) A neurotic (compulsive or psychasthenic) kind of impulse?

(3) An impulsive or rage reaction in an otherwise substantially normal person?

(4) The result of acute alcoholism? (See pages 10, 134.)

10. THE SIXTEEN CRUCIAL QUESTIONS: Before terminating the interview, the examiner would do well to review the following sixteen questions, to be certain that he can answer all of them, if asked on the witness stand.

a) What is the clinical psychiatric diagnosis?

b) Were there any significant physical or neurologic findings?

c) Was the defendant sane (1) at the time of examination; (2) at time of the offense?

d) What is his intelligence?

e) Is the defendant a chronic or periodic alcoholic?

f) Was defendant drunk at the time of the offense?

g) Is he a habitual taker of opiates, barbiturates, or marihuana?

h) Did he know the nature of the act charged?

i) Does he know the quality ("harmfulness" and consequences) of the act?

j) Does he know that his act was something which is generally considered wrong?

k) Does he understand the seriousness of his current predicament?

l) Is he capable of helping in his own defense?

m) Was he, at the time of the crime, capable of forming the degree of intent, premeditation, or willfulness called for in the indictment?

n) At the same time of the act, was he in the grip of a powerful impulse? (See 9*i* above.)

o) Does he assert loss of memory for the offense? If this amnesia is considered genuine, is it due to hysteria, concussion, pathologic intoxication, or some form of epilepsy?

p) What is the prognosis in terms of treatability and future dangers to society?

Note: It will be observed that an understanding of the defendant's motivation is not listed as one of the crucial questions. Naturally no psychiatrist worthy of that title is satisfied to study a case without trying to uncover motivation. However, for reasons elaborated in the text, this is of minor importance in terms of the patient's technical responsibility. On the other hand, intent (as distinguished from motive) is of major importance. If the crime was one of personal injury, did he *intend* to hurt the victim? If it was a theft, did he *intend* to convert someone else's property to his own use?

11. THE REPORT: For further details see Chapter 3. In general, the report should cover:

a) Review of the medical and psychiatric history of the defendant.

b) The neurologic, psychiatric, and medical findings.

c) A brief summary of the facts of the crime.

d) The diagnosis—psychiatric, psychologic, neurologic, and medical.

e) The offender's intelligence level, qualitatively and quantitatively.

f) Whether the defendant knew the nature and quality of the act charged and whether he was driven by an irresistible impulse.

g) Whether he knew he was doing something wrong.

h) Whether he can now cooperate in his own defense; and if not, why not.

i) The possibilities of therapy, including both the kind and the prognosis.

j) A simple exposition of the emotional mechanism behind the offense.

Note: If the defendant is stuporous, mute, or hopelessly uncooperative, Guide IV may be found helpful. See page 359.

Guide II. Examination of the Personal Injury Claimant

Note: It might be supposed that neuropsychiatric examination of a patient claiming injury would be no different from the conventional clinical examination. This, however, is an oversimplification. In a litigated case the doctor may be cross-examined on his techniques, findings and interpretations, whereas in ordinary clinical practice the examiner is accountable to nobody. Again, the examiner in a personal injury case has to record a good deal of non-medical information—details of the accident, names and addresses of the opposing attorneys, name of the insurance carrier, etc., because he needs these data in preparing reports and forwarding bills. Furthermore, there is a marked difference in motivation, with the claimant tending to overstress his disability, and (where the doctor is examining for the defense) with the patient often hostile to the physician. And much of the traditional privacy of the doctor-patient relationship is lost in medico-legal examinations. Finally, the examiner must have meticulous records (because they may be exhibited publicly in court) and must prepare reports comprehensible to laymen. Thus the examination of the personal injury claimant is, in practice, much different—at least in its peripheral features—from the normal clinical examination.

1. PRELIMINARY READING: Chapters 4 and 11 of this book.
2. PRELIMINARY HISTORICAL DATA:

    a) Name and identification of person or company referring the case.
    b) Description (including nonmedical details) of the accident.
    c) Nature of patient's work, with note as to possible exposure to toxic chemicals (in workmen's compensation cases).
    d) Patient's previous accident or industrial disease record.
    e) If patient alleges unconsciousness at time of accident, elicit what is meant by "unconscious"; how long he was in that state; where he was when he "woke up"; and whether there were any post-coma sequels.
    f) Hospital or office to which patient was taken for first-aid, how long he stayed there, what their findings, diagnosis, and treatment were.
    g) Names of attorneys and insurance companies involved.

3. PATIENT'S COMPLAINTS:

    a) First record patient's complaints *in his own words,* and without prompting him and without asking leading questions.

    (Juries and judges will look askance at a record which quotes an illiterate worker as complaining of "vertigo" or "photophobia"; hence, at the beginning, patient's own words are used.

To avoid the implication that the examiner "suggested" certain symptoms, the complaints should be set up in two paragraphs, the first listing those volunteered by the claimant without prompting, and the second those complaints brought out by normal medical questioning.)

b) In a separate paragraph list complaints brought out by questioning.

c) Describe accident or exposure in patient's own words.

4. PREVIOUS HISTORY:

a) Note specifically any record of previous accidents or industrial diseases, and whether patient received any financial awards as a result. (Failure to ask about this might lead to embarrassment on the witness stand.)

b) Record specifically the patient's habit history with reference to alcohol, drugs, food fads, smoking, and sleep. (Some psychoneurotic-like or psychotic-like symptoms could be due to chronic alcoholism, for instance.)

c) Determine whether patient had ever been rejected for insurance, military service, or employment because of physical or emotional disabilities. (Hypertension might mimic a post-concussion syndrome, and the doctor would look foolish if he ascribed the symptoms to the injury when it is later shown that he has been rejected for insurance because of hypertension producing the current symptoms.)

d) Note specifically if claimant had ever before been a hospital patient, and if so why.

e) Mention should be made of patient's school and job history, with particular emphasis on vocational and scholastic adjustment and reasons for leaving school and jobs.

f) Marital history (to anticipate possibility that emotional symptoms might be due to marital maladjustment rather than to the accident).

g) All this is superimposed on the conventional "past history" part of the usual medical examination. This traditional type of history-taking must not, of course, be omitted.

5. NEUROLOGIC EXAMINATION: (An examiner for a defendant or insurance company is likely to be vigorously cross-questioned as to the completeness of his examination and the time he spent on it. He cannot afford to omit any routine test, since the claimant's counsel may use that to "prove" that the examination was careless or biased.

The claimant's own examiner is less vulnerable here, since any omission would ordinarily not hurt the defendant's case. However, it might suggest a slovenly examination. Remember to record all negative findings.)

a) General appearance. Does patient undress without aid and with coordinate movement?

b) Gait and station. Does he swing arms as he walks? Does he limp, walk stiffly, stand steadily, festinate, watch floor as he walks, or show foot-drop? Is there a positive Romberg, and if so how much sway and in what direction?

c) Coordination. Check finger-nose maneuver, with eyes open, again with eyes closed; if abnormal note whether defect is in placement, past-pointing, short-pointing, or tremulousness. Have patient lift full water-glass, button and unbutton jacket, and fit key in key-hole, with and without eyes open. Obtain handwriting sample. (Keep it in the file.) Review possible cerebellar signs (hypotonus, rebound phenomenon, adiadochokinesis, dysmetria, asynergy, and movement slowness).

d) Motor system. (Also see Reflexes, below.)

(1) Is patient right-handed, left-handed, or ambidextrous?

(2) Look for tremors, particularly of eyelids, tongue, and extended hands, and note breadth of tremor, its regularity, its rate, and under what conditions it becomes better or worse. (Patient should also be questioned about this.)

(3) Strength. Use dynamometer if available. (An examiner who does much medico-legal work should keep a dynamometer in his bag.) Measure strength of hand grips, of power in lower and upper extremities comparing right with left and with theoretical normal.

(4) Make specific studies of motor power and coordination in areas where disability is alleged—a particular limb, for instance.

e) Cranial nerves. All twelve pairs must be tested, even though they could not possibly have been implicated. Any omission will be noticed by the cross-examining attorney and may be cited as evidence of a careless neurologic examination. To test cranial nerves properly, the examiner must have on hand the solutions for tasting and smelling, cards with the words Sweet, Sour, Bitter, Salt, written on them, flashlight, tuning fork, an ophthalmoscope, skin testing equipment, test type cards, and a transparent ruler.

(1) Olfactory nerve. Test each nostril separately. Use vials of non-irritating, easily recognizable, odoriferous solutions, such as peppermint, camphor, turpentine, or cloves. (Ammonia and vinegar test the fifth nerve, not the first.) The most frequent cause of anosmia is the common cold.

(2) Optic nerve. Retinoscopy should be routine, and every neuropsychiatrist should be able to do at least a cursory ophthalmoscopic examination. Vision may be tested with standard test types, and perimetry by confrontation. Tests for color blindness and detailed perimetric studies are best referred to the ophthalmologist.

(3) Oculomotor nerve. It is not practical to separate the examinations of the third, fourth, and sixth nerves. These are tested as a unit.

    (a) Pupils—size, eccentricity, contour, reaction to light and to accommodation. If pupils are unequal, measure each pupil with a transparent ruler and note the diameters.

    (b) Look for ptosis and check the ciliospinal reflex.

    (c) Look for nystagmus, both horizontal and vertical. Distinguish true nystagmus from normal nystagmoid jerks. If nystagmus is found, make record of direction of the quick component, and note on what extreme of vision (right, left, upwards or downwards) it is most pronounced.

    (d) Look for squint. Is it present on forward gaze or only on looking toward one extreme? Record it in detail.

    (e) Any double vision (or triple vision!)? Determine under what circumstances the images are seen and the position of one image relative to the other.

    (f) Symmetry of the ocular movements.

(4) The trochlear nerve. Included in e (3) above.

(5) The trigeminal nerve. Check strength and symmetry of masseter and temporalis muscles. Test for jaw jerk. Examine the area of each of the three sensory divisions (ophthalmic, maxillary, mandibular) in the conventional way, with pinprick and light touch.

(6) The abducent nerve. Included in e(3) above.

(7) The facial nerve. Look for facial assymetry, and check by having patient frown, whistle, smile, shut his eyes tightly, and raise his eyebrows. If facial asymmetry is found, de-

termine specifically whether forehead is involved in this. Impairment of taste sense is reviewed under the ninth nerve.

(8) The auditory nerve. The examiner varies his voice during the examination and notes any gross impairment of hearing. Then check hearing to watch-tick and to "ordinary" conversation noting distances for each ear separately. With tuning fork, apply both Rinne and Weber tests. Vestibular tests and more refined studies of hearing, as well as otoscopy, are best left to the otologist.

(9) Glossopharyngeal nerve. Taste is tested either with powdered ingredients or with solutions. Sugar, salt, citric acid, and quinine are the traditional tetrad of powders. Sugar and salt solutions, diluted vinegar, and an ordinary "bitter tonic" may be used. The patient points to the words "Sweet," "Sour," "Bitter," "Salt" written on a card. This is because each quadrant of the tongue is separately tested and if the subject speaks, he will roll the powder or solution over his whole tongue. The posterior third of the tongue is served by the ninth nerve, the rest of the tongue by the seventh. Test pharyngeal reflex and note position of uvula when at rest and when patient says "Ah."

(10) Vagus nerve. Have patient sip water and note (a) if he regurgitates, and (b) how he swallows. Laryngoscopic examination is best left to the laryngologist. Note hoarseness or dyspnea. Is speech "nasal"? Check rate and regularity of pulse.

(11) Accessory nerve. As patient turns head, note power of this movement (against examiner's hand) and behavior of the two sternomastoid muscles.

(12) Hypoglossal nerve. Have patient protrude and deviate tongue. Note symmetry of tongue movements, and tremors and atrophy of tongue, if present.

f) Reflexes. In practice, little is learned from a lengthy examination of the reflexes. Obvious and objective reflex changes usually occur in more advanced conditions, when diagnosis is not much in dispute anyway. However, reflexes have caught the popular fancy to such an extent that any omission in reflex examination is considered scandalous. There are hundreds of reflex tests, most of them obscure, and no examiner can cover them all. It is a favorite device of cross-examining attorneys to unearth some little

known reflex (usually from the footnote of an obsolete text) and
hurl this at the medical witness. In general, the following reflexes
should be tested in all cases:

(1) Jaw jerks.
(2) Radial and ulnar reflexes.
(3) Biceps and triceps reflexes.
(4) Abdominal skin reflexes.
(5) Knee jerks.
(6) Ankle jerks.
(7) Plantar reflexes and Babinski confirmatories.
(8) Cremasteric and scrotal reflexes.
(9) Check for Hoffman's sign.
(10) Check for ankle and patellar clonus.

g) Sensory system. Sensory examination is more important in
personal injury work than in general clinical neurology. This is
because hysterical hypesthesias are so common after injury, and
because peripheral nerves are so often injured in accidents. Care
must be taken that the patient cannot see the skin area being
tested. If necessary, the claimant is blindfolded during this part
of the examination. At first the general body areas are rapidly
covered: face, neck, each quadrant of the trunk, each quadrant of
the back, and both surfaces of each arm, forearm, hand, thigh, leg,
and foot. Then more detailed exploration is made of any area in
which findings are suspicious and of any area towards which patient directs any complaints. It is important to compare right and
left sides for any and every finding as well as to note any absolute
areas of anesthesia, hypesthesia, or hyperesthesia. When such
areas are found, the examiner determines whether the area abruptly terminates or whether the distorted sensation merges imperceptibly into an area of normal sensation.

(1) Look for areas of:
    (*a*) Reduced sensation—hypesthesia.
    (*b*) Lost sensation—anesthesia.
    (*c*) Perverted sensation—paresthesia.
    (*d*) Exquisite sensitivity—hyperesthesia.
    (*e*) Lost vibration sense—pallanesthesia.
(2) With respect to any area where any oddity is found:
    (*a*) Compare it with same area on opposite side of body.
    (*b*) Ascertain its limitations and mark its frontiers on a
        sketch or describe exactly, giving careful measurements
        from fixed bony points.

(3) The modalities normally tested are:

   (*a*) Light touch. Use brush or wisp of cotton pulled out from tip end of a cotton swab.

   (*b*) Pinprick. Since it is difficult for the examiner to apply a uniform degree of pin pressure, one of the special pin-pricking instruments should be used if possible.

   (*c*) Temperature sense. Use recently prepared tubes of hot water and ice water. Be sure that the tubes have been carefully dried on the outside before applying to the patient's skin.

   (*d*) Two-point discrimination. Use compass points or special instruments made for this purpose. Note smallest distance between points which patient discriminates as separate stimuli; and widest distance which he considers a single stimulus. (These figures are usually different.)

   (*e*) Vibration sense. Apply tuning fork to bony prominences and note if patient recognizes the peculiar "vibratory" or "electrical" quality of the contact. Stop the vibration manually and have patient call out when it has been stopped. Apply dead fork briefly, and after a moment snap the tines together and note if patient recognizes that vibration has started. Apply to the sternum, clavicle, several spinous processes, all four styloid processes, the olencranon, and the four malleoli. On the sternum, apply separately to right and left halves. (This being a single bone, patient should sense the vibration from all points, if he senses it from any one point on the sternum. Hemipallanesthesia of the sternum therefore suggests hysteria.)

   (*f*) Position sense in the fingers and toes. After moving a toe or finger up or down or sideways, examiner brings it into one position and notes if patient can tell in what position. This may also be used in testing recognition of position of the entire extremity.

   (*g*) Stereognosis. Have patient recognize a small, readily identified object (key, coin, matchbox, etc.) placed invisibly in his hand.

(4) Sensory modalities less usually tested—though examined when indicated—are:

   (*a*) Barognosis.

   (*b*) Sensitivity to deep-pressure pains.

h) Special Examinations. When indicated, certain special examinations of the nervous system may be done. These include:

(1) Tests for aphasia.

(2) Spinal fluid studies (pressure, cytology, color, culture, chemistry).

(3) Electrical responses to determine integrity of muscles and nerves.

(4) Electro-encephalograms.

(5) Studies of endocrine status.

(6) Consultations with otologist, ophthalmologist, and laryngologist.

(7) Pharmacologic tests of the sympathetic nervous system.

(8) X-rays, including air-studies and arteriograms, of head and spinal column.

i) A reminder: Record all negative findings.

6. APPRAISAL OF INTELLIGENCE: It is important to make some assay of the claimant's intelligence: *first* because this is an essential part of any neuropsychiatric study, *second* because it may be claimed that intellectual impairment resulted from the accident or industrial disease, *third* because it helps in interpreting the patient's history and in appraising his motivations. A psychologist should be asked to administer an appropriate psychometric test. If this is not practical, the psychiatrist should estimate intelligence by doing simple psychometric studies. This should be correlated with the claimant's school and work record.

7. GENERAL MEDICAL REVIEW:

a) The neuropsychiatrist should include a routine (even if only cursory) medical examination, in order to satisfy himself as to possible nonneurologic and nonpsychiatric causes of the symptoms. In particular, attention should be paid to:

b) Blood pressure findings (especially if headache is a major complaint).

c) Locating, measuring and charting all scars (possibility of other accidents and verification of claimed accident). Note if scars are tender, adherent, well-healed.

d) Measurements of weight at each visit. (Sick persons, whether the illness is of structural or emotional origin, seldom gain weight while sick.)

e) Cardiovascular examination.

f) Minor physical findings supportive of subjective complaints.

8. PSYCHIATRIC EXAMINATION:

   a) The conventional psychiatric examination is accomplished as a matter of course. Particular attention is paid to:

   b) Anxiety. Is this overt, latent, expressed through dreams, or converted into somatic symptoms?

   c) Cooperativeness with the examiner. (Note is made of hostility or overeagerness.)

   d) Crying spells—as reported by patient or witnessed during interview.

   e) Patient's emotional response (with somatic concomitants such as, e.g., blushing) to various types of questions.

   f) Patient's appearance and general behavior.

   g) His awareness of his surroundings, his attentiveness, his clarity, and his orientation.

   h) Delusional material and paranoid trends. (Note in particular whether any paranoid trends are elicited towards the insurance company, opposing lawyer, labor union, or employers. See section on attitudinal pathosis, page 63.)

   i) Psychomotor activity: restlessness, productivity, coherence, and general pressure of thought, activity, and speech.

   j) Evidence of hallucinations.

   k) Memory for recent and remote events; memory for details of the accident. If impaired memory is alleged, obtain specific examples from family.

   l) Mood: its appropriateness and stability.

   m) Some impression (admittedly often intuitive and nonobjective) of the patient's "sincerity" and motivation.

   n) The extent to which his play-life, as well as his work-life, is affected by the alleged disability.

9. CONSIDERATION OF POSSIBLE MALINGERING: Though it may be distasteful to do so, it is essential that the examiner weigh this possibility in any personal injury claim. See Chapter 11 for suggestions. (For malingered psychoneuroses, see particularly the criteria on page 170.)

10. FORMULATION OF THE CASE: The examiner will want to make two formulations after he has reached a diagnosis. These are: (*a*) relationship of the diagnosis to the accident or industrial disease, and (*b*) severity of the disability.

   a) If psychoneurosis or psychosis is diagnosed, which of the following best describes its relationship to the accident:

(1) The trauma was an adequate *cause*.

(2) The trauma was a *major precipitating factor*.

(3) The trauma materially *aggravated* a pre-existing condition.

(4) The trauma was a *minor factor* in maturing a previously well-developed psychosis or neurosis.

(5) The trauma is *unrelated* to the emotional disorder.

(6) The fright, emotional shock, or terror of witnessing, or being a victim of the accident, caused the disability; this, rather than any mechanical injury being the factor.

(7) The symptoms are due to suggestion—in the accident room, the hospital ward, the words of attorneys, adjusters or relatives.

(8) The desire for compensation, or hostility to the employer, is a conscious or unconscious factor in precipitating the disability or in maintaining it. (See attitudinal pathosis, page 63.)

b) Evaluation of disability. (See pages 51 to 54.)

11. FINANCIAL RECORDS: The financial records of the examinations and treatments may constitute an important part of the case, both in connection with measuring damages and in helping clarify the status of the physician. (The doctor's bill, in "negligence" cases, is itself part of the amount claimed in the suit.) These financial records become an intrinsic part of the "papers" and may be exhibited in court. In his bookkeeping record the physician should show:

a) Who is accountable for the medical bill.

b) To what address were bills sent, when, and in what amounts.

c) How much was paid, when, by whom.

d) How much is still owing and for what services (itemized).

e) If no bills have been submitted, why not.

12. THE REPORT: If a printed form is to be filled out, be sure to make at least one carbon copy and clip it to patient's office record. Also, type on the carbon copy the questions being answered. For example, a form might have printed headings like this: "When did the accident occur?" "When did you first see the patient?" "When do you believe he will be able to return to work?" If the doctor retains a simple carbon copy, he will have on this copy nothing but a collection of dates, and later on will not know what each date means. The solution to this problem is simple: type the questions as well as the answers on the copy.

If no form is furnished, or if it is supplemented by a narrative report, the following paragraphing will be helpful:

a) As a heading, the name of the claimant and the name of the defendant.

b) When and where the claimant was examined, and at whose request.

c) The past and present history as given by the claimant. Note previous accidents and previous work record.

d) Supplementary details about the accident, and the source of this information.

e) The patient's complaints in his own words.

f) Supplementary complaints furnished by members of family or others, and the source of this information.

g) Results of neurologic and physical examinations. If this is done on behalf of defendant, employer or insurance company, the findings should be systematically organized by body systems, such as "cranial nerves" or "motor system," etc. This is to indicate that nothing was left out; and the carbon copy then becomes a springboard for testimony, particularly during cross-examination. Suggested paragraph headings here are those in paragraph 5 of this guide, beginning on page 345.

If examination is done on behalf of claimant himself or his own attorney, it would be enough simply to list the positive findings and add a statement that "except for the above, all physical and neurologic findings were negative."

h) The diagnosis: medical, neurologic, and psychiatric.

i) The relationship between the diagnosis and the accident (or occupational exposure). If the diagnosis is "psychoneurosis" in any form, turn to 10*a* of this guide, and select the phrase which most closely delineates the relationship.

j) A note as to the severity and permanency of the disability. (See pages 51 to 54.)

k) Include a bill, and keep a record showing amount of bill, dates covered, and to whom the bill was sent.

Guide III. Examination of the Testator

Note: It is seldom that a psychiatrist is asked to examine a person prior to his signing a will. However, some attorneys take this precaution when the estate is large, the potential heirs litiginous or the testator eccentric; and also whenever challenge is anticipated. Sometimes a psychiatrist is examining a patient for some other reason and knows (or is told) that the patient has a large estate which may, some day, be thrown into the courts. Under those circumstances, the psychiatrist who has included this type of examination is fortunate because he can testify effectively if subsequent will litigation does develop. Before embarking on the examination, the doctor would do well to reread Chapter 7.

1. ORIENTING THE TESTATOR: If the testator himself asks for the examination and arranges the appointment, little orientation is necessary. He expects to be "tested." However, if his attorney or a member of the family makes the arrangements, the doctor should ascertain what the patient was told. Does he know that this is to be a psychiatric examination and why? Or was he told that this was some sort of business interview? It is awkward to plunge into a line of memory-testing and similar questions when the patient is totally unprepared for it. A testator resents this, considers it an aspersion on his sanity. It may, therefore, be necessary for the doctor to give the subject some kind of tactful orientation before launching the examination. This tact should, of course, be part of the psychiatrist's verbal equipment anyway. One has to know how to find out whether a person communicates with spirits, without just asking the question bluntly. (One possible line of questioning would be: When did your mother die? Have you thought much about her since her death? Do you ever dream about her? Does her influence still guide you in any way? etc., thus gradually leading up to the question of a belief in spiritualism. Usually the devotee of spiritualism will deliver the material spontaneously by this time.) Again, while delusions of marital infidelity are common in seniles, it would be gauche to ask bluntly: Is your wife untrue to you? This too has to be approached slowly and gently—usually *via* questions about the testator's general happiness, satisfaction with life, shared tastes with wife, etc.

2. THE SPECIFIC INTERVIEW: Circumstances will determine whether it is better to start with specific testamentary questions or better to do a general psychiatric interview first. If the testator knows that he is being interviewed to determine whether he can make a valid will, it is easier to start with specific questions dealing with testamentary

capacity. Otherwise, it might be better to do the general examination (paragraph 3, then 2) first. In the specific interview the points to be covered are:

a) If the matter of making a will has come up, testator is encouraged to talk freely about this, so that it may be determined whether, in fact, he knows he is making a will.

b) If (*a*) does not apply, the examiner determines from the testator's general intelligence whether he is *capable* of knowing, when he is making a will, that that is what he is doing.

c) The testator is then asked to name the members of his family, indicating their relationship to him, and their approximate ages. This is then checked with information furnished by the attorney or others. The examiner watches particularly for delusions that long-deceased relatives are still alive, and for misidentifications.

d) Continuing from (*c*) the examiner draws the testator out about his feelings towards the various members of his family, looking particularly for evidences of paranoid or other delusional trends, and for unreasonable prejudices.

e) The testator is asked whether he owns his own home, how much the taxes are, and at what it is assessed. Also for information about any automobile, business, stocks, bonds, or acreage that he may own. The attorney should have prepared the patient for this, since otherwise it may seem like an impertinent battery of questions coming from a doctor. The information furnished is then checked against data supplied by the lawyer or obtained from other sources, to see if it is substantially correct. The examiner particularly looks for fantastic overevaluations, claims to ownership of property or other assets which might be delusional, and ideas of poverty.

f) The examiner is on the lookout for eccentric ideas, particularly ideas touching on:

(1) Belief in spiritualism.
(2) Eccentricities of dress or manner.
(3) Ideas of marital infidelity.
(4) Ideas that children or other relatives are ungrateful or are persecutory.
(5) Fanaticism in any field.

g) Information must be obtained from the subject (and independently checked) about the testator's tastes in alcohol, addiction to "sleeping pills," and habits generally.

h) Discussion should be free enough for the examiner to determine whether any person or organization seems to have an undue hold on the testator's affections or interests; whether he is engaged in any crusades; whether he is abnormally devoted to any society, movement, individual, or "cause."

i) By now, the examiner should be able to form some opinion about the testator's general intelligence. See paragraph 3*b* below.

j) The testator's standing in the community and position in his business and/or profession, as well as his vocational competency, should be ascertained and noted.

k) Ability to understand what he is reading and writing should be checked, if patient will permit, by having him read and explain newspaper items and by having him write simple phrases from dictation. Similar tests may be done with simple arithmetical problems. Watch particularly for evidences of aphasia.

3. GENERAL PSYCHIATRIC EXAMINATION: Either before or just after the specific inquiry (paragraph 2 above) the doctor should accomplish a general psychiatric examination.

a) Note testator's behavior, attitude, cooperativeness, and general appearance.

b) Note his clarity, brightness, and awareness. If practical, a psychometric test should be administered to gage his actual intelligence. If this is not practical, enough data should be accumulated both from the examination and from other sources to make an evaluation of his intelligence possible.

c) Note psychomotor activity: restlessness, speed of thinking, productivity, articulateness, coherence, and general pressure of thought, speech, and activity.

d) Note depth, appropriateness, and stability of mood. Does testator readily exhibit anger, tears in eyes, indignation or depression?

e) Note orientation and general contact with reality.

f) Test memory for recent and remote events. Senile patients usually recall remote events with great vividness; may be vague about more recent events. Also note ability to recall and retain simple facts given early in the interview and raised again towards end of the examination.

g) Note evidence of delusions and hallucinations. Of particular interest here are delusions with respect to friends, servants and relatives, and with respect to ownership of property.

h) Testator's opinion of his own mental state, including his opinion about his own memory and ability to concentrate.

Is there any evidence of "neurotic" behavior or activity, specifically with respect to anxiety, hypochondriasis, complaints of "nervousness," abnormal shyness, sense of inadequacy, tics, mannerisms, or other complaints or findings suggestive of psychoneurotic reaction?

j) Make personality evaluation. Is testator an aggressive or recessive person? Introverted or extroverted? Moody or stable? Hostile or amiable? Impulsive or deliberate? Mature or immature? Lazy or energetic? Ambitious? Self-satisfied?

4. NEUROLOGIC AND MEDICAL EXAMINATION: Many testators are elderly, and a will is often challenged because the disappointed relatives argue that old age is tantamount to doddering senility. It is therefore important to evaluate the physical and neurologic evidences of senescence as well as to do a neurologic and medical examination for general diagnostic purposes.

a) Look for evidences of senility—arcus senilis, cataracts, hypertension, arteriosclerosis, etc.

b) Look for tremors—especially of tongue, eyelids and hands. Obtain and keep a specimen of patient's handwriting. Cross-check with *2k* above.

c) Look for evidences of alcoholism (enlarged nasal skin capillaries, enlarged liver, tremors, etc.).

d) Note presence or absence of hemiparesis or hemiplegia. Compare tendon reflexes and plantar reflexes bilaterally. Slight hemiparesis may be uncovered and this, in turn, may suggest a mild degree of aphasia—a matter of importance in interpreting testator's ability to write a will. Hence note whether patient is right-handed or left-handed.

e) Specifically test for aphasia.

f) Determine vision, whether eyeglasses are worn or needed, and whether vision is suitably corrected thereby. This may be important if will is challenged. Consultation with ophthalmologist may be indicated.

g) Determine hearing. Are hearing-aids worn or needed? This too may be important if will is challenged, and consultation with otologist may be indicated.

h) Note whether patient dresses and undresses without aid; whether he is coordinate in buttoning clothing; whether he walks freely, needs cane.

i) Look for classical signs of paralysis agitans and specifically note if no such signs are found.

j) The neurologic examination detailed on page 345 of Guide II (personal injury claimant) may be followed here. Note that comparison of reflexes, unimportant in personal injury examination, is important in this type of study because of possible cerebral vascular disease.

k) Give general physical examination, with particular attention to possibility of any wasting or debilitating disease, any condition producing frequent pain, any disorder accompanied by attacks of fever, disorientation, confusion, or delirium.

l) Give supplementary examinations as indicated: X-rays, spinal taps, special psychologic tests, special eye or ear studies, electrocardiograms, electro-encephalograms, etc.

5. THE REPORT: The following paragraph headings may be helpful:

a) Identifying data, including when and where examination was done and at whose request; with note as to whether patient previously understood, or was given to understand, purpose and scope of the examination.

b) Significant physical and neurologic findings.

c) Significant psychiatric and psychologic findings, with particular mention of testator's awareness, intelligence, coherence, and grasp of reality.

d) Diagnosis—physical, neurologic, psychologic, and psychiatric.

e) Answers to specific questions: At the time of the examination—

(1) Did he know, or was he capable of knowing that he was making a will?

(2) Did he know the nature and extent of his property?

(3) Could he identify his closest relatives and friends?

(4) Were any delusions elicited or implied with respect to (2) and (3)?

(5) Did he have any eccentricities or bizarre prejudices? If so, were they consistent with (1), (2), (3), and (4) above?

(6) Is he unusually gullible, or too easily influenced?

f) General conclusion as to testamentary capacity (based on material developed in Chapter 7), plus findings on current examination as indicated by headings in this guide).

Guide IV. Examination of Mute Patients

Note: This is a guide to the examination of the patient who, because of psychosis or physical disease, is unable to answer questions. A patient may, of course, refuse to answer questions on advice of counsel; or because he adheres to a philosophy of "not talking."

1. ORIENTATION OF THE EXAMINER: Determine from facts available whether patient is mute because of (*a*) his physical condition, (*b*) his mental state, (*c*) advice of counsel, or (*d*) deliberate refusal to talk for fear that it will get him into trouble. Indicate applicable reason in report.

2. BRIEFING OF THE EXAMINER:

   a) Preliminary: accumulate from records, reports of friends, relatives, attorney, and probation officers, whatever can be obtained as to patient's past and present history.

   b) Concurrent: from guards, nurses, interns, attendants, friends, etc., obtain current information as to:

   (1) Whether patient dresses and undresses himself. Does he tear off his clothing?
   (2) Whether he ever talks and under what circumstances.
   (3) How he sleeps; and whether he talks in his sleep.
   (4) Whether he asks for or accepts, cigarets.
   (5) Whether he asks for or accepts, food and water.
   (6) What he does about urination and bowel movements.
   (7) Whether he writes or reads letters.
   (8) Whether he looks at newspapers or magazines.
   (9) Whether he is violent or disturbed.
   (10) Whether his mutism is constant and persistent.

3. GENERAL FINDINGS:

   a) Note clothing; how he walks; his attitude toward examiner.
   b) Note his posture: incumbent, in chair, floor-pacing, rigid, shaky?
   c) Note gross findings such as convulsions, stupor, waxy flexibility, and the like.

4. THE FACE: Note his facial expression, whether (and under what conditions) it changes; whether it displays interest or any other emotion; whether his glance is stary, furtive, or shifty; whether he keeps eyes closed, and if so whether they can be readily opened.

5. RESPONSE TO PAIN: Approach with pin, and note if there is shrinking or other evidence of anticipated pain; prick skin and note physical and emotional reactions.

6. UTTERANCES: Subject may be generally mute, but utter occasional remarks. Note these, indicate what seems to have precipitated them, whether the utterance bears any obvious relationship to its apparent stimulus, and whether it is in the nature of echolalia or verbigeration.

7. WRITING: Offer patient pencil and paper. If he neither throws it away nor writes spontaneously, try asking questions; if no response, try writing down questions, see if patient will write answers.

8. PHYSICAL EXAMINATION: Note extent to which patient cooperates. Follow pattern of standard physical examination including a rather thorough neurologic examination. If patient appears to be in coma or stupor, keep these in mind:

   a) Smell breath for alcohol, acetone, or other odors.
   b) Catheterize patient and have urine carefully examined.
   c) Consider advisability of doing lumbar puncture.
   d) Venupuncture and examination of blood for sugar, nonprotein nitrogen, etc., as indicated.
   e) Blood counts.
   f) Skull and other X-rays as indicated.
   g) Electro-encephalogram.
   h) Take temperature and pulse; count respirations.
   i) Do careful ophthalmic study, noting especially size and equality of pupils and status of eyegrounds.
   j) Examine skin areas for scars, redness, needle marks, extravasations, and rashes.

9. CHEMICAL STIMULI TO PRODUCTION: Consider possibility of intravenous injection of barbiturates. Determine legal propriety of such a measure first. Also review page 37 this book for "medical" value of narcosynthesis. If legal clearance is given, and medical indications seem valid, consider intravenous barbiturate injection, and questioning of patient under narcosynthesis. Alcohol may also be used as a tongue loosener, either by offering the patient some whiskey or by introducing it into the stomach *via* a tube.[1] The ethical and legal properties may, however, prevent use of this technique.

---

[1] Catton mixed whiskey with the patient's food and, after imbibing five ounces of it, the defendant's mutism vanished. See Joseph Catton, *Behind the Scenes of Murder* (New York: W. W. Norton & Co., Inc., 1940), p. 178.

10. OTHER STIMULI TO PRODUCTION : Numerous stimuli have been used, with varying success. These include electrical skin shocks, conventional and subshock (nonconvulsive) electrical shock therapy modalities, exposing the patient to moving pictures, handing him Rohrschach cards, adding to the mutism by giving insulin and then terminating the insulin coma abruptly, waking the patient suddenly from a deep sleep, administration of scopolamine, and mechanical devices to prevent the patient from sleeping in the hope of "breaking" his resistance. There is grave doubt about the ethical, if not the legal, propriety of many of these techniques.

11. CONSIDERATION OF POSSIBLE MALINGERING: See Chapter 11, especially page 162.

Guide V. Examination of the Allegedly Drunken Driver

Note: Many police departments furnish forms or guides to be used by physicians in examining allegedly drunken drivers. A physician who lives in a community where such forms are not used would be well advised to obtain the forms adopted by the police department of the nearest large city. The following guide will also be found helpful. Chapter 9 should be reviewed.

1. History. Ask the Defendant:

   a) What he had to drink during the last eight hours, how much, when, and whether it was taken on an empty or full stomach.

   b) Whether he habitually uses or has recently used a mouth wash. If so, brand of mouth wash, or (if it was a prescribed wash) name of dentist or physician who prescribed it. When was mouth last washed? (This is to anticipate a possible defense that the alcohol odor on the breath was due to a mouth wash.)

   c) Whether he has diabetes. If so, name of treating physician and last administration of insulin. (This is to anticipate defense that swaying is due to acidosis or insulin overdosage.)

   d) Whether he has had any head injuries in the past year; if so, name of treating physician or hospital, and additional details about any postconcussion symptoms. (This is to anticipate defense that staggering or confusion is due to a postconcussion state.) If there was an automobile accident prior to the examination, the physician should obtain from the police enough information about the accident to determine whether the defendant sustained a concussion.

   e) What his sleeping habits are; how much he slept last night; whether he takes sleeping pills; if so, their name (or name of prescribing physician) and when they were last taken. (This is to anticipate a defense that staggering and confusion are due to insomnia or barbiturate overdosage.)

   f) Whether he had sustained a back injury recently or during the past year; if so, who the treating physician is. (This anticipates the defense that the incoordinate walking might be due to back injury.)

   g) Whether he is under any kind of medical treatment; if so, who the doctor is. (This anticipates the defense that the symptoms are due to medication other than alcohol.)

   h) What his present medical or nervous complaints are.

2. HISTORY. FROM POLICE OR BYSTANDERS:

a) Was anti-freeze used in radiator of car? If so, is it an alcohol medium anti-freeze? (To anticipate defense that this accounts for the odor to the defendant's breath.)

b) How defendant behaved when arrested or (if there was an accident) on leaving the scene.

c) Whether the road was dusty and the car an open model. (To anticipate defense that red eyes were due to dust.)

d) The defendant's general behavior while awaiting the physician: was he sleepy, bellicose, clownish, or what?

e) Whether any therapeutic, stimulating, or restorative measures had been applied subsequent to the arrest but prior to the examination; if so, what.

Note: It is probably best *not* to ask whether the defendant has a "record" of alcoholism. While medically such a question is perfectly proper, it is forensically bad tactics. It suggests that the doctor may allow the answer to prejudice him. Theoretically the diagnosis is to be based on findings at this one examination.

3. CLINICAL EXAMINATION:

a) Clothes: Are they tidy? Stained with blood, vomitus, or beverage? Do the clothes smell of alcohol?

b) General appearance: Are eyes bloodshot? Is defendant grossly incoordinate? Is he loud-mouthed? Hiccoughing? Red-faced?

c) Does his breath smell of alcohol, or of any popular, readily-recognized "killer" of alcohol odors?

d) Coordination: Try the standard line-walking, finger-nose, balance, and turning tests.

e) Articulation of speech: Thick, stuttering, slurred, or whispering?

f) Content of speech: Coherent, sarcastic, overamiable, overhostile, suggestive of delusions or hallucinations, or flighty?

g) Tremors: Hands, eyelid, tongue, general body, any suggestion of of delirium tremens?

h) Eyes: Dilated pupils? reddened conjuctivae? glassy appearance?

i) Mentality: Orientation, clarity of thought, euphoria, excitement, depression?

Note: These suggestions are over and above the usual routine physical examination which should not be omitted. (For example: Heart disease may cause some suggestive symptoms, and the examiner will be made to look foolish later in court if he is asked whether he examined for heart disease and has to say "No"; the defendant might have alleged that his apparently intoxicated condition was due to the heart disease.)

4. CHEMICAL TESTS: Urine, blood, expired air. See page 138 for further details.

5. THE REPORT: The following paragraphing may be helpful:

   a) Name of patient; when and where examination was done; exact hour; at whose request the examination was made.

   b) Objective findings: all items listed in 3 above. Include verbatim transcript of significant things the patient said.

   c) The history, especially items a, g, and h of 1 above; and, when appropriate, the other items in this paragraph. Indicate that this material came from the patient himself. Then include the items in 2b, 2d, and 2e, with a note as to the source of that information.

   d) Indicate whether any chemical tests (blood, urine, breath) have been ordered; whether accused agreed to submit, or whether he refused and, if so, the reason; and, if results are available, what they are and what they mean. If tests have been ordered but not yet reported, indicate laboratory which is performing them, and when results can be expected.

   e) All diagnoses should be listed, even if some of them appear irrelevant to the question of drunken driving.

   f) Conclusion as to the defendant's fitness to operate a motor vehicle.

Guide VI. Examination of the Juvenile Offender

Note: The examiner can expect the probation office or the interested social agency to prepare a detailed history of the case covering the child's background and the circumstances of the current delinquency. He will want to study this report before seeing the child. He will ask to have one or both parents available during his interview though, of course, at some time during that period he will see the child alone. He often can determine the place of the examination. If so, he will exercise that option, selecting the first available of the following places: (1) his own office, (2) a hospital or clinic, (3) office of a social agency, (4) a room in a school building, (5) a conference room in the probation office, (6) a conference room in the court house or other government building, (7) the place where the child is detained.

1. PRELIMINARY BRIEFING: Look for, and note when appropriate—

   a) General data identifying the child and describing his home.

   b) Child's role in the home (his attitude towards it, his duties, how much hold the home has on him).

   c) Status of the parents, including whether they are living together, their own educational and vocational backgrounds, their economic status, their attitude towards their children as sensed by the social worker or probation officer.

   d) History of the child's early development with respect to age of talking and walking, development of eating habits, habits and conditions of sleep, interest in and play with other children, and the like.[2]

   e) Child's current and past school record with respect to grade, quality of school work, scholastic weaknesses and strengths, school attendance, relations with teachers, his attitude towards school, and intelligence test scores.

   f) Probation officer's or social worker's judgment about the type of discipline and control exercised by the parents.

   g) Details of past and present delinquencies.

   h) A picture of the cultural milieu in which the child lives (essential). Probation office and social agency reports usually describe the neighborhood in vivid detail. Is it a delinquency-breeding environment, an area where to be delinquent is to be "normal?" Is it a neighborhood filled with socially disorganizing facilities? Is it a neighborhood where the streets are more attractive than the homes?

---

[2] Probation office histories are often deficient in this item, and the examiner may have to assemble this information from personal interview with the parents.

2. INTERVIEW WITH PARENTS:

   a) Verify developmental history detailed in 1*d* above.

   b) Child's past and current health. Convulsions, sickness, accidents, operations, "nervousness" (obtain examples of what the parents mean by this), sleeping and eating habits, and health status in general.

   c) Parents' account of child's recreational life, relationship with siblings and with other children, and their concept of his personality. Include their picture of the child's interests and hobbies (movies, television, spectator sports, reading preferences, etc.).

   d) Parents' account of the difficulties they have had with the child, giving concrete examples, their own explanation of this behavior, what they did about it, and how the child reacted to their actions.

   e) Verify facts about the economic, cultural, intellectual, educational, and vocational status of the parents.

   f) Facts about other adults (boarders or relatives) in the home, their influence on the child and child's attitude towards them.

   g) The parents' own hopes and plans for the child, and their own explanation (in their words if possible) of why he has gotten into this trouble.

   h) Examiner's impression of the intelligence and emotional stability of the parents and their attitudes towards their children.

3. PHYSICAL EXAMINATION OF THE CHILD:

   a) Orientation: The doctor is introduced to the child as a physician, and opens his interview with the familiar equipment of the doctor; the tongue depressor, the stethoscope, etc. (If the examiner is a psychologist, and a Ph.D., he is best introduced simply as "doctor." Child will assume he is a physician, though of course no physical examination is done. This practice, though perhaps ethically deplorable, seems tactically necessary in winning the cooperation of the child.)

   b) Height and weight, distribution of fat, gross endocrine defects. Is child unduly large, small, fat or lean for his age?

   c) Note any gross defects, particularly with respect to physical handicaps.

   d) Soundness of heart and cardiovascular system generally.

   e) Presence of adenoids, enlarged tonsils, swollen lymph nodes.

   f) Examination of respiratory system.

   g) Examination of skin for scars, bruises, exanthemata, and evidences of allergic reactions.

h) Dental survey for caries, missing teeth, etc.

i) Neurologic examination—see section 4, below.

4. NEUROLOGIC EXAMINATION OF THE CHILD:

a) By this time examiner will have observed whether child stutters, lisps or stammers; and if so, this should be noted here.

b) Examination of eyes, particularly for visual defects and conjunctivitis.

c) Gross tests of hearing, with reference to otologist if indicated. Examination of eardrums.

d) Examination of motor system, with particular reference to tics, tremors, lefthandedness, and incoordination. Also observations on gait and station. See page 345.

e) Cranial nerves should be tested (though not necessarily in such detail) as suggested on page 346.

f) Sensory system is not readily examined in children, but the general body area (each quadrant of the trunk and of the back, and each surface of each extremity) should be explored for gross defects in touch, pain, and vibration sense. Testing for temperature sense is seldom practical and rarely necessary.

g) Special tests and consultations as indicated. This might include consultations with pediatrician, allergist, otologist, cardiologist, urologist, or ophthalmologist; electro-encephalograms, X-rays, blood counts, urine analyses, and (very rarely) blood chemistries and spinal taps.

5. PSYCHIATRIC INTERVIEW WITH THE CHILD:

a) By this time the examiner will have absorbed a good deal of information about the child's personality and intelligence. This should be organized and recorded now.

b) Intelligence. Scores are usually on record already and, if the reported I.Q. is consistent with child's school standing and general behavior, need not be repeated. In doubtful cases the child should be sent to a psychologist for a battery of intelligence tests. If this is impractical, the psychiatrist should be prepared to do at least a cursory test for the purpose of determining (1) the child's intelligence or mental age level, and (2) the qualitative nature of his intelligence with respect to ability to handle abstract concepts, to handle things, to handle words.

c) The child's own picture of what his parents, siblings, playmates, home, and school are like should be solicited, interpreted, and recorded.

d) Note should be made of his own plans, ambitions, fears, day-dreams, and nocturnal dreams.

e) He is encouraged to report on his own hobbies, interests, and recreations.

f) Item *c* above is now further explored with reference to his picture of what parental and school discipline are like and what he thinks they ought to be.

g) At this point it should be possible to explore the more obvious neurotic indicators: what he is afraid of, what makes him lose his temper, and what seems to be producing anxiety. His knowledge of sexual activity, guilt feelings about it, if any, and general sexual orientation may be elicited.

h) Evidence of psychosis, if any, should be clear by this point. Psychoses are rare in children; but psychotic children often get into trouble. Look particularly for hallucinations and fantasy-formation which seems beyond (or, more accurately, below) the child's maturity or intelligence level.

i) This interview may produce some sort of overt emotional response: laughing, crying spells, silliness, blushing, confusion, or hostility. The response itself, and the points at which it develops, are noted.

j) Can the examiner now figure out just what values the child was seeking to obtain from his delinquency? What did he do during school hours, while he was truant? What did he expect to buy with the money he stole? The answer will not come from the child himself; at least the significant part of the answer will not be articulated. But by now perhaps the examiner can see what purpose the delinquency was serving.

k) The child's own "explanation" for his delinquent behavior should be the penultimate question. It is amateurish to ask this question early in the interview. Indeed, it may block further expression by the child.

l) Finally, the child may be asked what he thinks the judge should do.

6. THE REPORT: It is suggested that before writing his report, the examiner review Chapter 10. Note particularly the paragraphs beginning on page 149.

a) Identifying data, including place of examination and at whose request the child was examined.

b) Compact summary of the specific delinquent act responsible for the current juvenile court appearance.

c) Significant details of the personal, family, social, and school history (from sections 1 and 2 of this guide).

d) Significant physical findings. Negative findings should not be detailed unless the child or parents have made an issue of them. Include positive neurologic findings here.

e) Intelligence, both in terms of mental age and qualitatively, should be recorded (and interpreted) in a separate paragraph. See 5b of this guide.

f) The psychiatric interview should be summarized. See section 5 of this guide.

g) Diagnosis. There should be at least one entry under each heading. Thus:

    (1) Physical: Substantially healthy child; or
              Healthy except for dental caries and hypertrophied tonsils.

    (2) Neurologic: No significant neurologic abnormalities; or
              Epilepsy, petit mal; or
              Chorea, acute.

    (3) Intelligence: Substantially normal; or
              Mental age (Binet) 6½; I.Q. 64; (moron); or
              Mental age (name test) 9¼; I.Q. 85 (dull normal).

    (4) Psychiatric: Primary conduct disorder, see next paragraph; or
              Post-encephalitic conduct disorder; or
              Substantially normal personality; or
              Schizophrenia, hebephrenic.

h) Mechanism of the delinquency. In this paragraph the examiner writes a brief account, in lay language, of what he thinks caused the child to deviate from "normal" behavior.

i) Recommendation. Usually one of the nine following recommendations will be made. See paragraphs beginning on page 152.

    (1) Dismiss the matter.

    (2) Reprimand the child and dismiss the matter.

    (3) Have the child make restitution of the amount stolen (or reimburse for damage done) from his own allowance or by money earned after school.

    (4) Send the child to a mental hygiene clinic or (if family can afford it) to a private psychiatrist for psychotherapy, or to a social agency for case-work services.

(5) Transfer the child to a different school or to a different kind of school or to a different kind of class in the same school. (Give type of class needed and reasons.)

(6) Place in a foster home or with relatives. (Give details of what is aimed at by this recommendation.)

(7) Place the child on probation. (Include suggestions as to the scope and kind of probationary supervision recommended.)

(8) Commit the child to a colony (or state school) for mental defectives, a public or private child-treatment center, a mental hospital, or other special medical or educational institution. (Recommendation should be specific.)

(9) Commit the child to a reformatory, state home, or other type of correctional institution.

Note: Some recommendations of course may be combined; and some given in the alternative. Thus number 6 and number 7 may be combined, or number 5 may be contingent on accomplishing number 6, etc.

Guide VII. Determination of Competency

Note: As used in this guide, "competency" means ability to handle one's own affairs.[3] This does not cover ability to make a will (see Guide III) nor competency to sign one's self into a hospital, to testify, or to consent to an operation.

1. HISTORY: Usually the request that the doctor determine competency is made by a relative, attorney, court, or creditor, rarely by the patient himself. The petitioner will ordinarily give a brief history showing that, at a certain point in the recent past, the patient began to squander money, or to announce his intention to squander money; that he developed an unhealthy attachment to some person who was exercising undue influence over him; that he developed a burning interest in some "cause" or crusade; or that he developed peculiar ideas which caused him to hoard his money and deny himself or his family the necessities of life. The point at which the aberration first became obvious is here called the "break-point." The examiner should seek the following data:

   a) Patient's vocational, social, and medical history *prior* to the break-point. How did he manage his affairs then? Obtain specific examples of good judgment and sound behavior during that period. If it is now alleged that he has fallen prey to some designing person, obtain examples of his ability to resist such persons prior to the break-point. Note patient's health, vigor, clarity of speech and thought prior to the break-point.

   b) A narrative account of the events leading up to the break-point.

   c) A narrative account of the current behavior; specifically the features which make the petitioner feel that the patient is incompetent. The examiner should not be content with vague statement as to "poor judgment" or "imprudent expenditures" or an "unsound marriage." He should ask for specific examples of the allegedly poor judgment and so forth.

   d) An account of the patient's current medical condition, with emphasis on any evidence of paralysis, speech defect, memory defect, convulsions, tremors; and sleeping, eating, and drinking habits, as well as injuries and operations.

   Note: Occasionally a patient asks a psychiatrist to determine his competency in order to thwart a relative's plan (real or fancied) to

[3] The conceptual basis of "competency" is discussed more fully in Chapter 13, particularly on pages 185 to 189 which should be reviewed before applying the guide.

have him declared incompetent. The history under these circumstances will be vague since the patient is not likely to offer evidences of his own bad judgment. The examiner's point of entry here is the question about the relative's *motive* in seeking to have the patient declared incompetent. If the patient is questioned repeatedly about this, he will eventually advance his theory of the petitioner's motive. This serves as a wedge into a fuller investigation of the patient's mental state. Another approach would be: "What in your behavior makes your brother think you need a guardian?" Either the patient says, "I don't know," or he recites some behavior which the relative considers foolish. If he says he doesn't know, this leads back to the question of the relative's motive.

2. PHYSICAL EXAMINATION: [4] Look for—

   a) Evidences of hypertension and general or cerebral arteriosclerosis.
   b) Evidences of senility or pre-senility.
   c) Evidences of alcoholism.
   d) Evidences of intoxication with bromides or other sedatives.
   e) Evidences of malnutrition or general enfeeblement.
   f) Evidences of any other chronic disorder.
   g) Special laboratory tests as indicated.

3. NEUROLOGIC EXAMINATION: [4]

   a) Evidences of aphasia. Check for ability to understand the spoken word, the written word, and gestures; and for ability to reply coherently in words and gestures.
   b) Handedness. Determine if patient is basically lefthanded or righthanded.
   c) Evidences of cerebral-vascular disorders. Compare reflexes, size of pupils, and contour of face on both sides. Look for pathologic reflexes. (The point here is to determine if patient has possibly had a "minor" cerebral-vascular insult.)
   d) Evidences of epilepsy, including fugue states and psychomotor equivalents.
   e) Do a sensory examination to determine areas of anesthesia or hypesthesia in connection with possible hysteria or possible parietal lobe involvement.
   f) Coordination, synergy, gait, station, and diadochokinesis should be determined.
   g) Check acuity of hearing. Report in figures, either audiometric

---

[4] This, of course, is in addition to the conventional physical examination.

or in terms of distance at which conversation can be heard. Consult with an otologist if necessary.

h) Determine acuity of vision with and without glasses. Check eyegrounds for arteriosclerosis, hemorrhages, papilledema, or other lesions.

i) Any evidence of brain injury?

4. PSYCHIATRIC EXAMINATION:

a) Determine intelligence at time of examination. Compare with I.Q. scores made available from previous employment, school, or Army-Navy records; or inferred from patient's educational and vocational history. If psychologist is available, have him determine intelligence by appropriate tests, and have him look for evidences of deterioration or organic brain disease.

b) Make note about patient's general appearance: tidiness, attitude, odor of breath (acetone, alcohol, etc.), anxiety, hostility, and cooperativeness.

c) Note emotional responses shown during the examination and indicate what form they take and what seems to precipitate them.

d) Note patient's awareness of his surroundings: orientation, attentiveness, and clarity.

e) Observe level of psychomotor activity: restlessness, talkativeness, coherence, productivity, and general pressure of speech, talk, and thought.

f) Explore possibility of delusional material and paranoid trends.

g) Special interests, hobbies, and "causes" in which patient is interested or to which he is devoted—including whims, fads, and fancies.

h) Test memory for both recent and remote events, including ability to recall.

i) Observe stability and appropriateness of the patient's mood.

j) Is there any evidence of hallucinosis?

k) Focus now on the material of the break-point and obtain patient's own interpretation of what has been going on.

l) Form some judgment as to the patient's suggestibility.

m) Any evidence of psychoneurosis, particularly obsessional or dissociative?

n) Discuss his plans for the future; specifically what he wants to do with his money. Relate this to the nature of any delusional material uncovered now or previously.

o) Before terminating the examination, be certain that there is enough material to permit answering the following questions:

(1) Is patient sane or insane?

(2) Is his intelligence normal? changed from its previous level? dull, defective, or superior?

(3) Does he have aphasia? If so, what kind?

(4) Is he so suggestible (either in general or to some particular and favorite person) as to fall ready prey to a designing individual?

(5) Does he have periods of recklessly bad judgment? If so, are these epileptic, hysterical, alcoholic, or psychotic in nature?

(6) Are his personal plans sound and indicative of good judgment?

(7) Does he have delusions or obsessions which would cause him to hoard his funds and deny himself or family the comforts of life?

5. THE REPORT: This should be focussed sharply on the specific question of competency. It would be unwise to include irrelevant material touching on criminal responsibility, on whether patient should be committed, on type of treatment recommended, and so forth. These other items, though important, belong elsewhere in the examiner's relationship with the case. They are not part of the question of competency, and introducing them unnecessarily will open the examiner to a wider field of cross-examination. Of course, if the psychiatrist has been retained for a general psychiatric opinion and recommendation, he has to explore all these other problems too. But this guide is constructed for an examiner who is asked simply the one question: Can the patient handle his own business affairs?

a) Identifying data, and place of examination. At whose request was the examination made?

b) A concise account of the circumstances which led the family (court, attorney, or patient, as the case may be) to question the subject's competency.

c) Physical and neurologic findings. Include all diagnoses reflecting any medical or neurologic disorder.

d) Appraisal of patient's current intelligence. Use mental age rather than I.Q. if intelligence is below normal. Indicate if this represents a deterioration from a previously higher level.

e) The major psychiatric findings, including types of memory defects, evidences of undue suggestibility, of confusion or lack of contact, of delusions or hallucinations, of patient's own plan for his future, of emotional stability or instability, and of any neurotic traits.

Where impairment of judgment is recorded, this should be supported by specific examples—either those developed during the examination or those reported in the history. Similarly with findings as to undue suggestibility or gullibility: the conclusion should be supported.

f) The psychiatric diagnoses.

g) Conclusion as to competency:

(1) Does he have a mental disorder? What is it?

(2) Does this disorder cause bad judgment?

(3) As a result of the bad judgment, is it expected that the patient will:

(*a*) Squander his funds imprudently?

(*b*) Hoard his funds to the detriment of himself or family?

(*c*) Fall prey to designing persons?

Appendix D

MODEL ACT FOR THE CERTIFICATION OF THE MENTALLY ILL

In 1949, at the request of the National Advisory Mental Health Council, the Public Health Service (Federal Security Agency) developed a model State certification law, the text of which follows.* See also Chapter 12 (page 181) for an analysis of some of the features of the proposed act. The committee which drafted the proposed law included Dr. Robert H. Felix, Dr. James V. Lowry, Dr. Winfred Overholser, Dr. Riley Guthrie, Mr. Israel L. Sonenshein, Miss Gladys Harrison, and Mr. Franklin N. Flaschner.

In the text which follows, the letters X, Y, and Z are used:

X indicates the space in which should be written the name of the appropriate court.

Y indicates the space in which should be written the name of the department responsible for administering state mental hospitals.

Z indicates the space in which should be written the name of the appropriate *local* health authority.

An Act Governing Hospitalization of the Mentally Ill [1]

I. Definitions.
II. Voluntary Hospitalization.
III. Involuntary Hospitalization.

PART I—DEFINITIONS

As used in this Act, terms shall have the following meanings:

(a) *Mentally ill individual.*—An individual having a psychiatric or other disease which substantially impairs his mental health.

(b) *Patient.*—An individual under observation, care, or treatment in a hospital pursuant to this Act.

---

* In May 1951, the Utah Legislature enacted a certification law largely patterned on this "Model Act." This is the first state law to use the "Model Act" as a basis.
[1] From *Public Health Service Publication 51* (Washington, D. C.: U. S. Government Printing Office, 1951). This is a publication of the Federal Security Agency, entitled "A Draft Act Governing Hospitalization of the Mentally Ill."

(c) *Licensed physician.*—An individual licensed under the laws of this State to practice medicine and a medical officer of the Government of the United States while in this State in the performance of his official duties.

(d) *Designated examiner.*—A licensed physician registered by the (*central administration*) as specially qualified, under standards established by it, in the diagnosis of mental or related illness.

(e) *Hospital.*—A public or private hospital or institution, or part thereof, equipped to provide in-patient care and treatment for the mentally ill.

(f) *Head of hospital.*—The individual in charge of a hospital, or his designee.

(g) (*Central administration*).—The (State) (Department of Health) (Mental Health Commission) (Department of Mental Hygiene); here designated as Y.

PART II—VOLUNTARY HOSPITALIZATION

2. *Authority to receive voluntary patients.*—The head of a private hospital may and, subject to the availability of suitable accommodations, the head of a public hospital shall admit for observation, diagnosis, care, and treatment any individual who is mentally ill or has symptoms of mental illness and who, being 16 years of age or over, applies therefor, and any individual under 16 years of age who is mentally ill or has symptoms of mental illness, if his parent or legal guardian applies therefor in his behalf.

3. *Discharge of voluntary patients.*—The head of the hospital shall discharge any voluntary patient who has recovered or whose hospitalization he determines to be no longer advisable. He may also discharge any voluntary patient if to do so would, in the judgment of the head of the hospital, contribute to its most effective use in the care and treatment of the mentally ill.

4. *Right to release on application.*—(a) A voluntary patient who requests his release or whose release is requested, in writing, by his legal guardian, parent, spouse, or adult next of kin shall be released forthwith except that

(1) if the patient was admitted on his own application and the request for release is made by a person other than the patient, release may be conditioned upon the agreement of the patient thereto, and

(2) if the patient, by reason of his age, was admitted on the application of another person, his release prior to becoming 16 years of age may be conditioned upon the consent of his parent or guardian, and

(3) if the head of the hospital, within 48 hours from the receipt of the request, files with the X court or a judge thereof, whether in session or in vacation, a certification that in his opinion the release of the patient would be unsafe for the patient or others, release may be postponed on application for as long as the court or a judge thereof determines to be necessary for the commencement of proceedings for judicial hospitalization, but in no event for more than 5 days.

(*b*) Notwithstanding any other provision of this Act, judicial proceedings for hospitalization shall not be commenced with respect to a voluntary patient unless release of the patient has been requested by himself or the individual who applied for his admission.

PART III—INVOLUNTARY HOSPITALIZATION

5. *Authority to receive involuntary patients.*—The head of a private hospital may and, subject to the availability of suitable accommodations, the head of a public hospital shall receive therein for observation, diagnosis, care and treatment any individual whose admission is applied for under any of the following procedures:

(*a*) Hospitalization on medical certification; standard nonjudicial procedure.

(*b*) Hospitalization on medical certification; emergency procedure.

(*c*) Hospitalization without endorsement or medical certification; emergency procedure.

(*d*) Hospitalization on court order; judicial procedure.

6. *Hospitalization on medical certification; standard nonjudicial procedure.*—(*a*) Any individual may be admitted to a hospital upon

(1) written application to the hospital by a friend, relative, spouse, or guardian of the individual, a health or public welfare officer, or the head of any institution in which such individual may be, and

(2) a certification by two designated examiners that they have jointly examined the individual and that they are of the opinion that

(A) he is mentally ill, and

(B) because of his illness is likely to injure himself or others if allowed to remain at liberty, or

(C) is in need of care or treatment in a mental hospital, and because of his illness, lacks sufficient insight or capacity to make responsible application therefor.

An individual with respect to whom such a certificate has been issued may not be admitted on the basis thereof at any time after the expiration of 15 days after the date of examination, exclusive of any period of temporary detention authorized under section 11. The head of the hospital admitting the individual shall forthwith make a report thereof to the Y.

(*b*) Such a certificate, if it states a belief that the individual is likely to injure himself or others if allowed to remain at liberty, shall, upon endorsement for such purpose by the head of the Z or by a judge of any court of record of the county in which the individual is resident or present, authorize any health or police officer to take the individual into custody and transport him to a hospital designated in the application.

7. *Hospitalization on medical certification; emergency procedure.*—(*a*) Any individual may be admitted to a hospital upon

(1) written application to the hospital by any health or police officer or any other person stating his belief that the individual is likely to cause injury to himself or others if not immediately restrained, and the grounds for such belief, and

(2) a certification by at least one licensed physician that he has examined the individual and is of the opinion that the individual is mentally ill and, because of his illness, is likely to injure himself or others if not immediately restrained.

An individual with respect to whom such a certificate has been issued may not be admitted on the basis thereof at any time after the expiration of 3 days after the date of examination. The head of the hospital admitting the individual shall forthwith make a report thereof to the Y.

(b) Such a certificate, upon endorsement for such purpose by the head of the Z or a judge of any court of record of the county in which the individual is present, shall authorize any health or police officer to take the individual into custody and transport him to a hospital as designated in the application.

8. *Hospitalization without endorsement or medical certification; emergency procedure.*—Any health or police officer who has reason to believe that

(a) an individual is mentally ill and, because of his illness, cannot be allowed to go unrestrained pending examination and certification by a licensed physician, or

(b) an individual who has been certified under section 6 or 7 as likely to injure himself or others cannot be allowed to go unrestrained pending the endorsement of the certificate as provided in those sections

may take the individual into custody, apply to a hospital for his admission, and transport him thereto. The application for admission shall state the circumstances under which the individual was taken into custody and the reasons for the officer's belief.

9. *Hospitalization upon court order; judicial procedure.*—(a) Proceedings for the involuntary hospitalization of an individual may be commenced by the filing of a written application with the X court by a friend, relative, spouse, or guardian of the individual, or by a licensed physician, a health or public welfare officer, or the head of any public or private institution in which such individual may be. Any such application shall be accompanied by a certificate of a licensed physician stating that he has examined the individual and is of the opinion that he is mentally ill and should be hospitalized, or a written statement by the applicant that the individual has refused to submit to examination by a licensed physician.

(b) Upon receipt of an application the court shall give notice thereof to the proposed patient, to his legal guardian, if any, and to his spouse, parents, and nearest known other relative or friend. If, however, the court has reason to believe that notice would be likely to be injurious to the proposed patient, notice to him may be omitted.

(c) As soon as practicable after notice of the commencement of proceedings is given or it is determined that notice should be omitted, the court shall appoint two designated examiners to examine the proposed patient and report to the court their findings as to the mental condition of the proposed patient and his need for custody, care, or treatment in a mental hospital.

(d) The examination shall be held at a hospital or other medical facility, at the home of the proposed patient, or at any other suitable place not likely to have a harmful effect on his health. A proposed patient to whom notice of the commencement of proceedings has been omitted shall not be required to submit to an examination against his will, and on the report of the designated examiners of refusal to submit to an examination the court shall give notice to the proposed patient as provided under paragraph (b) of this section and order him to submit to such examination.

(e) If the report of the designated examiners is to the effect that the proposed patient is not mentally ill, the court may without taking any further action terminate the proceedings and dismiss the application; otherwise, it shall forthwith fix a date for and give notice of a hearing to be held not less than 5 nor more than 15 days from receipt of the report.

(f) The proposed patient, the applicant, and all other persons to whom notice is required to be given shall be afforded an opportunity to appear at the hearing, to testify, and to present and cross-examine witnesses, and the court may in its discretion receive the testimony of any other person. The proposed patient shall not be required to be present, and the court is authorized to exclude all persons not necessary for the conduct of the proceedings. The hearings shall be conducted in as informal a manner as may be consistent with orderly procedure and in a physical setting not likely to have a harmful effect on the mental health of the proposed patient. The court shall receive all relevant and material evidence which may be offered and shall not be bound by the rules of evidence. An opportunity to be represented by counsel shall be afforded to every proposed patient, and if neither he nor others provide counsel, the court shall appoint counsel.

(g) If, upon completion of the hearing and consideration of the record, the court finds that the proposed patient

(1) is mentally ill, and
(2) because of his illness is likely to injure himself or others if allowed to remain at liberty, or
(3) is in need of custody, care or treatment in a mental hospital and, because of his illness, lacks sufficient insight or capacity to make responsible decisions with respect to his hospitalization,

it shall order his hospitalization for an indeterminate period or for a temporary observational period not exceeding 6 months; otherwise, it shall dismiss the proceedings. If the order is for a temporary period the court may at any time prior to the expiration of such period, on the basis of report by the head of the hospital and such further inquiry as it may deem appropriate, order indeterminate hospitalization of the patient or dismissal of the proceedings.

(*h*) The order of hospitalization shall state whether the individual shall be detained for an indeterminate or for a temporary period and, if for a temporary period, then for how long. Unless otherwise directed by the court, it shall be the responsibility of the Z to assure the carrying out of the order within such period as the court shall specify.

(*i*) The court is authorized to appoint a special commissioner to assist in the conduct of hospitalization proceedings. In any case in which the court refers an application to the commissioner, the commissioner shall promptly cause the proposed patient to be examined and on the basis thereof shall either recommend dismissal of the application or hold a hearing as provided in this section and make recommendations to the court regarding the hospitalization of the proposed patient.

10. *Hospitalization by an agency of the United States.*—(*a*) If an individual ordered to be hospitalized pursuant to the previous section is eligible for hospital care or treatment by any agency of the United States, the court, upon receipt of a certificate from such agency showing that facilities are available and that the individual is eligible for care or treatment therein, may order him to be placed in the custody of such agency for hospitalization. When any such individual is admitted pursuant to the order of such court to any hospital or institution operated by any agency of the United States within or without the State, he shall be subject to the rules and regulations of such agency. The chief officer of any hospital or institution operated by such agency and in which the individual is so hospitalized, shall with respect to such individual be vested with the same powers as the heads of hospitals or the Y within this State with respect to detention, custody, transfer, conditional release, or discharge of patients. Jurisdiction is retained in the appropriate courts of this State at any time to inquire into the mental condition of an individual so hospitalized, and to determine the necessity for continuance of his hospitalization, and every order of hospitalization issued pursuant to this section is so conditioned.

(*b*) An order of a court of competent jurisdiction of another State, or of the District of Columbia, authorizing hospitalization of an individual by any agency of the United States shall have the same force and effect as to the individual while in this State as in the jurisdiction in which is situated the court entering the order; and the courts of the State or District issuing the order shall be deemed to have retained jurisdiction of the individual so hospitalized for the purpose of inquiring into his mental condition and of determining the necessity for continuance of his hospitalization, as is provided in subsection (*a*) of this section with respect to individuals ordered hospitalized by the courts of this State. Consent is hereby given to the application of the law of the State or District in which is located the court issuing the order for hospitalization with respect to the authority of the chief officer of any hospital or institution operated in this State by any agency of the United

States to retain custody, transfer, conditionally release, or discharge the individual hospitalized.

11. *Transportation; temporary detention.*—(*a*) Whenever an individual is about to be hospitalized under the provisions of section 6, 7, 8, or 9, the Z shall, upon the request of a person having a proper interest in the individual's hospitalization, arrange for the individual's transportation to the hospital with suitable medical or nursing attendants and by such means as may be suitable for his medical condition. Whenever practicable, the individual to be hospitalized shall be permitted to be accompanied by one or more of his friends or relatives.

(*b*) Pending his removal to a hospital, a patient taken into custody or ordered to be hospitalized pursuant to this Act may be detained in his home, a licensed foster home, or any other suitable facility under such reasonable conditions as the Z may fix, but he shall not, except because of and during an extreme emergency, be detained in a nonmedical facility used for the detention of individuals charged with or convicted of penal offenses. The Z shall take such reasonable measures, including provision of medical care, as may be necessary to assure proper care of an individual temporarily detained pursuant to this section.

12. *Notice of hospitalization.*—Whenever a patient has been admitted to a hospital pursuant to section 6, 7, or 8 on the application of any person other than the patient's legal guardian, spouse, or next of kin, the head of the hospital shall immediately notify the patient's legal guardian, spouse, or next of kin, if known.

13. *Medical examination of newly admitted patients.*—(*a*) Every patient admitted pursuant to the provisions of section 6, 7, 8, or 9 shall be examined by the staff of the hospital as soon as practicable after his admission.

(*b*) The head of the hospital shall arrange for examination by a designated examiner of every patient hospitalized pursuant to the provisions of section 7 or 8. If such an examination is not held within 5 days after the day of admission, or if a designated examiner fails or refuses after such examination to certify that in his opinion the patient is mentally ill and is likely to injure himself or others if allowed to remain at liberty, the patient shall be immediately discharged.

14. *Transfer of patients.*—(*a*) The Y may transfer, or authorize the transfer of, an involuntary patient from one hospital to another if the Y determines that it would be consistent with the medical needs of the patient to do so. Whenever a patient is transferred, written notice thereof shall be given to his legal guardian, parents, and spouse, or, if none be known, his nearest known relative or friend.

(*b*) Upon receipt of a certificate of an agency of the United States that facilities are available for the care or treatment of any individual heretofore ordered hospitalized pursuant to law or hereafter pursuant to section 9 of this Act in any hospital for care or treatment of the mentally ill and that such individual is eligible for care or treatment in a hospital or institution of such agency, the Y may cause his transfer to such agency of the United States for hospitalization. Upon effecting any such transfer, the court ordering hospitalization, the legal guardian, spouse, and parents, or if none be known, his nearest known relative or friend shall be notified thereof immediately by the Y. No person shall be transferred to an agency of the United States if he be confined pursuant to conviction of any felony or misdemeanor or if he has been acquitted of the charge solely on the ground of mental illness unless prior to transfer the court originally ordering confinement of such person shall enter an order for such transfer after appropriate motion and hearing. Any person transferred as provided in this section to an agency of the United States shall be deemed to be hospitalized by such agency pursuant to the original order of hospitalization.

15. *Discharge.*—The head of a hospital shall as frequently as practicable, but not less often than every 6 months, examine or cause to be examined every patient and whenever he determines that the conditions justifying involuntary hospitalization no longer obtain, discharge the patient and immediately make a report thereof to the Y.

16. *Conditional release; rehospitalization.*—(*a*) The head of a hospital may release an improved patient on the condition that he receive out-patient or nonhospital treatment or on such other reasonable conditions as may be specified by the head of the hospital. Whenever conditional release of a patient has extended beyond 1 year, the head of the hospital shall re-examine the facts relating to hospitalization of the patient and, if he determines that in view of the condition of the patient hospitalization is no longer justified, he shall discharge the patient and make an immediate report thereof to the Y.

(*b*) The Y is authorized to issue an order for the immediate rehospitalization of a conditionally released patient who has failed to fulfill the conditions of his release if it has reason to believe that conditions justifying hospitalization continue to exist. Such an order, when endorsed by a judge of any court of record of the county in which the patient is resident or present, shall authorize any health or police officer to take the patient into custody and transport him to a hospital designated by the Y.

17. *Right to release; application for judicial determination.*—(*a*) Any patient hospitalized under the provisions of section 6, 7, or 8 of this Act who requests to be released or whose release is requested, in writing, by his legal guardian, spouse, or adult next of kin shall be released within 48 hours after receipt of the request except that, upon application to the court or a judge thereof, whether in session or in vacation, supported by a certification by the head of the hospital that in his opinion such release would be unsafe for the patient or for others, release may be postponed for such period not to exceed 5 days as the court or a judge thereof may determine to be necessary for the commencement of proceedings for a judicial determination pursuant to section 9.

(*b*) The head of the hospital shall provide reasonable means and arrangements for informing involuntary patients of their right to release as provided in this section and for assisting them in making and presenting requests for release.

18. *Position for re-examination of order of hospitalization.*—Any patient hospitalized pursuant to section 9 shall be entitled to a re-examination of the order for his hospitalization on his own petition, or that of his legal guardian, parent, spouse, relative, or friend, to the X court of the county in which he resides or is detained. Upon receipt of the petition, the court shall conduct or cause to be conducted by a special commissioner proceedings in accordance with such section 9, except that such proceedings shall not be required to be conducted if the petition is filed sooner than 6 months after the issuance of the order of hospitalization or sooner than 1 year after the filing of a previous petition under this section.

PART IV—PROVISIONS APPLICABLE TO PATIENTS GENERALLY

19. *Right to humane care and treatment.*—Every patient shall be entitled to humane care and treatment and, to the extent that facilities, equipment, and personnel are available, to medical care and treatment in accordance with the highest standards accepted in medical practice.

20. *Mechanical restraints.*—Mechanical restraints shall not be applied to a patient unless it is determined by the head of the hospital or his designee to be required by the medical needs of the patient. Every use of a mechanical restraint and the reasons therefor shall be made a part of the clinical record of the patient under the signature of the head of the hospital or his designee.

21. *Right to communication and visitation; exercise of civil rights.*—(*a*) Subject to the general rules and regulations of the hospital and except to the extent that the head of the hospital determines that it is necessary for the medical welfare of the patient to impose restrictions, every patient shall be entitled

(1) to communicate by sealed mail or otherwise with persons, including official agencies, inside or outside the hospital;
(2) to receive visitors; and
(3) to exercise all civil rights, including the right to dispose of property, execute instruments, make purchases, enter contractual relationships, and vote, unless he has been adjudicated incompetent and has not been restored to legal capacity.

(*b*) Notwithstanding any limitations authorized under this section on the right of communication, every patient shall be entitled to communicate by sealed mail with the Y and with the court, if any, which ordered his hospitalization.

(*c*) Any limitations imposed by the head of the hospital and on the exercise of these rights by the patient and the reasons for such limitations shall be made a part of the clinical record of the patient.

22. *Writ of habeas corpus.*—Any individual detained pursuant to this Act shall be entitled to the writ of habeas corpus upon proper petition by himself or a friend to any court generally empowered to issue the writ of habeas corpus in the county in which he is detained.

23. *Disclosure of information.*—(*a*) All certificates, applications, records, and reports made for the purpose of this Act and directly or indirectly identifying a patient or former patient or an individual whose hospitalization has been sought under this Act shall be kept confidential and shall not be disclosed by any person except insofar

    (1) as the individual identified or his legal guardian, if any (or, if he is a minor, his parent or legal guardian), shall consent, or

    (2) as disclosure may be necessary to carry out any of the provisions of this Act, or

    (3) as a court may direct upon its determination that disclosure is necessary for the conduct of proceedings before it and that failure to make such disclosure would be contrary to the public interest.

(*b*) Nothing in this section shall preclude disclosure, upon proper inquiry, of any information contained in such certificates, applications, records, or reports, or information as to his current medical condition, to any members of the family of a patient or to his relatives or friends.

(*c*) Any person violating any provision for this section shall be guilty of a misdemeanor and subject to a fine of not more than $500 and imprisonment for not more than 1 year.

24. *Detention pending judicial determination.*—Notwithstanding any other provision of this Act, no patient with respect to whom proceedings for judicial hospitalization have been commenced shall be released or discharged during the pendency of such proceedings unless ordered by the court or a judge thereof upon the application of the patient, or his legal guardian, parent, spouse, or next of kin, or upon the report of the head of the hospital that the patient may be discharged with safety.

25. *Additional powers of Y.*—In addition to the specific authority granted by other provisions of this Act, the Y shall have authority to prescribe the form of applications, records, reports, and medical certificates provided for under this Act and the information required to be contained therein; to require reports from the head of any hospital relating to the admission, examination, diagnosis, release, or discharge of any patient; to investigate complaints made by any patient or by any person on behalf of a patient; and to adopt such rules and regulations not inconsistent with the provisions of this Act as it may find to be reasonably necessary for proper and efficient hospitalization of the mentally ill.

26. *Unwarranted hospitalization or denial of rights; penalties.*—Any person who wilfully causes, or conspires with or assists another to cause, (1) the unwarranted hospitalization of any individual under the provisions of this

Act, or (2) the denial to any individual of any of the rights accorded to him under the provisions of this Act, shall be punished by a fine not exceeding $........ or imprisonment not exceeding ...., or both.

X—Designation of appropriate court
Y—State Department responsible for administration of mental hospitals
Z—Local Health authority.

TABLE OF CASES CITED

INDEX OF NAMES

INDEX OF SUBJECTS